G000016736

INCIDENTALLY CRICKET

MORE cricket and confusion from the Outcasts C.C.

Alan Haselhurst

Illustrations by 'Hoby'
(David Haselhurst)

Queen Anne Press

First published in Great Britain in 2003 by
Queen Anne Press
a division of Lennard Associates Limited
Mackerye End, Harpenden
Hertfordshire AL5 5DR

A CIP catalogue record for this book
is available from the British Library

ISBN 1 85291 655 9

Editor: Kirsty Ennever
Jacket design: Paul Cooper

Printed and bound in Great Britain by
Biddles

CONTENTS

For Monton Sports Club (cricket, lacrosse, tennis, squash)

in celebration of its centenary –

the only cricket club which has ever made me its chairman.

I remain grateful and I remember it well.

ACKNOWLEDGEMENTS

The response to *Eventually Cricket* was pleasing. Friends who know me well enough to say otherwise were encouraging – sometimes flattering. 'You have mastered the perfect blend of de Selincourt and Tom Sharpe': thank you CHG of London for that. 'Congratulations, you've done it again': my gratitude to CS of Windermere for those words. Believing (not too vainly, I hope) that I have created some enjoyment, the occasional chuckle and a good read, I have been tempted into further effort.

My wife has again borne the brunt. All 95,000 words have had to be deciphered from my increasingly erratic longhand, made worse when committed to paper on a moving train (not that actual movement can be guaranteed on my railway line). A series of drafts has then had to be produced, as correction has followed correction. She has been wonderfully patient and hard-working and my appreciation knows no bounds.

David, my cartoonist son, has produced another set of drawings which demonstrate his developing talent. I hope that his skills will soon earn a greater circulation than my books can provide. In the meantime, many thanks Hoby.

One of my former parliamentary assistants, Ross Jackson, was a helpful source of Japanese names. Some are his and some are mine: his are authentic and mine are pure invention. I hasten to add that I am not anti-Japanese; I simply got carried away.

My publisher has continued to show faith in me. We share a love of cricket which seems to have survived his realisation that he has no J. K. Rowling on his hands. I greatly appreciate his enthusiasm and support.

I am grateful to everyone (willing or otherwise) who has pored over the text and been helpful with suggestions and the elimination of errors. One thing I have learned from the preparation of books for publication is how easy it is to be word-blind. No matter how conscientiously you think you have scoured the proofs, some mistake seems to squeeze through. To my chagrin both previous books contained little mistakes I had failed to spot. So in the expectation that I remain fallible I apologise in advance for any glitches in this book.

In the end it is simply meant to be a bit of fun. You do not have to be a complete devotee of cricket to enjoy what I write, but it may help. If you are not, as a distinguished American friend of mine tells me, you can just concentrate on the pub scenes.

MEMBERS OF THE OUTCASTS CRICKET CLUB

Alan Birch
Stewart Thorogood
Dean Faulds
Jon Palmer
Winston Jenkins
Phil Cole
Colin Banks
Greg Roberts
Tom Redman
Nigel Redman
Basil Smith
John Furness
Kevin Newton
Charlie Colson
David Pelham
Rashid Ali
Tim Jackson
Ray Burrill
Harry Northwood

Simon Crossley (Scorer)
Syd Breakwell (Umpire)

OUTCASTS C.C.

versus

DOREDELL C.C

THE TWO TEAMS
(in batting order)

DOREDELL C.C.
Jim Flote
Howard Tiller
Haydn Bliss
Adrian Wills
Ray Beckett
Kris Vertz
George Summermore (w/k)
Farley Richardson (c)
Ed Fylder
Fred Ranger
Tom Amwell

12th man : Hugh Smith

OUTCASTS C.C.
Jon Palmer
David Pelham
Dean Faulds
Rashid Ali (w/k)
Winston Jenkins (c)
Phil Cole
Ray Burrill
Harry Northwood
Kevin Newton
John Furness
Greg Roberts

12th man : Tim Jackson

PRELIMINARIES

Something was wrong. The landlord of the Sink and Plumber edged nearer to the door. Behind it in his snug there was supposedly in session an extraordinary general meeting of the Outcasts Cricket Club. Whilst all general meetings of the Outcasts bordered on the extraordinary, what was truly exceptional about this evening was that the door against which the landlord's ear was pressed had not opened for fully twenty-five minutes. The landlord did not keep a log, but since the Outcasts had made their headquarters in his pub, he had never known such a long gap to occur between rounds. So far no more than two rounds had been served and this was well below par for the occasion.

The landlord could hear little and that too was unusual. He began to entertain a wild theory. Just under an hour ago his wife had provided a supper of venison pie and chips. She had said that it was a new recipe albeit taken from a scrapbook belonging to her grandmother which she had found in a trunk. If this set of customers had somehow suffered food poisoning and were then to desert the Sink and Plumber, his turnover would be severely reduced. He need not have feared. The Outcasts were in shock, but it had nothing to do with the venison pie, which had been devoured with complete satisfaction.

What had reduced the Outcasts to relative silence and sobriety apart from a number of belches (the pie had been unusually rich) was an announcement by fixtures secretary Winston Jenkins that Doredell Cricket Club had written to invite the Outcasts to play another fixture in the village. So startling was this news that a hush had descended on the room. It had been short-lived, being broken by a particularly loud belch from Alan Birch, who had partaken more fully than anyone of the venison pie. Alan had claim to the title unusual in a cricket club of gourmet-general. Slowly reactions were triggered from other members. Temporarily beer was forgotten – unlike last season's escapade in Doredell.

Thirteen of the Outcasts had been on the previous season's trip to Doredell on the Essex/Cambridgeshire border. All of them could rely on vivid memories even though some had been dulled by excess. In light of all that had happened the question on everyone's mind was why on earth they had been asked back. The combination of incident, accident, mistake and indiscretion had made it an outing remarkable even by Outcasts' standards. Not only did they wonder in retrospect whether they might be forever barred from the village, but also they feared that their reputation might have wider repercussions. So an invitation couched in cordial terms was in its way breathtaking, not to mention belch-inducing.

An intense debate was provoked. That it occupied the span of what would normally be two rounds was an indication of the doubts and different opinions which were aired. It took the voice of the landlord reminding them that 'last orders' was getting close to galvanise the Outcasts towards resolution of their debate. The landlord was stretching the truth, but he had felt that desperate measures were necessary. The prevailing view in the Outcasts' conclave was that they could not carelessly let fixtures drop, because, if the clubs they visited were going to be over-censorious, they would end up without any matches at all. However, acceptance was conditional on Winston Jenkins making discreet enquiries lest some dastardly act of retribution against them was being planned in this extremity of Essex. Then, exhausted by the unaccustomed intensity of their discussion, the Outcasts managed to sink four pints each before being the last customers to be ejected on to the streets of south-west London.

It was not until the following morning that the big, black Welshman began hazily to recall the task with which he had been entrusted. Only after advising a client that he doubted the bank could see its way to help to finance what looked like a thinly-disguised chain of bawdy houses in English market towns 'to exploit a previously untapped rural potential' did Winston Jenkins have a moment to reflect. Basically he had been tasked to examine a gift horse in the mouth. This would be a delicate operation and he had not worked out a way of performing it before his phone rang and he was having to explain to a local builder that the bank would not extend the present £1 million overdraft limit to a business whose annual turnover had now sadly fallen to rather less than half that amount.

So the day had continued. When Winston Jenkins finally stepped out of the bank's offices leaving the carcasses of businesses and business plans strewn behind him, a twin realisation hit him. He had not moved forward an inch on the Doredell case and he had nothing in the flat for his supper. He accelerated his step in the direction of the Bombay Heaven where the dilemma whether to eat there or take away was resolved by his remembering that he had recorded highlights of a one-day international between New Zealand and Bangladesh - something to brighten up the winter's evening. And it was in the Bombay Heaven that he had a chance meeting which was to prove significant.

When Winston Jenkins passed through the gates of the Bombay Heaven he was already set on what his order would be: lamb rogan josh, onion bhaji, vegetable curry, pilau rice and two poppadums. In the ordinary way he would have been in and out in fifteen minutes, the crossword in his evening paper, with any luck, completed. What interrupted the plan was an encounter with Mr Sunil Aryani, who was both the proprietor of the restaurant and a business client. Winston Jenkins found Sunil Aryani in an expansive mood. An effusive greeting was followed by extravagant promotion of his new, extended menu, which contained 'many exciting and original dishes'. So overwhelming was the restaurateur's sales patter that when Winston Jenkins left the premises he was carrying portions of heavenly chicken tandoori, palak paneer, dal mashalla, nan bread and saffron rice all at higher prices than he usually paid. But he also carried something else: a clue. Printed on a box to which his attention had been directed were three words: nice, hayste, cambs.

The trigger for the revision of the menu at the Bombay Heaven had been a change of supplier of the spices which Sunil Aryani purchased for what he regarded as his unique new range of recipes. It has to be said that the choice of new supplier owed nothing to Sunil Aryani's eternal quest for customer satisfaction. What had happened was a take-over of his established supplier, a long-established family business in Cambridgeshire. The successful purchaser had supplanted the familiar range of spices with his own and it had been left to customers such as the owner of the Bombay Heaven to make adjustments. It was less a matter of certain spices becoming unavailable and more a question of cost. Nice Spice did not come cheap.

The anatomy of this take-over was displayed in papers on Winston Jenkins's desk within an hour of his resuming work the following morning. This hour was uncharacteristically later than usual. Winston Jenkins had had a poor night. The heavenly chicken tandoori and its accompaniments had not rested as easily in his stomach as his more accustomed selection. With his appointments perforce re-scheduled Winston made connections. The name Nice Spice rang a bell. He had met someone from that company. Finally he remembered where: it had been in the Yorkshire village of Gigton, the scene of previous Outcasts excesses, when a sudden vacancy for an umpire had been filled by a passing stranger. Hayste was easier to recall even without recourse to a map. It was the next-door village to Doredell; he had seen the directional signs on last year's visit. Newspaper reports told the rest. Nice Spice had acquired Fingerbarrows Flavours amid promises of radical reorganisation and huge new investment. The only hard evidence of change to date had been redundancies.

One connection still eluded Winston Jenkins. Without knowing why he felt it had to be there. Profiles of Cranley Nice, founder, owner, chairman and chief executive of Nice Spice all made mention of his passion for cricket. One newspaper cutting revealed that he had a regular hospitality box at The Oval. The arrival in Hayste and the adjoining village of Doredell of this self-confessed cricket fanatic must, Winston Jenkins reckoned, have some bearing on the Outcasts being asked to renew the fixture with the local team. But there was a lot left to be filled in and he realised that an investigatory journey to the Essex border would have to be undertaken before he could submit a reliable report to his fellow Outcasts.

A reconnaissance in Doredell was not without risk in the wake of the Outcasts' previous visit. With his size and colour and his faint Welsh accent, Winston Jenkins imagined that he might be the least forgettable of the thirteen who had gone to play the Doredell village team last year. The starting point for some gentle enquiries might ordinarily have been the local pub, the Pink Pedlar, but Winston Jenkins knew that there could be no question of that. The day he chose to travel was bitterly cold. Thus his initial exploration was conducted from the comfort of his car.

The appearance of the Doredell cricket ground was such as to filter the memory of what had taken place last year. In winter a cricket ground can look desolate. Allowing for that, Winston Jenkins still thought that the Doredell ground was in poor shape. The distant wooden pavilion had an almost abandoned look about it. The grass had not been cropped. Winston was no expert, but he was left wondering whether it could be nursed back to an acceptable playing condition within just three months. Motoring on, he appreciated for the first time exactly how close to each other the villages of Doredell and Hayste actually were. The thin dividing line was the River Widdle (an apt name for this minor watercourse) whose only significance was that it marked the county boundary between Essex and Cambridgeshire. It then became apparent to Winston that the spice and flavours factory straddled the border.

It was an uneven division. The bulk of the works lay in Cambridgeshire with the principal access for employees and visitors via Hayste. The warehouse and storage sheds, together with the recreational centre, works canteen and sports ground, were on the Essex side of the Widdle. To any industrial complex are attached advantages and disadvantages. Most of the jobs went to the people of Hayste and the shops in that community gained most from the trading opportunities which were generated by the presence of the factory. The effects on Essex were less benign as juggernaut lorries invaded the territory. Verges and hedgerows were clipped and mangled by these mighty beasts. Pedestrians, cyclists and horse-riders were put in fear of their lives. The deterioration of the road surface was an added hazard for everyone.

And then there were the smells. It is an inescapable truth that a factory which specialises in the production of smells produces smells, which in turn prove themselves well capable of escaping from their immediate environment. The prevailing wind in those parts ensured that the odour drift was in the direction of Doredell.

Sometimes the swirling scent could be quite pleasant, but there were too many occasions when the atmosphere was sickeningly sweet or powerfully pungent. There was no redress for the long-suffering villagers. They had to console themselves with the realisation that the factory provided work for at least a few of them and that night brought relief. The displacement of Fingerbarrows Flavours by Nice Spice swept away even those crumbs of comfort.

The two watchwords of Cranley Nice's undoubtedly successful business career were profit and quality. Employee welfare and community relations were a long way down the list. He reconciled profit and quality by means of a fanatical obsession with productivity. Assets had to be worked. When necessary new equipment capable of producing more at less cost had to be acquired. Nice Spice had steadily gained market share, but not without leaving blood on a number of living-room carpets. In any production unit operated by Nice Spice, twenty-four hour shift working quickly became standard; more slowly the workforce was contracted. These effects were beginning to be felt in Hayste and Doredell, and especially in Doredell.

Not all of this was visible to Winston Jenkins as he wound his way round the lanes which comprised the highway network of Doredell. Iris Pearlhammer filled in some of the details. 'Convenience store' was the least apt description for the establishment over which this formidable lady had presided for the last thirty years. Sited in a somewhat obscure location the newcomer needed determination to find it. In appearance the shop's commercial role was well disguised. Not even its function as the village post office was advertised by the usual signage despite the best efforts of Post Office Ltd. 'They know where I am', Mrs Pearlhammer had very firmly told the man sent from regional office in a vain attempt to persuade her to conform. Her claim was only partly true.

The Post Office apart – and she had always accounted to them scrupulously and with precision – Iris Pearlhammer had managed to conceal herself from a large part of officialdom ('snoopers' in her lexicon) for years. The regulatory hand of local councils and agencies of government had been kept at bay. What she sold and how she sold it satisfied her customers even if her standards and practices did not conform to those laid down and prescribed by the Health and Safety Executive, the Food and Hygiene Regulations, the Trading Standards officer and probably others. Had Iris Pearlhammer understood the word metric, the chances of her dealing in such measures would have been remote. Her little business had survived (prospered would have been too strong a term) because she was the simplest exemplar of supply and demand.

Whilst it was plain that a negligible amount of her turnover could be attributed to passing trade, she could be found if the searcher was sufficiently assiduous. The armed raid on her Post Office a few years ago got no publicity. The gun-toting young man who invaded her space got more than he was expecting. Brought up in the East End of London, Iris Pearlhammer knew a thing or two about gangsters. She felled him with a heavy-based frying pan (the last of what had been slow-moving stock), trussed him hand and foot with a nylon washing-line and gagged him with a yellow duster. She managed to drag him into the back of her estate car and then at a later hour she had deposited him, conscious and terrified, in a bus shelter on the main road into Cambridge. Finding a purse, on a whim she extracted a £10 note to cover her expenses: the cost of washing-line, duster and petrol. She pinned a note to his windcheater to advise whomsoever rescued him 'I am a crap robber'. She had had no more trouble.

It should be acknowledged that the procedure adopted by Iris Pearlhammer falls into the category of 'don't try this at home'. However, it stands comparison with more orthodox techniques. The young man in question, having been no more than an apprentice

gangster, opted for a total career change. He enlisted with a voluntary organisation and thereafter pursued a virtuous path. He was last heard of doing good works in some of the least developed parts of South America. Not the most minor of his good works was coaching primitive tribesmen in the art of cricket in which task he was helped by access to the MCC Advanced Coaching Manual on the Internet.

This hitherto unrevealed part of Doredell history explains why the appearance of Winston Jenkins in a bulky anorak, balaclava and dark glasses held no terrors for Iris Pearlhammer. As her visitor seemed ready to be a paying customer she was ready to pass the time of day whilst keeping the heavy-based frying pan within reach. When the subject of Nice Spice was introduced, just after Winston Jenkins had invested in a full sheet of second-class stamps, Iris Pearlhammer held back neither information nor her feelings. Nice Spice had not just taken over the company, the new owners had practically taken over the village without, it seemed, doing local inhabitants a lot of good. Having listened to this tale of corporate infiltration, Winston Jenkins was puzzled. Why Doredell particularly and not Hayste? The shopkeeper thought she knew the answer to that, but kept her reply mysterious and ambiguous: 'They want to keep us quiet, they do.' That struck Winston as distinctly odd. When her customer asked about the cricket ground, Iris Pearlhammer did not see any possible link. That was a network into which she was not plugged.

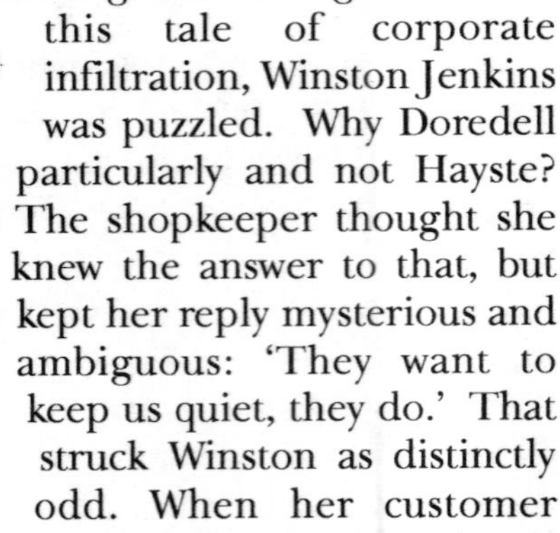

Winston Jenkins thought nevertheless that he was almost there. From all the gossip which had poured from Iris Pearlhammer's lips it was a reasonable inference that Nice Spice must have muscled in on the village cricket club. It obviously still existed, for otherwise the Outcasts would not have received an invitation to play. A second visit to the ground, this time with a closer inspection, confirmed Winston Jenkins' opinion that, wherever cricket was to be played in Doredell, it would not be at its old home. That seemed to leave only one place. It did not entirely explain why the Outcasts had seemingly been forgiven for last year's indiscretions. Perhaps, Winston reasoned in coming to a conclusion, there had been a change of club officials and perhaps Cranley Nice, with his notorious regard for cricket, had been persuasive, especially as it looked as though matches were intended to be played on the company's sports ground. And that was only the half of it.

Another lively evening at the Sink and Plumber enabled the Outcasts to hear Winston Jenkins's report. His account was very plausible, but he had to field a great many questions before a decision - on a majority vote - was made. The fixture this year was set for May, much earlier in the year than last year's encounter. It left less time for the memory to fade, as Basil Smith, one of the team's off-spinners, drily observed. Team selection had to be given very careful thought. Availability was far from being the only factor to be taken into consideration.

Availability, however, was the factor which accounted for the first two discards. Nigel and Tom Redman possessed a serially ill mother. For a surprisingly large part of the previous season they had been dispossessed of her. Incredibly for one who on most days could scarcely make it downstairs, Muriel Redman had undertaken a family visit to Australia which had encompassed experience of hospitals in three states. The Southern Hemisphere had apparently agreed with her so much that she had stayed much longer than anyone, including her hosts, had expected. She had finally returned to British soil on the climactic day of the Outcasts' cricket season, the day of the match against Doredell. She left the aircraft in a wheelchair although a later telephone conversation with an Australian relative established that she had had not a trace of difficulty in being ambulant at the departure gate. Once home Muriel Redman convinced herself (but not her doctor) that she was a victim of deep vein thrombosis. This thought helped to ensure that she wintered badly. Her sons found themselves more exploited than ever. For the moment they had reluctantly put aside the possibility of weekend cricket, preferring to concentrate instead on ways of persuading their much beloved mother to emigrate. It was a goal which, had he heard of it, the chief executive of the National Health Service would have enthusiastically supported.

Alan Birch, who was a retail pharmacist and wholesale gourmet, was genuinely able to excuse himself on the grounds that his wife, Margaret, had booked them into the exclusive Dappletree Manor for the weekend as a birthday treat. So sought after was this acclaimed establishment that the booking could not be rearranged. And nor, added Alan Birch, could his birthday. Although none of his friends had any direct acquaintance with this paradise for the bon vivant, many of them had heard of it via a feature on television. Unlike many celebrity chefs, the owner of Dappletree Manor, Stanislaus Dubrovsky (it was not his real name), was far too mercurial and hot-tempered a character to submit to the discipline of a six-part series extolling the dishes which he had created. The producer was grateful to be relieved of such a responsibility. A single feature programme about the restaurant had been all that Stanislaus Dubrovsky had been prepared to tolerate (business after all was business and there was no such thing as too much demand). Having completed the filming the producer suffered a minor nervous breakdown, which later led to a complete collapse and early retirement.

Stewart Thorogood was another Outcast who would miss the return to Doredell. His absence nearly always subtracted something significant from the strength of the team. Stewart could probably claim to be the club's leading all-rounder. Apart from opening both the batting and bowling, he could also bring another craft to the side: cunning. He was never without a scheme or two if things got desperate. But tucked away inside Stewart Thorogood there still lay a kernel of political ambition, despite his unsuccessful foray into the selection process of the South West Essex Conservatives a while ago. When Amanda Sutton had come into his life he had put aside such thoughts. Even cricket had taken second place to his passion and for an interval (actually no more than a few days) he had been off his ale. After Amanda had moved in with him and they had become a settled item, Stewart found that his partner, far from being hostile to his interest in politics, encouraged it.

That was why both he and she were booked into a seminar in a

West Country rural retreat when the Outcasts were scheduled to go to the outer reaches of Essex. The venue was Polesdene Manor and the theme of the gathering was 'Politics and business: the ethical partnership'. Amanda, herself a competent businesswoman, had assured Stewart that he would be mixing with the movers and shakers and should be able to make contacts which would turn out to be useful to him. The list of leading contributors was undoubtedly impressive. Mega-industrialist Sir Storm Mackintosh, said to have the ear of political leaders across the world, would conduct the seminar. The keynote speech would be made by Lord Rugswell who, as Mr Slingsby Woodbinder, had been Minister of Trade with the World when Britain's balance of payments had moved from a surplus of £800,000 to a deficit of £2.2 billion inside three years. His reward had been a seat in the Lords and confirmation in the same job.

Another speaker was to be the renowned philanthropist, J. Darvill Eaglesworth, at the very mention of whose name people would appreciatively and wisely nod. It remained true, however, that no one had quite succeeded in identifying any of the beneficiaries of his generosity. Yet everyone agreed that he was a very important man. The City interest was to be represented by Leonard Molebarrow from what was described (mainly by him) as a leading firm of stockbrokers. There was no doubting that Leonard Molebarrow had made his own fortune even if not all his clients had been quite so lucky. To represent the female business tycoon the organisers had chosen the Hon. Lavinia Hooker. As events were to prove more attention should have been paid to the name and less to the title. Her rapidly expanding empire was outside the usual mainstream, but her presence at the seminar was to add to its enjoyment (at any rate for the chosen few).

If Tom, Nigel, Alan and Stewart were the four who were unable to play in the Doredell match, there were three whom the Outcasts simply could not risk. Top of the list was Colin Banks, their quickest bowler and fastest flirt. After the invitation from Doredell had been received, Colin had put in an anonymous call to the bishop's office and established that the Vicar of Doredell was the same incumbent. That settled it. He could not go anywhere near the place. Last year's embarrassment made him persona non grata. The Outcasts still thought it a huge laugh that Colin Banks had found himself naked in the vicar's bedroom. The residents of Doredell had shown not a flicker of amusement either then or since. Up to that point, Colin Banks recalled as he stretched for another pint in the Sink and Plumber, the visit to Doredell had gone rather well. The highlights of Colin's life were romance and cricket, usually alternately. Without a steady girlfriend, he specialised in a regular sequence of girlfriends ensnared by his dashing good looks. Between encounters his cricket was more likely to hit its peaks.

Arriving woman-less in Doredell Colin had bowled straight and fast, picking up three wickets in each of his two spells and a warning for an obscene gesture in one of them. Assuming that his batting would not be a crucial element in the encounter, he had generously slaked his thirst and lain down on a grassy bank to keep a sleepy eye on the Outcasts' reply. That was where she had encountered him.

She was young. She was shapely. She was blonde, her curly hair bubbling in the slight breeze. She was also the vicar's wife. All bar the last and most salient point was immediately apparent to Colin Banks. The path to her bedroom was strewn with misunderstandings. Fay Andrews was far from being an empty-head, but there was an element of unworldliness in her make-up. She was a good person with a pronounced sense of charity. The cause presently nearest her heart and which had brought her amongst the modest crowd attending the cricket match was Orphans in Africa. She was selling raffle tickets and she was sure, she said when she thought she had Colin Banks' attention (there was no problem about that), that he would buy some. And then she smiled. It was a smile which could have sold the Encyclopaedia Britannica to the Eskimos. Colin's hand, which had been moving towards his small change, transferred to his wallet. Further encouraged by a dazzling beam it selected a £10 note. Fay's grateful demeanour proved a fateful temptation.

Fay Andrews was much the most beautiful woman he had met in two weeks. Both that and the belief that his role in the cricket match was by now over, as Stewart Thorogood and Alan Birch were applying themselves positively and profitably to their task, led Colin Banks to say that there was no cause closer to his heart than Orphans in Africa. Fay Andrews's eyes widened (delightfully) and Colin responded with the declaration that Africa as a whole was one of his passions. It was as well that none of his friends heard this preposterous claim; several of them were aware that Colin's only passion for Africa had taken the form a couple of years ago of a striking

Zambian girl and even that had been short-lived. But Fay Andrews was taken in. Believing that she had found a new recruit for her good causes (Orphans in Africa did not have a monopoly of her attention), she wondered whether Colin would like to see her collection of Africana together with graphic photographs of pestilence, famine and deprivation. He declared himself eager for this heart-stirring experience. Step by step they marched on, each blithely misreading the other's intention. When Fay Andrews flashed another smile, blushed coyly and said she had some etchings upstairs, Colin Banks could perhaps be forgiven for the assumption that the person he took to be the daughter of the house was encouraging him. Not even the sight of walls covered in artwork sowed doubt in Colin's mind, because he had eyes only for the low bed with its zebra-skin cover.

Colin was never able to satisfy his friends as to the exact word, gesture, look or combination thereof which persuaded him to strip, but when Fay Andrews said (meaningfully, he thought) that she would be back in a moment, he convinced himself that he was on the threshold. But he was not in fact prepared for what happened next. His intended partner returned still fully clothed carrying an African artefact which on sight of Colin she promptly dropped. She screamed. Being well acquainted from her photographs with a surfeit of the naked male form, her reaction was more likely to have been caused by the breakage of the objet d'art than by Colin's metamorphosis. The next sound Colin heard was an enquiring male voice from downstairs. In a split second he realised it was getting nearer. Whoever the newcomer was, Colin thought that an introduction would be difficult. Snatching up his clothes he lunged for the door of the ensuite bathroom and shut himself inside.

From his refuge Colin Banks could both hear and to some extent see (it was an old house with home-made panel doors) what ensued. The newcomer comforted a distraught Fay Andrews. Such was the manner of the comfort that no immediate disclosure of his whereabouts was forthcoming. Expecting a pounding on the door and demands for his submission, Colin certainly did not expect what next took place. Through a narrow slit in the door he could see two things, neither of which was pleasing. On the zebra-skin covered bed the vicar (his collar betrayed him) was making love to Fay; and on the impala skin bedside rug, sheltered by a larger piece of the fractured artefact, lay the jockstrap which he had failed to gather in his rush for the bathroom.

Stunned by the activity being graphically portrayed before him (he was as yet unaware of the true relationship between the older man and the younger woman), Colin still had enough wit to work out his next move. An exit strategy was rapidly required but he could not envisage one which included the retrieval of his jockstrap. Clothed in his remaining items of kit he inspected the window and what lay below it. With the help of a conveniently large bath-towel he lowered himself part of the way to the ground. The remaining distance involved a painful working-over by a prolific climbing rose. He was a scratched and torn figure when he returned to the cricket ground. His was not the only transformation which had occurred.

A potted résumé of this episode and its aftermath often enlivened the gatherings at the Sink and Plumber. It had become part of the Outcasts' folklore. When the tale was recalled (as from time to time it most assuredly was) it was not uncommon for it to be brought to life with impromptu renditions by Alan Birch and David Pelham in the parts of the vicar and his wife. Such a performance lent weight to the conclusion that Colin Banks could not possibly be risked in the forthcoming visit to Doredell. Re-enactment of his folly also goaded Colin into retaliation, fastening first on Kevin Newton.

Kevin, who worked as a local planning officer for an authority neighbouring one of the London boroughs, was the Outcasts' second choice wicket-keeper behind Rashid Ali. For the first two or three years of his association with the Outcasts, Kevin was second choice by some distance. His original long blond hair had been thought to be a serious impediment to his sighting of the ball. Eventually a piece of harmless vanity had persuaded him to sport a closely cropped style. This coincided with a step change in his ability behind the stumps. Kevin had never admitted the connection. However, there had been something else too. The new style had appeared to pay dividends in Kevin's social life.

Buoyed by a series of pleasurable but transient relationships, Kevin had thrown himself neck and crop at a stunningly beautiful Danish girl who had arrived last summer in his local authority headquarters on a thirty-day secondment. On Kevin's part it was love at first sight and he worked hard - pathetically hard in the view of his colleagues in the office - to insinuate himself into her life. The visitor, Kirsten Sindersen, was doubtless flattered by his attentions. Perhaps in a strange country she was glad to be befriended and at the same time not in the least put off by someone who had a touch of Scandinavian good looks about him. But so far as Kirsten Sindersen was concerned that was the limit of it. It was a limit which Kevin Newton neither recognised nor understood. He bid for most of her attention. Towards the end of her stay she began to find his willingness to please almost intimidatory. When he spoke of coming over to see her in Copenhagen she decided that she had to put him straight. There was a long-standing boyfriend back home. Kevin was put straight, straight into depression. He had never previously felt so deeply about any girl. He had still not got over the shock of his rejection by the time of the match against Doredell. This was how he excused his subsequent behaviour.

In response to his rejection Kevin Newton had not (more than usually) taken to drink. It was in cricket that he sought his solace. He began to attend indoor nets, which for him and most Outcasts was an unusual occurrence. Even more amazingly, he went along to these nets five nights a week. He threw himself into practice with burning intensity, plying the cricket school's coaches with questions and avidly following their advice. In the two matches he played for the Outcasts ahead of the Doredell game, his change of attitude was marked. On the field he was all energy and animation. He kept up a continuous flow of chivvying comments and encouragement. Even his batting in the one innings he was called upon to play was transformed. He made thirty, which was the first time he had reached double figures since his extraordinary knock against the wild schoolboys of Rockcliffe. It was not just the runs, but the classy way in which they were made that caused curious comment amongst his friends.

It was this born-again cricketer who came to Doredell. When the home team had chosen to bat he had helped Colin Banks to achieve half of his six-wicket haul with three good catches. He had conceded no more than six byes which was in itself noteworthy. On this occasion Kevin was not expected to bat until number eight in the order. As Alan Birch and Stewart Thorogood built their opening stand, Kevin himself did not expect to have to bat. He had reckoned without Mostyn Winchope.

Mostyn Winchope had been full-time head security guard at Fingerbarrows Flavours and part-time umpire for Doredell Cricket Club. When in June he had reached the age of sixty-five, these roles were reversed in what was almost certainly a more appropriate allocation of his time. The management of Fingerbarrows had never identified the precise cause of

Mostyn Winchope's failure to forestall a damaging break-in earlier in the year. The company's paternalistic approach to their employees, especially those of long standing, dictated that Mostyn Winchope could continue to work for a few hours a week under a newly appointed supervisor. The man himself was in no way displeased by this arrangement. Indeed he was thankful.

The dogmatism and bullheadedness which had characterised Mostyn Winchope's approach to security equally dominated the position of authority he occupied on the cricket field. He now saw Doredell Cricket Club as his only power base. Home had long been the sovereign territory of Mrs Audrey Winchope. But when he was in charge of a match Mostyn Winchope relished the sensation of having complete authority. He did not suppose for a moment that his 'slight' hearing loss, on which Mrs Winchope commented so acidly, was in any way detracting from his performance as a firm but fair dispenser of justice at the crease. She also said that he needed glasses.

For most of the match in which Doredell played the Outcasts, Mostyn Winchope had played a passive role. The majority of the appeals had come at the other end and been dealt with by the visiting umpire, Syd Breakwell, the ex-policeman who had served the Outcasts for a number of seasons with diligence, good humour and occasional accuracy. The second innings of the game was already long under way and Mostyn Winchope had had to do no more than turn down an appeal for LBW. It had been palpably too high, the ball having hit the batsman in the stomach which in Alan Birch's case was better accustomed to receiving soft, tasty delicacies internally and not hard, round objects externally. Mostyn Winchope chafed at finding himself no more than a bit part player. However, it was not to be long before he moved centre stage.

The slide in the Outcasts' innings had already begun before Mostyn Winchope turned it into an avalanche. Doredell had resorted to a rarely-employed leg-spinner once it appeared to their captain that the game had slipped irretrievably away from them. The rarely-employed leg-spinner had straightaway caused confusion to the batsmen and umpires alike. He had a strange, contorted bowling action which had Syd Breakwell, standing at square leg, in two minds about whether he should no-ball him for throwing. This was a step which Syd Breakwell had never so far taken in his umpiring career, but he was always keen to extend his repertoire. His indecision was only sustained by worry about the crisis which such a dramatic intervention might create. He should not have worried, because mayhem was just around the corner.

The rarely-employed leg-spinner bowled round the wicket on a slanting run which took him between the stumps and the umpire. At the point of delivery he perfectly obscured the umpire's vision. Whether the umpire himself was standing too much to the right or whether the bowler's follow-through was causing him to tread illegally on the pitch, the umpire should have taken steps to correct the situation. Even if Mostyn Winchope had been in the process of turning his mind to this - and there was no evidence to suggest that he had - his concentration would have been shattered as completely as Fay Andrews' artefact by the bloodcurdling cry which the bowler emitted. The rarely-employed leg-spinner had hardly ever had occasion to appeal. So when the moment came he gave it everything. Mostyn Winchope's first thought was to reckon that perhaps he had overestimated his hearing loss, but he then quickly assessed what he saw. What he saw was Winston Jenkins playing back to a ball which had palpably struck his pad in line with middle stump. Up went his finger. What he had not seen, as the bowler's left shoulder had been in the way, was that the ball had pitched six inches outside leg-stump. It was charitably supposed by Winston Jenkins that, had he seen where the ball had pitched, the umpire would have known enough about the laws of cricket to have turned down the appeal. However, as the match did not appear to be in danger, Winston Jenkins walked off without any show of dissent.

Excited by his feat in turning the ball as sharply as he had done, the rarely-employed leg-spinner tried again. The batsman was David Pelham, who liked to be thought of as an all-rounder. His performances did not consistently underline this theory. His fellow Outcasts preferred to think of David as a bowler who could bat. This did not turn out to be the day when the exception proved the rule. The ball he received did pitch in line with leg-stump. That at least could be said for it. Obligingly for the bowler it also turned. Playing safe, David Pelham dabbed it down in the direction of slip who pounced on it and claimed a catch. So obviously did the ball hit the ground before he gathered it that no other fielder near the bat joined in the appeal. To Mostyn Winchope, however, it looked like a catch and he gave it. Had he even thought to consult his colleague at square leg it would have made no difference, because Syd Breakwell, still ruminating about the odd bowling action, had been looking at the bowler and not at the slip fielder. David Pelham departed with rather more concern than Winston Jenkins had felt it necessary to display.

Into this somewhat tense and uncertain atmosphere had stepped Kevin Newton, keen to give another demonstration of his lately-discovered prowess with the bat. The rarely-employed leg-spinner was beside himself. He had never before had occasion to deliver a hat-trick ball. Given as is customary at such moments a more attacking field, he became over-excited. The ball he delivered was faster, flatter and fuller. It did not spin. It had no chance to spin. What it did do was take Kevin Newton by surprise. He should have hit it hard into the open spaces which the attacking close-in field had created, but he was too late with his stroke and instead thick-edged it into his pads. It was enough for the psyched-up bowler who let out a mighty yell. It was enough for Mostyn Winchope who had heard the appeal, but not the sound of bat on ball which had clearly carried to the boundary, if not beyond. It was too much for Kevin Newton when he saw the finger raised. The raising of his own finger in the direction of the misguided umpire was merely the start of what proved to be an unedifying altercation.

As another round was purchased at the Sink and Plumber in the wake of Colin Banks' firm conclusion that there was no question of Kevin Newton making an early return to Doredell, the spotlight inevitably switched to Charlie Colson. His 'crime' after all had been the most heinous. On the field Charlie Colson's performances could often surprise. Mainly a gentle, medium-pace bowler he could never be described as the spearhead of an attack and yet on occasions he had taken wickets as an opening bowler. His batting was even less consistent, but in his time with the Outcasts he had batted in virtually every position, not always (although fairly often) badly. Off the field he was more consistent. When it came to beer consumption he led the averages. Of all the Outcasts on last year's trip to Doredell he had been the most drunk the most often. Even the next most drunk of his companions had been sufficiently in command of his faculties to attest to that. So Charlie had been named thirteenth man and took no part in proceedings on the field. It was the part he played off the field, both during and after proceedings, which caused the trouble.

After a nap to help him recover from the journey and what he had consumed during it, Charlie Colson thought that he would be performing a service by renewing acquaintance with the village pub – just to check that it was still there he told himself. He seemed to remember that it was called the Hungry Goat. When he stumbled upon it he was confused. A pub it undoubtedly was. Yet its appearance had changed. So had the name. It was now the

Pink Pedlar and the outside décor was in keeping with the title. Curiosity spurred him through the door. Inside it was partly recognisable. An effort had clearly been made to maintain a local village environment. At the same time the stall had been set out to attract a wider trade. Flowers were not usually in abundance in the Outcasts' favourite drinking haunts. The theatrical prints and photographs would have been more in place in a West End establishment. They contrasted oddly with scenes from rugby matches which also proliferated.

The new proprietors responsible for this makeover – Charlie Colson had vaguely registered the names above the entrance: G. Poppledown and H. Bliss – were not in evidence. The young man behind the bar said that they were resting. Charlie Colson ignored the wink with which this information was delivered. He was more interested in the delivery of a pint of Hoppenhall's Charger bitter, a superb real ale which he was relieved to see had survived the changes. A few pints of this product were well worth having despite an atmosphere of glitz. And a few is precisely what Charlie proceeded to have. Eventually, conscious (just about) that even a thirteenth man should be cheering on his team, Charlie made his way back to the ground noting on his way that the neighbouring field had now filled with cattle. When he got back he found that it was nearly time for the tea interval.

Forlorn and unprepossessing from the outside the old Doredell cricket pavilion might have been, but inside there had always been a warm welcome for the cricketers at tea-time. (Sadly the same could not be said of the showers at close of play.) However, this time there was a snag – in itself only a minor snag, but the trigger for something much more major. The admirable ladies in charge of cricket teas were one short of their usual complement. A day earlier Mary Cornwell, having finally succumbed to pressure from Mr Cornwell, who said he could stand her complaining no longer, had had her bunions treated. To her horror she was told to put her feet up for a day before doing much standing or walking. To avoid another round of wailing, Mr Cornwell had taken himself off for a day's fishing. His wife was left to fume at her incapacity. She had not missed a cricket tea in nine years. Ever conscientious, she promised Florence Tilt, current mistress of the pavilion kitchen, that she would send a substitute. Her daughter, Lisa, was nominated. This was to be a bad decision.

Surprisingly for someone well plugged in to the local newsround, Mary Cornwell was not up-to-date with a late item, namely her daughter's interest in Darren (son of Florence) Tilt, a slim (some would say skinny) young man, who aspired to play cricket for Doredell. In fact Darren Tilt aspired to play cricket for England, but it was not yet proven that he was good enough even for his village team. One of Mary Cornwell's tasks was to collect the milk from Iris Pearlhammer's shop and take it to the cricket pavilion. No doubt Lisa Cornwell would have remembered to discharge this responsibility if, after setting out from home, she had not bumped into Darren Tilt. He was going to the cricket ground and so she went with him, forgetting the necessary diversion to the village store. She had eyes and thoughts only for Darren Tilt. This made her almost unique among the female population of Doredell. For all his good looks Darren Tilt was not the kind of young man mothers hoped their daughters would bring home to tea. Whilst generally thought of as trouble (the more kindly ascribed his attitude to life as lacking in confidence) he was on this occasion no more than the innocent cause of there being at the outset no milk for the cricketers' tea. Disaster came from an entirely different source.

Awareness of the absence of milk came late. Distracted by the sight of her son locked not only in conversation with her friend's daughter, Florence Tilt had failed to cast her supervisory eye over the tea-table. The ladies who helped her would not have dared to say a word even if they had noticed that the milk jugs were empty, because they knew that Mrs Tilt always had everything under control. It was only when Darren Tilt tore himself apart from Lisa Cornwell in response to an insistent shout that he was required to bat, that his mother recovered her composure and emerged from the kitchen to carry out a late check that all was well. Members of the Doredell team were already hovering. With Darren Tilt at the crease and Colin Banks rampant in his second spell, the arrival of the rest of the players was imminent. A cry went up. It was not Kevin Newton appealing for a catch behind the wicket (that would come ten seconds later), but Florence Tilt's wail of lament that her record of impeccable efficiency was unexpectedly besmirched.

Charlie Colson, on his return from the Pink Pedlar, hovered near the pavilion, at the giggly stage of his drunkenness. Having grasped (vaguely) the cause of Florence Tilt's cry of horror he found his own way of responding. All the other players had assembled for tea and begun to tackle the ample sandwiches when Charlie led the animal into the pavilion. With the salutation, 'I think you'll get all the milk you want now, missus', Charlie departed, laughing uncontrollably. The animal did not.

Charlie's promise was unfulfilled. His condition was such that he had not been able to make the most fundamental of distinctions. The animal he introduced to the cricket pavilion was unable to provide milk. It was a young bullock. What it did provide was pandemonium. Anyone who was witness to the spectacle would contend that the expression 'bull in a china shop' should give way to 'bull in a cricket pavilion' as a way to describe chaos. In these unfamiliar surroundings the animal was nervous and at first stood quite still. The people in whose company he now found himself were also nervous and after a short period of shock did not stay still. The sudden movement caused the bullock to lash out with his hind legs. Unfortunately poor Darren Tilt was standing directly in the line of fire. With a terrible cry he fell to the floor. In one and the same action the cricket club was denied part of its bowling strength and the young ladies of Doredell any risk of sexual harassment.

The attention directed to the stricken Darren Tilt allowed the young bull a few more moments of madness. Tables were overturned. Women screamed. The trophy cabinet (its singular title being appropriate) was smashed. Pictures fell off the walls. The tea urn was punctured. The flow of boiling hot liquid excited the animal to the extent that it relieved itself with an astonishing liberality from which few people escaped. The only cool head

on the premises belonged to George Summermore, Doredell's wicket-keeper and, more relevantly, someone who had been brought up on a farm. He eventually got the right side of the animal and brought it under a level of control which, later, the Outcasts wished they had been able to exert on Charlie Colson. The bullock left behind an unbelievable mess. Never in this kind of occasional cricket had there been such willingness on the part of players to resume the match – and that was despite the fact that what they were wearing now bore a closer resemblance to combat fatigues than cricket gear. As to the pavilion itself, there were some who said that the smell was never banished throughout its remaining period of use.

After this pastoral triumph Charlie Colson fell asleep again. Not for the first time he was to display astonishing recuperative powers. He awoke on cue when the teams were ready to set off for the pub for the after-match de-brief. He insisted that he was up for it, but to a discerning eye his pallor might have warned otherwise. Having been no more than annual visitors, the Outcasts had found the Hungry Goat a perfectly acceptable pub in view of the fine ale it served. They were less enamoured of its conversion to the Pink Pedlar. Serious drinkers amongst the beer-loving residents of Doredell had been more tolerant, being unwilling to take to the alternative beverages at the next nearest pub, the Red Barrel in Hayste. And, of course, the Pink Pedlar was the only hostelry in walking distance. The Outcasts could allow themselves a more critical eye and did not feel entirely at ease. On early acquaintance the new owners failed to dispel this feeling. An early retirée from the oil industry, Geraint Poppledown, and occasional ballet dancer and rugby player Haydn Bliss, were a curious couple. But there was still no excuse for Charlie Colson's later outburst.

The first rumblings of disaster had begun with the return of Colin Banks's jockstrap. Recollections differed as to whether it was during the second or third round that they were joined in the lounge bar by the vicar. It was quickly evident that he had not come for a drink. He obviously felt that this was not the occasion for a customary greeting or introduction for his first words were a question. 'Mr Banks?' Colin Banks thrust himself from a gaggle by the bar and reddened (his friends insisted) on sight of the newcomer. There was no time for pleasantries. The vicar thrust in Colin's direction a paper bag containing the garment which Colin of necessity had had to leave as a souvenir of his visit to the vicarage. Tracing its owner had not required a feat of brilliant detection. On the waistband in laundry ink the name was clear enough as was also the verb with which it rhymed (a late night inspiration of Colin's flat-mate, Greg Roberts).

It quickly became plain that the vicar had come to deliver judgement and not just the offending garment. 'May God forgive you your evil and lascivious behaviour and cleanse your mind and body.' This was received by the listening Outcasts mostly in stupefied silence marred only by a few suppressed giggles. Colin Banks might have accepted the rebuke in silence and the vicar in turn might have said no more had not Charlie Colson ostentatiously raised his glass and said "Amen". It was then the vicar's turn to change colour. Had his earlier invocation been a prayer or not, no such construction could be put on what he was then provoked to say. The bit about defiling young women was too much for Colin Banks, who still had a misconceived idea of the relationship between Fay and the vicar. Unwisely he aired his belief. Thirty years of attachment to the cause of pacifism deserted the vicar in as many seconds. Order was restored with only minimal damage done and that mainly to glassware. The licensees, with the ballet-dancing rugby player to the fore, persuaded the vicar to leave. This was quick thinking on their part: they knew the vicar was a teetotaller whilst their more numerous clients patently were not. Even so Messrs. Poppledown and Bliss drew a distinction between the vicar's custom and his reputation.

There was no hiding-place for Colin Banks. Explanations were demanded from him by colleagues who had no difficulty whatsoever in disbelieving lasciviousness on the part of their leading fast bowler or his constant readiness to commit what the vicar of Doredell would regard as sins of the flesh. It was the vehemence of Colin's counter-allegation which had taken them aback. Equally the truth, which locals in the bar were able to confirm, had shaken Colin. Thereafter, with the help of more ale, the discussion became more uproarious and, inevitably, vulgar. As a reaction to his humiliation Colin was embellishing his tale to such enormous lengths that Haydn Bliss felt moved to intervene from behind the bar to defend the honour of the vicar and his wife.

The reproof brought silence, but not for long. Tongues were loose. One tongue in particular was very loose indeed. It belonged to Charlie Colson. His addled mind had taken against the proprietors of the Pink Pedlar, the pub itself in its new guise and now the criticism from behind the bar. He allowed himself a coarse remark, the target of which was all too obvious. Sober, Charlie Colson was a liberal-minded man, but he had gone several pints ahead of his brain. Trade notwithstanding, this was too much for the Pink Pedlar's resident couple. Within minutes the Outcasts were outside – barred. It was not Charlie Colson's finest hour.

Thus it was that the team for this season's surprise return to Doredell picked itself. Only Jon Palmer and Dean Faulds (both batsmen), Basil Smith and Harry Northwood had not made the trip to Doredell last season. The first three had been to the village for earlier, less sensational matches. Only Harry Northwood, also a batsman, had never been seen in the place. The twelve names did not represent a balanced side. Attack was hardly the word to apply to the combination of bowlers on which it would be forced to rely: three off-spinners and two (to be honest) nondescript medium-pacers. The batsmen would have to perform particularly well if the Outcasts were to make a game of it. With those strategic reflections, members of the Outcasts Cricket Club stumbled from the Sink and Plumber into the February night, it having finally been decided that the rotating captaincy/match managership (as was the club's wont) should rest with Winston Jenkins in view of the spadework he had already done.

A decision had to be made about transport. It was influenced by two factors. Over the years the Outcasts had most regularly availed themselves of the services of Executive Sporting Coachways, who specialised in providing seedy coaches for uncritical and often unruly sportsmen and women. The Outcasts, whilst themselves not consistently the wildest of the coach company's customers, could tolerate the standards on offer. Eventually the regulatory authorities decided they could not and for a while Mr Bill Blimp's company had been forced to withdraw from the field. But not for long. Soon this resourceful entrepreneur was back, but not with the most ideal vehicle. A double-decker was altogether too big for most of Bill Blimp's regular contracts, too cumbersome for some of the roads it had to take and too expensive in terms of fuel for the owner's comfort. Nevertheless whilst the search for a more practicable single-decker continued, the big bus had to be used. Bill Blimp overcame the most pressing of his handicaps by converting the upper deck into a bar.

In the conversion Bill Blimp had spared every expense. What greeted the passenger was crude but functional. There were a few soft drinks (Bill Blimp knew that there was a good mark-up on these), cans of lager and in pride of place a barrel of real ale. These were not the ideal conditions for the carriage and keeping of such an excellent commodity, but the Outcasts were ready to make a small compromise. Their first encounter with the mobile bar had been last year's trip to Doredell. It had proved to be, through the agency of Charlie Colson, the genesis of their woes.

The yellow double-decker had jolted into the small car park at Doredell Cricket Club. Some of its passengers had begun to regret the relaxation of their general rule not to drink beer which might not have fully settled. One or two, who had imbibed with great gusto on finding this new facility available, had particular cause to regret it. Bill Blimp might have converted his new acquisition into a travelling bar, but he had not thought to provide for the logical consequences. There was no lavatory on board. This had already caused one interruption to the journey, the net effect of which had not helped. The outstretched hand of David Slaybrooke, the captain of the Doredell team, was brushed aside by those who were first off the bus in an unseemly sprint for the pavilion. In the visitors' changing-room the single WC was occupied (Syd Breakwell had travelled separately to Doredell). The expedient adopted by Charlie Colson and David Pelham had not endeared them to their hosts and the visit was off to an uneasy start.

Despondency spread when Alan Birch returned from the toss to announce that they should get ready to field. There were some who felt more ready for bed. Alan Birch assured his groaning colleagues that this had not been his decision. He had lost the toss. With a mixture of heavy heads and aching stomachs, eleven men took the field. Their expectations of the day were not high. But after a few overs from Colin Banks they had changed. They would change again.

Winston Jenkins was quite clear in his mind that they could not possibly take the double-decker to Doredell again. He would also have ruled out a Blimp single-decker had one been available, because to risk a Blimp driver in Doredell would have been foolhardy. Winston could still visualise the mangled wreckage of two of the Doredell players' cars as Bill Blimp's second son, George, sought to turn the double-decker round in the confined space of the cricket club car park.

Winston Jenkins doubted whether he would ever have had second thoughts on this matter, but any fleeting possibility of them was driven from his mind after a phone call from Tim Jackson. Tim was the Outcasts' party-maker-in-chief, no great cricketer, but a tremendous social asset. He could understand the reasoning for his being in the chosen twelve for Doredell, but he had not wished to go there. There happened to be a prestigious race meeting at Newmarket that week and Tim's principal passion was racing. However he also had good social contacts in horse-racing country, so if he was to miss the racing itself, the next best thing was to salvage some worthwhile bash from the loss. He had come up trumps, he told Winston, but it was a bit of a special party – fancy dress and up-market. He suspected that not all his friends would want to go, but it made the outing hard to reconcile with Executive Sporting Coachways. Tim agreed to sound out opinion and Winston continued to struggle with the logistics.

There were no such problems in the new home of Doredell Cricket Club where Cranley Nice had been installed as honorary president. There was not too much of the honorary about it, because Cranley Nice intended to be more than an adornment. A convenient vacancy for the post of captain allowed the honorary president to propose, without much fear of contradiction, his newly-appointed factory manager, Farley Richardson. Cranley Nice was the kind of man who would have achieved his objective even if there had not been a convenient vacancy. However, no scheming had been necessary. The former captain, David Slaybrooke, had left the village in a hurry to live with his wife in Cornwall following her discovery of the existence of her rival in Doredell.

Cranley Nice felt that he could smarten up and sharpen up Doredell Cricket Club if he could shift it in-house. The company's facilities were far superior to those which Doredell's cricketers had previously enjoyed and Cranley Nice was prepared to put some extra money in the pot. Several members of the club were company employees and he felt that discipline could be improved if senior management was in charge. Otherwise he ordained that there should be no change. The usual fixture list would be maintained and he was deaf to suggestions that there were sound reasons in some cases, especially one, for change. The boss had spoken and his (modest) bounty silenced criticism. For the moment.

The Outcasts' early season form ahead of the fixture with Doredell was hard to assess. One match had been won in what in every sense had been a tight finish. Two others had been abandoned, one because of unrelenting rain which had set in before the interval and the other because of unrelenting drunkenness which had set in after the interval. In the only completed match - against Parrstone - the Outcasts had fielded first. Without the aid of Colin Banks to spearhead the attack - he was holidaying in the Caribbean with the current light of his estate agent's life - their motley variety of seamers had dismissed the opposition for just under two hundred runs. Stewart Thorogood had been particularly impressive and even Winston Jenkins and Phil Cole had found conditions sufficiently helpful to compensate for their inability to maintain full control of line and length. With a batting line-up on paper of Stewart Thorogood, Jon Palmer, Dean Faulds, Alan Birch, Rashid Ali and Ray Burrill, it should not have been a struggle to make one hundred and ninety-nine to win the match.

One of the most pleasing features of the Parrstone ground was the village pub nestling on its perimeter. There was a hint of romance (or possibly lust) in its name, the Groom and Milkmaid. It was as always a natural drop-in for thirsty cricketers, but it had enhanced pulling power on the day of the Outcasts' visit by virtue of a canvas sign stretched above the entrance which announced a Festival of Real Ale. Early inspection, that is before the toss, revealed an array of Outcasts' favourites, two of which had to be sampled before the commencement of play. No time was lost in instructing Dean Faulds, who was captain for the day, that winning the toss meant fielding first. This was duly accomplished, creating the prospect of early release for those who were lowest in the Outcasts' batting order.

Much as in the game against Doredell the previous year, appearances were deceptive. A good opening partnership had been put together by Jon Palmer and Stewart Thorogood against bowlers who had themselves managed a drop or two of ale during what had been a tea interval only in name. Even when both were out in successive overs for forty apiece, there seemed no cause for alarm. Dean Faulds and Alan Birch were quickly into their stride and the score moved forward at more than five an over which put the Outcasts comfortably ahead of the asking rate. Had Dean Faulds paid more pre-match attention to the pitch than to the saloon bar of the Groom and Milkmaid he might have anticipated what was to come. The strip was unusually dry for April. Dean Faulds had not had much resort to his spinners when Parrstone had batted, because equally unusually the quicker bowlers had largely done the job for him.

The Parrstone captain had obviously left it as late as he dared before introducing his spinners. By this time the Outcasts were more than half-way to their target and more than half of their team was ensconced in the Groom and Milkmaid. After about fifty overs mostly bowled by quick or medium-pace bowlers over and round the wicket the already dry pitch was breaking up to an extent which would have made the great Doug Wright's mouth water. Parrstone did not have anyone of Doug Wright's ability in their team, but it was only a matter of being able to put the ball in the right place and spin it a little to be effective in the conditions which by then prevailed. Parrstone had a leg-spinner and an off-break bowler who (most of the time) could put the ball in the right place and spin it a little.

To their credit the Outcasts did not collapse, but batting became an altogether different proposition. Wickets began to fall more steadily and rather less steadily players in the lower reaches of the batting order were having to make their way back from the Groom and Milkmaid. The lower their place in the order, the more their already modest capacity with the bat was reduced. The saving grace was Rashid Ali, whose skills against the turning ball were far and away above those of his fellow players. Even his powers of salvation seemed unequal to the task when with twelve runs needed and nine wickets down, the last man approached the crease.

Tim Jackson was not the man any captain would call upon in a batting crisis. Into his sixth season with the Outcasts his aggregate of runs was still in single figures. The number of ducks recorded against his name would have stood comparison with any recreational cricketer in England. Were the research practicable it is possible that his level of prowess might well have outclassed international competition. In another startling statistic known only to a few he had come to the wicket against Parrstone with a total of pints consumed in a single session in excess of his career run aggregate. He was not happy to be where he was. Nor was his partner happy to see him where he was and how he was. There were two balls in the over left to face and not a lot of time for a tutorial in which Rashid Ali might have instructed Tim Jackson how to cope with them. Rash hoped that he had got across the simple point that, if the leg-spinner pitched the ball outside leg-stump, Tim could safely use his pads to knock it out of harm's way. From a dreamy look in Tim's eye, Rash's hopes were not high. He assessed the best chance of the team's survival as the grabbing of a leg-bye if the slightest opportunity presented itself.

Rashid Ali was not confident that even this lifeline would be available. Tim Jackson's manner at the wicket had an unreal look about it. The speed with which he eventually took guard did not suggest that technical proficiency would form part of his game plan. His look around the field was perfunctory at best. As he leant on his bat while the leg-spinner prepared to bowl, to Rash's horror, Tim winked. Rash groaned. He knew all too well what to expect. Such judgement as Tim possessed when a cricket bat was in his hand must have drained from him as the excellent beers at the Groom and Milkmaid had drained into him.

The sound of shattering glass caused heads to turn not in the direction of the Groom and Milkmaid from which it could so easily have emanated, but towards the row of cars which lay beyond the mid-wicket boundary. The owner of the vehicle with the broken windscreen was the first to spot the damage. Ironically it belonged to the leg-spin bowler. In all honesty it had not been a great ball, but on close analysis it could be shown that the quality of the delivery was not the principal factor determining its fate. Going down on one knee, Tim Jackson had despatched the ball with a languid swing of the bat. The effect of this heroic shot was somewhat spoilt when it became apparent that coming up off one knee was an operation the batsman was unable to perform without assistance. In one blow Tim Jackson had exceeded his cumulative total of two seasons, but what he had seen from the non-striker's end had convinced Rashid Ali that nemesis was close at hand.

The conviction grew when Rash tried once more to convey to his partner, now wearing an awful glassy smile, a sense of how delicately the match stood. With only one ball left in the over he stressed the value of survival over aggression. 'For goodness sake, Tim', he concluded his appeal, 'use your head.' And that is precisely what Tim Jackson proceeded to do. The leg-spinner, whose mood and accuracy had declined in equal measure, sent down a flatter, shorter delivery which tempted Tim Jackson to go for broke. Flinging himself forward he stumbled and met the ball not with his pad, not with his bat, but with his head. His momentum was such that the ball went shooting back to the bowler. The leg-spinner's first instinct was to throw it to the wicket-keeper to effect a run-out, because Tim Jackson had fallen well clear of the crease. However, his instinct was blunted by the chivalry of his team-mates who rushed to the assistance of the stricken batsman. In the melee which ensued, Rashid Ali took charge and in the process of attending to Tim, dragged him discreetly back within his ground.

Tim Jackson insisted on resuming, but had a look of even greater impermanence about him. Rashid Ali, realising that there was no time to be lost, struck the Parrstone off-spinner for two fours and completed victory for his side. After four more pints in the after-match celebration, Tim Jackson declared himself completely recovered, but no one was prepared to bet on how many more matches would come and go before his next run would be scored.

This promising start to the Outcasts' season was not advanced by the two matches which followed. In the rain-ruined game at Odworth the home team had batted and only David Pelham could be said to have distinguished himself and then only in the sense that his one wicket had cost twenty-one runs off nine overs whereas the other few to fall had cost substantially in excess of that. On their next outing the Outcasts were merry on arrival in Kettlemore and thoroughly drunk very soon thereafter. They had found a depleted home side which had already taken advantage of a sensational half-price offer from their local brewery for two barrels of a new bitter they were test marketing. When the Outcasts had got there the test was already well advanced. By mutual consent a different sort of contest was arranged and this was played to a finish. The lead-up to the match against Doredell did not bode well.

What the Outcasts did not know was that Doredell Cricket Club had also had, to put it mildly, an indifferent start to its season. Whereas the Outcasts' record to date caused no kind of internal recrimination, a failure to perform effectively by Doredell Cricket Club was a matter of greater concern and urgency within the corporate walls of Nice Spice. Defeats by three wickets, six wickets, nine wickets and one hundred and forty-eight runs did not go unnoticed by Cranley Nice. Farley Richardson was summoned in late April to a meeting in his chairman's office and he knew it was not about production costs and the latest sales figures. But Farley Richardson did not attend the meeting in trepidation. He had covered his back whilst presiding over a series of defeats of increasing severity. He intended to demonstrate that in spite of what was recorded in the scorebook against his name he could not possibly be blamed for his team's dismal record.

His gloss on events had it that his dismissal caught at the wicket in the first match, LBW in the second and run out in the third had all been the product of absurd umpiring decisions. To this he added that in the most recent match he had been the not out batsman at the end. For all the slickness of this explanation Farley Richardson could not conceal the fact that he had failed to score a single run. So he had come armed with scapegoats to divert attention from his failings. He claimed disaffection on the part of two members of the team who had lost their jobs in the wave of redundancies which had followed the Nice Spice takeover. It was agreed that the cricket team should be progressively rebuilt on the basis of discipline and loyalty to the company. For the moment Cranley Nice gave Farley Richardson the benefit of the doubt, for there was no doubt that production costs and the latest sales figures were both headed firmly in the right direction.

Farley Richardson was an intelligent businessman, but not a wise cricketer. He had oversold his cricketing knowledge and skills in the belief that this could be the decisive factor in the selection process when he had sought the senior management post on offer at Nice Spice. He should not have over-egged the pudding. His business qualifications and commercial record had been impressive enough to ensure his appointment. It had been foolhardy to create the risk that Cranley Nice would see him as an arm of his cricketing policy which aimed to identify Nice Spice as closely as possible with the cricket clubs in the vicinity. Cranley Nice believed that strong managerial control applied as much to cricket as to the production of spices and flavours. So Farley Richardson had made himself appear to be the man to put in charge of Doredell Cricket Club in the wake of his being put in command of the erstwhile factory of Fingerbarrows Flavours. The appearance was wholly deceptive.

The benefit of the doubt continued to attach itself to Farley Richardson. In the match which followed the inquisition by Cranley Nice, the umpire reprieved Farley Richardson on nought when he was to most other eye witnesses as plumb LBW as it is possible to be. He went on to accumulate seventeen runs with a variety of ungainly shots. Whether his team's total of one hundred and forty-five would have been sufficient to stem the sequence of defeats was never put to the test as torrential rain intervened and no further play was possible. Farley Richardson let it be known (and foolishly believed) that a corner had been turned.

His hopes were further buoyed by the discovery of a new talent. Ray Beckett was a sledgehammer of a man who had just been taken on by Nice Spice as a fork-lift driver deployed mainly in the stores. Farley Richardson would not usually have ventured as far from his comfortable office as the draughty stores building on the perimeter of the site. However, when driving into the works one morning he remembered that he wished to speak to the stores manager who had been uncontactable by telephone the previous day. Parking his car on company-imposed double yellow lines he entered the stores. His search for the store manager's office had scarcely begun before he was almost mown down by a fast-moving fork-lift truck driven by a young man of mountainous proportions. Summary dismissal of this lunatic was at the forefront of the works manager's mind when he spotted something poking out of the man's overalls which surprised him. It was the latest issue of *Wisden Cricket Monthly*. This was not a journal which ever found its way on to Farley Richardson's reading list and he would not have expected it to have much of a circulation amongst the employees of Nice Spice. It was this thought which persuaded him to postpone remonstration whilst the fork-lift truck driver's interest in cricket was probed.

Ray Beckett's interest in cricket was total. He also proved himself to be extremely garrulous. Farley Richardson was bowled over by a torrent of words almost as effectively as he might have been moments earlier by the fork-lift truck. Having asked the question, Farley Richardson was stuck for twenty minutes while he got the answer. He was beginning to grind his teeth with impatience when he suddenly heard Ray Beckett refer to playing for a club 'down Romford way'. Breaking into the flow, he established by some rapid-fire questions that Ray Beckett was new to the village, had played regular club cricket, was a left-hand bat, would be interested in playing for Doredell and was free to attend mid-week nets. With this prize under his belt and a satisfactory meeting with the stores manager, Farley Richardson's pleasure was only dissipated by finding that his car had been clamped.

The Outcasts were first made aware of an impending local government by-election in Doredell when their motorcade passed a field lined with posters. These advertised the availability to the neighbourhood's electorate of Jim Flote, the Independent candidate. After a few minutes it became clear that what was on offer was a choice between two men untrammelled by party political partisanship. Half a mile down the road the Outcasts were greeted by placards displaying the smiling face of Adrian Wills, 'your Really Independent candidate'. The two images alternated throughout the rest of the journey into Doredell.

The vacancy in the Doredell ward of the Vale of Widdle District Council had been caused by the sudden departure of Casper Fulworth who had (not without skill) misrepresented the people of Doredell for ten years. Such had been his power and influence in the area that he had always been elected unopposed. It was a remarkable record, but not half so remarkable as the misuse to which he had put his office and the rewards it had brought him. This programme of wealth creation - a model of its kind - might easily have been prolonged if Casper Fulworth had not fallen in love outwith the bonds of his marriage. In the course of pillow talk he had imparted to his new partner much about himself (a subject to which he readily turned) and how he had reached his present eminence. Too much. As love turned sour his partner began to see the outline of her own wealth creation programme. The blackmail was not long advanced before Casper Fulworth worked out that the rate of his wealth destruction was likely to prove swifter than its creation. He recognised the moment for decisive action. Recompensing his foreign bank account with one last king-size fraud, Casper Fulworth wrote a letter of resignation (to the local authority, not his wife) and disappeared. The people of Doredell prepared for the novelty, for them, of a contested election.

It was unusual for the Outcasts to arrive at their cricket venues in procession. Travelling in their own cars was not conducive to the fulfilment of the social aims of their outings. The visit to Doredell was different. As Tim Jackson had anticipated, the function he had lined up for the evening following the match was not to the taste of all of his friends. The Outcasts were therefore divided into two natural groups: those who had opted for a long evening's progress towards dignified inebriation and those who had wanted the fastest possible route to post-match leglessness. It had been decided to hire two mini-buses to accommodate these conflicting objectives. The potentially restrictive effect of having two self-drive vehicles on a mission of this kind was overcome by happy chance.

Jon Palmer's wife, Adrienne, had fancied the posh fancy dress party when it had been mentioned to her. She stuck with her decision to attend even when she realised that other ladies of the Outcasts' clan were not making the trip. Adrienne was at the earliest stage of believing that she might be pregnant. In this state of uncertainty she had suspended even her moderate level of drinking. Without full explanation she had declared to Jon that she was willing to be a driver. More extraordinarily Greg Roberts was another one available for this task. He had been tempted into a bet by Colin Banks. After a heated argument between them in the Sink and Plumber one night about alcohol dependence, Greg was taunted by his flat-mate that he could not get through the month of May without a drink. When Colin's initial offer of £100 was rashly doubled Greg took the bet. That was why he was willing to be at the wheel of the other mini-bus making its way to Doredell.

The two mini-buses were followed by the second newest and

prized possession of club scorer Simon Crossley and his wife, Sophie. This was an extremely stylish estate car which they had acquired nearly new from a friend of Sophie's uncle who traded in Dollis Hill. It had been mainly reliable. So far the warranty had had to be invoked only once. The estate gave them ample space for the impedimenta carried of necessity when they travelled with their first and most prized possession, Brian Sachin Crossley. Now eleven months old, Brian Sachin was showing a tendency to favour the right hand, but he had not yet had his first full net. The Crossley estate car also conveyed Syd Breakwell, the umpire, who seemed to find the often noisy presence of a baby a more soothing journey companion than the main body of the Outcasts at their most uproarious.

To the intense dismay of Harry Northwood the final car in the line-up contained his parents. Harry was the newest and youngest recruit to the Outcasts. He had quickly demonstrated that he possessed all the drinking tastes, prejudices and, not least, capacity which might be expected to endear him to them. As a bonus he had turned out to be a talented batsman with an eye for the aggressive stroke. Harry Northwood had fallen in (and sometimes down) with the Outcasts whilst he was still at school. He was now in what he was pleased to call his gap year ostensibly keeping open the possibility of taking up the university place he had been offered.

Harry's parents were less pleased with the little they could tell about the constituent elements of their son's gap year. Part-time low grade jobs, surfing the net, sleeping, playing cricket and drinking, Mr and Mrs Northwood thought, hardly amounted to ideal preparation (others with insight would disagree) for the university course which they hoped their son would pursue. They became increasingly curious about the band of men with whom Harry had noticeably been spending more of his time and not just in the cricket season. An invitation to dinner with friends in Cambridge provided them with a convenient and innocent-sounding excuse 'to come and watch you play cricket'.

Harry was thunderstruck. It was not that his parents were narrow-minded. They had already experienced the style of modern living practised by Harry's elder brother, Eddie. Overlooking the fact that Eddie, despite a string of girlfriends, was on his way to his second million, they did not wish to make the same 'mistake' with

Harry. They knew that their younger son drank and they knew that he partied. They believed (correctly) that he neither smoked nor did drugs. How far his sex life had gone they had no idea. What worried Harry was that contact between his parents and the Outcasts in full flow would encourage them to put the worst possible construction on the nature of their son's social life. This could lead to the application of unwelcome pressures. Harry felt that he had to try every possible device to frustrate his parents' desire to go to Doredell.

Injury was the first ploy to come to mind. Harry needed to invent an injury which would be enough to persuade his parents that his only role in the match could be that of twelfth man. They would surely not want to go out of their way to watch him sit in the pavilion all day. It had to be an invisible injury. He wondered about a groin strain, but dismissed the thought immediately; it risked giving his mother an altogether wrong idea. Back strain was another possibility, but then he remembered that his mother was very friendly with a local chiropractor and he could predict what might happen if he volunteered this complaint. Then it occurred to him that he might leave it in the air as to whether he had actually been picked to play in the match against Doredell. If he could keep the likelihood of his inclusion sufficiently vague, he might be able to put his parents off the idea of leaving so early for their trip to Cambridge. He had laid the first trail of this doubt when unfortunately for him it was exploded by an unexpected development.

Basil Smith could be described as the Outcasts' specialist off-spinner. This accolade should not imply that Basil was the leading wicket-taker of the trio of Outcasts who bowled in this mode. What it actually meant was that his sole contribution to the side was to bowl off-spinners whereas Ray Burrill and David Pelham both had pretensions to batsmanship. Basil was also an accountant, but his wizardry with figures did not extend to the management of dates. Back in February at the Sink and Plumber when the team for Doredell was being established, Basil Smith had not appreciated the significance of the date of the fixture. It was only later, when his wife, Jane, reminded him that he had promised to take her for a weekend in Paris on their next wedding anniversary, that realisation dawned dawned. To be sure of her treat she had booked their hotel, the restaurants where they would eat and tickets on the Eurostar. Jane Smith had made it crystal clear, when Basil had half-heartedly begun to demur, that there was no way his promise could be dishonoured.

Basil's withdrawal set alarm bells ringing in Winston Jenkins's ears. As a precaution he first rang the other players on his team-list to confirm their availability. In Harry Northwood's case his father had taken the call. From that moment on Harry's Plan A was dead in the water. His presence at Doredell was guaranteed. So too was the presence of his parents.

Whilst Harry Northwood's mind turned to the formulation of Plan B, Winston Jenkins was faced with the more urgent task of restoring the basic strength of his team. He was now down to four bowlers unless he included Greg Roberts, whom he had provisionally nominated as twelfth man. Counting Greg Roberts as one of the eleven to which he had been reduced did not materially add to the bowling strength. Other Outcasts who might have done so remained firmly resistant to entreaty. It then came down to a case of making up numbers. Even then, Winston Jenkins drew a blank although he did detect a note of hesitation in the voice of Kevin Newton which caused him to turn again in that direction. Winston suggested a drink in the belief that, if Kevin was biddable, his resistance might more easily be overcome after three pints or more of good ale. On his way to Kevin's nearest local, the Hunched Dwarf, Winston recalled that he had not in fact seen his colleague since February. For reasons about which Winston was vague, Kevin had not played in any of the season's opening fixtures. Kevin's appearance had changed. He had allowed his hair to grow to its original, notorious length and he had grown a beard. Winston did not need three pints or more of good ale (he would still have them) to see that the original objection to Kevin Newton being part of the team to play Doredell could easily be overcome. Their opponents would surely not recognise him. Not picked for the game against Parrstone and having since been debilitated by flu, Kevin was keen to get into action again. But, he questioned after the third pint of the guest bitter (Wigmouths Windmill Ale), their opponents would remember his name. After, as it happened, two more rounds, Winston Jenkins assured Kevin Newton that he had the answer.

That is how Harry Northwood came to be sitting next to 'Boris

Wigmouth' in a mini-bus bound for Doredell. It was hard to estimate which of the two had the most to say. Between stopping his friends laughing, Kevin Newton was urging them to practise his nom d'occasion. Since foregathering at the point of departure Harry Northwood had been engaged in a damage limitation exercise. He had refused to travel in his parents' car on the ground that he needed to be involved in team talk during the journey. Despite the fact that the team was split between the two mini-buses Harry's assertion was correct, but not in the way he had led his parents to think. He desperately needed to plead with the team to spare his blushes during the course of the afternoon. By the time they reached Doredell, Harry was not sure he had got the message across even to that half of the team with which he had been closeted. As for Boris Wigmouth, he was harbouring serious doubts about his agreement to take part in the subterfuge. He sensed that, if he was to have an uncomfortable match, the trouble was more likely to come from his team-mates than from the cricketers of Doredell and their umpire.

Kevin Newton need have had no fears about bother from the Doredell umpire with whom he had so infamously clashed last year. Mostyn Winchope had been replaced. Another costly break-in at the factory site had put his continued employment, even on a part-time basis, under close scrutiny. That he had neither seen nor heard the nocturnal activity in the administration block which had been relieved of its contents of computer equipment and a safe was just possibly credible, but the unanswered question was how the company's van in which the thieved items had been stowed could have left the premises without apparent let or hindrance. Scrutiny of time-sheets suggested that Mostyn Winchope had spent part of the evening in the gatehouse. Other staff were interviewed in an attempt to pin down who might have seen whom and when. The build-up of suspicion against Mostyn Winchope was only part of the reason behind his precipitate departure from Nice Spice. When Farley Richardson learnt the name of the security officer who had been responsible for the clamping of his car, no quarter was given.

There was no question of the procession of vehicles carrying the Outcasts and their supporters sweeping into the company sports ground which had become the enforced home of Doredell Cricket Club. They were obliged to pass through security. Passage was not straightforward. The recent heist had led to a greater degree of surveillance being imposed. Cranley Nice readily agreed to Farley Richardson's recommendation that security should no longer be handled in-house. That was why the visitors found themselves in the insensitive and inflexible hands of the men (and there were only men) of Stopp Security Systems. In uniform which would have been the envy of a military head of state in a totalitarian country, Bert Bullmore and his lieutenants descended on the first vehicle, the mini-bus driven by Greg Roberts.

Despite Farley Richardson having left word that a party of cricketers was expected, the security guards insisted on every passenger getting out of the mini-bus. Each was then subjected to a brusque body search. Everything had to be taken out of the bags. Abdominal protectors were closely examined. Even bats were tapped and prodded as if they might be hollow containers for combustible materials. Finally they were waved through, only for the second mini-bus and its occupants to be subjected to the same process. Every last piece of baby apparatus was stripped from the Crossley estate car to be minutely inspected as though it might somehow be reconfigured as an offensive weapon. The three adults were greeted as though they might have been industrial spies. Almost reluctantly Bert Bullmore accepted that they were more nearly a cricket umpire and scorer with wife. Mr and Mrs Northwood did not have even this cover story. They might easily have been turned away had Harry not returned to the scene and rather against his better judgement persuaded Bert Bullmore of the filial connection. So eventually the whole party was in the ground after an ordeal simpler only than that usually endured by an England cricket captain trying to gain access to Headingley. The contrast with last year's arrival in Doredell could not have been more complete – and Winston Jenkins was prepared to be thankful for that.

The side led by Winston Jenkins did not have Colin Banks nor indeed anything recognisable as a purposeful bowling attack. This was a situation with which the Outcasts had to come to terms as they got changed in conditions which were light years away from those they had experienced on their previous visit to Doredell. Some of them could all too vividly recall the squalor and drabness of their then surroundings although it was true that on that occasion the squalor had been to some extent imported with them. The changing facilities in the spice company's sports pavilion had recently been refurbished. They were clean, spacious and generously endowed with showers and (always a vital facility when Outcasts were around) lavatories.

The ground too looked to be in excellent shape. Farley Richardson seemed content for the toss of the coin to take place in front of the pavilion steps, but Winston Jenkins preferred to go out to the middle. He felt that by an elaborate inspection of the pitch he might convey the impression to his opposite number that the Outcasts were raring to have a bowl. Winston Jenkins did not know at that stage how easily in cricketing matters Farley Richardson could be fooled. However, the subterfuge proved unnecessary. Winston called correctly when the coin was spun. Without any outward sign of relief and appearing to deliberate for a few seconds, Winston finally said the Outcasts would have a bat. Quite apart from the cricketing merits of this decision it also delayed the moment when the Outcasts would be exposed en masse to the home side allowing memories of last year to be rekindled.

Members of the Doredell team by contrast were prominently on view. From the shelter of the pavilion the Outcasts got their first impression of how their opponents had altered since the last encounter. There were new faces – as much as half of the team reckoned Winston Jenkins, as he gazed in fascination at a series of exercises being orchestrated by Farley Richardson. The impact of Nice Spice was readily apparent. The kit being worn by the Doredell team was pristine. It bore a logo larger than the norm pronouncing Spice to be Nice. Winston thought that it was probably unnecessary for the message to be repeated on both front and back of the shirts and even on each leg of the trousers. Caps, or sunhats where preferred, took up the same theme. Winston Jenkins thought it more a uniform than a cricketer's normal outfit.

There was not even a hint of uniform about Harry Northwood who, never having previously set foot in Doredell, was the only Outcast abroad at this time. His parents were puzzled that he was not in his whites. Harry could not afford to enlighten them, for by now he had been briefed on the role expected of him. It involved more than batting in the middle of the order. He was to be his team's gofer with a very tightly drawn job specification. Being the only Outcast unknown to anyone in Doredell and the joint licensees of the Pink Pedlar in particular, Harry was in charge of the acquisition and carriage of suitable quantities of bitter beer. He had two worries. The first was to work out how he was actually going to discharge this duty (in which he had a close personal interest); the second was how he could avoid raising the suspicions of his mother and father in the process.

Simon Crossley had no worries. The facilities at Nice Spice's sports ground were a scorer's dream. The scorebox was an adjacent but integral part of the pavilion. Without the encumbrance of tin plates and canvas rollers, electronic gadgetry controlled the information displayed to players and spectators. All this was in sharp contrast to the arrangements in previous years when he had rested his book on a plank supported by two rusty oil drums. He and his fellow Doredell scorer, Billy Gorman, had had to take turns in shouting out the score from time to time. There would be no shouting out this year, thought Simon, and no Billy Gorman.

One look at the extant scorebooks of Doredell Cricket Club had convinced Cranley Nice: not only did performance have to improve, but so too did the keeping of records. Good housekeeping was a key feature of the way in which the owner of Nice Spice ran his factories. It had to apply to the cricket team as well. Billy Gorman was a dear old boy, but he was undeniably old. With age had come an increasing dependence on a drop of rum. The effects showed as the scorebooks became messier in appearance and sketchier in detail. Even the old regime had doubted how much longer they could put up with this, but there had been reluctance to upset the village's favourite pensioner. No such sentimentality held back Cranley Nice. He went for the jugular, ordering that scoring in future would be done with a lap-top computer directly linked to a new scoreboard he would install. It was entirely within his duplicitous character to send a message of thanks and regret to the departing scorer. Billy Gorman bowed to the inevitable – and swore revenge.

Simon had got on well with old Billy Gorman, who had taken a kindly interest in Simon's marriage, his wife and then his prospective baby. There was no danger of the same interest being shown by Billy Gorman's successor. Rather it was with horror that he greeted Simon's arrival with wife and baby. There was no understanding, only distaste over the scorebox's transformation into a virtual crèche. Robert Vine's horror and distaste were not very well disguised. An only child and a gauche bachelor, he was not good with small children, let alone babies. He was not particularly good with the game of cricket either, but had taken a chance. For three years Robert Vine had toiled in a junior capacity in the company's accounts department. He did understand figures, computers (he thought) and the main chance. When a volunteer was called for, he saw it as a way of ingratiating himself with management. He did not have much in common with Simon Crossley although they did both sport an earring. It was evident that Sophie Crossley had continued to make headway with her husband's fashion make-over. By now Simon had just about got over the slings and arrows of outrageous Outcasts' rudeness.

In the umpires' room by contrast there had been a familiar face, but not the one Syd Breakwell had been expecting. An introduction still had to be made before full recollection came back. Rodney Corrington. They had met at Gigton. Rodney had been a casual visitor who became a stand-in umpire, albeit an umpire in a hurry. It clicked in Syd's mind where he had seen the legend Spice is Nice before: for a white coat Rodney had used his factory issue. In the intervening period Rodney Corrington had become Cranley Nice's favourite salesman. As well as selling the company's wares Rodney could talk a good cricket match. So Rodney's presence had been commanded by Cranley Nice when he was entertaining important customers and suppliers at cricket matches – which done in style was his favourite form of entertainment. Faced with an umpiring vacancy in his new fiefdom it had not taken Cranley Nice long to summon Rodney Corrington into the breech where at least Syd Breakwell was pleased to find him. They strolled out to the middle in animated conversation. At a somewhat faster pace Rodney Corrington returned for the bails. Having put them in place he looked up to see Syd Breakwell depart in search of the match ball.

FIRST INNINGS

Having at last secured the umpire's attention, Jon Palmer took guard, paused and looked around him. He then looked up in the direction of the bowler. Fred Ranger had opened the bowling for Doredell for five years or more, but never with the field now set for him by Farley Richardson. Three slips and a gully flattered Fred Ranger and so he bent his back to justify such an attacking ploy. He was unable to do so. By the end of the first over Jon Palmer had twelve runs under his belt without breaking sweat. Farley Richardson did not immediately learn the lesson. With a sense of satisfaction for a job well started, Jon Palmer leant on his bat. He watched Doredell's other opener, Tom Amwell, prepare to bowl. He remembered him from two years ago. No problem there, he thought. He could foresee a harvest of runs. He was sure he could match the success of Alan Birch and Stewart Thorogood in the match he had (thankfully) missed last year. He was less sure about David Pelham for whom the term makeshift opening batsman was glorious exaggeration. Twelve more runs later the harvest appeared to be taking shape, but there was scope for doubt about the longevity of the partnership. Unlike Jon Palmer's crisp blows through the gaps in front of the wicket, David Pelham scratched two boundaries through the slips (one shot should have gone to hand) and another was credited as leg-byes. Farley Richardson was encouraged in his belief in a policy of attack.

The fact that a mere six runs came off Fred Ranger's next over perpetuated the captain's illusion that he was on the right track. A combination of good length balls from the bowler and missed opportunities on the part of the batsman explained the comparatively low yield. It was then David Pelham's turn again. Before taking guard he carried out a rapid appraisal. Yes, he told himself, the number two spot in the batting order was neither commensurate with his ability nor favourable to his chances of amassing a decent score. Going in at seven or eight when the bowlers were tired enabled his more rustic strokes to prosper except, of course, if the Outcasts were 26-6 as they had been on one occasion (and very quickly 26-7 David Pelham reminded himself). On the other hand, his appraisal continued, the Doredell bowling looked ordinary and the pitch seemed good for batting. If he concentrated, runs might come. Supposed concentration did not prevent him chasing a ball outside off-stump which he was lucky to miss. Thereafter he played four respectable defensive shots and then nonchalantly took a single to steal the bowling. This was nearly his undoing.

From a discreet position inside the pavilion and with the aid of binoculars, Winston Jenkins studied the opposition. So far he had had close encounters only with Farley Richardson, who was a new face to him, and the Doredell twelfth man, Hugh Smith, who was not. If Winston remembered aright, it seemed that only five of the players on the field were familiar from last year. But then in a burst of activity another face from the past presented itself. As Jon Palmer pushed Fred Ranger through extra cover a fielder gave frantic chase. His cap fell off and a mop of golden curls was revealed. Recognition was instant. Shock quickly followed. Winston Jenkins had not expected to see Haydn Bliss on the cricket field. His presence could be a serious impediment to the refreshment arrangements which Winston thought he had in place. Harry Northwood had to be warned.

There was no risk of the warning failing to be delivered. Harry Northwood was still very visible within the curtilage of the ground. Indeed he seemed confined to the curtilage of his parents. Winston Jenkins kept him in sight whilst forbearing to break into the family circle. Harry himself was desperate for someone do exactly that. In a well-meaning way his father was plying him with questions about his cricket, the prospects for the game and how he hoped to get on when it was his turn to bat. His mother's questions Harry found less well-meaning. With all of a mother's instincts Mrs Northwood had begun to press her son about the nature of the company he was keeping. Even from the distance of the pavilion the Outcasts had given off an aura to which she had been sensitive. As he tried to dodge nimbly around the parental probe, Harry suspected that he had been booked for mission impossible.

In pre-match planning it had been thought that Harry was the only one of the Outcasts who could enter the Pink Pedlar with impunity. For the operation to be successful he had to be able to depart from the Pink Pedlar not simply with his own needs satisfied, but with a sufficient quantity of ale to provide necessary succour to his fellow Outcasts. This, the best plan which could be concocted in advance, was freely admitted to be flimsy. The quantity aspect had been addressed by the inclusion in the Crossley impedimenta of two large enamel jugs which were reckoned to have an eight pint capacity. No real thought had been given to the credibility of asking the publican to fill two jugs which had been carried on to the premises. A great deal was being asked of Harry in terms of ingenuity and improvisation. However, the attentive presence of Mr and Mrs Northwood had prevented him so far from getting even to the starting gate.

Fred Ranger was reinvigorated by having a plainly less able Outcasts batsman in his sights. Unable to persuade Farley Richardson that three slips and a gully were not an essential accompaniment to his bowling, Fred had little alternative but to buckle down and strive for accuracy. And buckle down he did. A study in concentration David Pelham might have thought himself, but a neutral observer would have thought otherwise as the batsman gave an impression of surviving rather than coping. Jon Palmer at the non-striker's end felt equally censorious as he mentally rehearsed the shots he would have played and counted the runs he would surely have scored. But he would not have scored off the sixth ball which Fred Ranger delivered. From somewhere the bowler found an in-swinging yorker which crashed into David Pelham's pads. Fred was almost too surprised to appeal, but the rest of the team, as coached by Farley Richardson, went up in chorus. All eyes turned to the umpire.

Coincidentally, in a not very distant place another appeal was being formulated. Mildred Askern worked in the packaging department of the spice factory. She had worked for Fingerbarrows Flavours for thirty-two years. She had lived all her life in Hayste. She was a popular figure both in and out of the workplace. It was true that Mildred had not been able to change quite as fast as working practices. The productivity deficit had grown over the years, but Mildred's cheerfulness, reliability and popularity with her fellow workers had allowed management to continue to cast a benevolent eye in her direction – the management of Fingerbarrows, that is. The new management was inherently less comfortable with the situation in the packaging department. Whilst there was awareness of the factory politics involved it was thought that Mildred Askern's presence for ten more years could seriously impede productivity and, more importantly, profitability. It was decided to up the ante.

To the surprise of Nice Spice's management, Mildred Askern did not object to Saturday working with the result that they were slowed down over six days instead of just five. Neither had new machinery helped. It went faster, but Mildred did not. Overall output barely changed. In an unusually enlightened step for Nice Spice re-training was offered, but Mildred had declined. 'No love', she had told her zone manager, 'the packaging department is where I belong. I've lived here and', she added with a chuckle, 'I suppose I'll die here.' The zone manager thought to himself without mirth that such an outcome might have to be arranged. In the short term it was decided to intensify the degree of supervision in the hope that an atmosphere less congenial to Mildred Askern could be created. This stratagem worked brilliantly, but not in the way that management had anticipated.

Trade union activity at the spice factory had only ever been low key. The family style management of Fingerbarrows had left room for few grievances and those which had arisen had been dealt with wisely and efficiently. The onset of a more abrasive management style with the arrival of Cranley Nice and his team positively called out for an organised response. The call was answered by Andy Lizzard. After years of declining fruitfulness in his native Merseyside, Andy Lizzard had finally made a break and brought his modest skills as an electrician to East Anglia. He had found both a home and a job in Hayste with relative ease. Complementing his modest skills as an electrician was Andy Lizzard's experience as a trade union shop steward, an endowment which he had taken care not to highlight when he had presented himself at the gate of the spice factory. Once on the payroll he bided his time. When Mildred Askern was told that she would have to lose her tea break to catch up with her work, Andy Lizzard recognised the perfect cause to which his advocacy could be applied. The shop floor waited agog.

Out on the sports ground the players waited for the umpire's response to the LBW appeal. Syd Breakwell as ever looked a magnificent symbol of authority. From head to toe his turn-out was immaculate. That could always be relied upon. The same could not be said of his decisions. Syd Breakwell had studied the appearance and mannerisms of umpires from across the world and had developed his own style which erred on the side of floweriness. He had not studied the laws of cricket with quite the same attention. His acquaintance with them was as of a friend and not a disciple. Usually, however, he covered his inadequacies with a bluff certainty which deterred even if it did not extinguish doubt. At the moment of Farley Richardson's orchestrated appeal Syd Breakwell had uncharacteristically allowed his mind to wander. Horrifically on his mind was the impending visit of his wife's sister and her husband. They had recently cruised in the Caribbean covering many miles and Syd feared that they would be armed with comparable miles of videotape from which there would be little chance of escape. On hearing the shout he chastised himself and re-focused on the batsman facing him. David Pelham had done what all canny batsmen do in such circumstances and shifted his position. Being in genuine doubt, Syd Breakwell gave himself the benefit of it. 'Not out!' he bellowed, adding with temerity: 'Going down the leg side, I fancy.' His fancy was not shared by everyone on the fielding side, but they swallowed their indignation. David Pelham heaved an inaudible sigh of relief.

Jon Palmer was keen to get back into the action. Tom Amwell's bowling held no terrors for him as he proceeded to demonstrate. With the field set as it was runs were easy to come by. Jon Palmer consistently found the gaps. Perhaps his over-eagerness had affected him, because his timing went slightly adrift. Strokes which should ordinarily have earned boundaries were getting only twos. A total of ten runs was not a bad yield from the over, but, ever seeking perfection, Jon Palmer was cross with himself. He brooded through another over in which David Pelham patted and prodded more with a view to survival than prosperity.

Those who had played alongside him on previous occasions did not know that Tom Amwell had a slower ball. This impression may have been heightened by awareness that Tom Amwell's repertoire hardly included a faster ball. Even Tom Amwell would not have rushed to claim that he could vary his pace at will. Yet what left his hand as the fourth ball of his fourth over would not have been disowned by Darren Gough. The first ball had been a line and length delivery which had commanded Jon Palmer's respect. The second had been too full and erring to leg; the batsman hit it firmly, but without complete conviction; two runs were added. The next ball had given the batsman width and the present was gratefully accepted. Jon Palmer got it together again in a glorious square drive which no fielder came near. Thus encouraged Jon Palmer was less wary than he should have been with the consequence that the universally unexpected slower ball struck his boot and not his bat. Before the appeal had died in Tom Amwell's throat the ball had rolled on and dislodged a bail. A bewildered and frustrated Jon Palmer took his leave. His annoyance was compounded when his successor, Dean Faulds, struck the two remaining balls of the over for four. Tom Amwell had tried to re-create the slower delivery – with dire results. The Outcasts passed fifty.

Two more extremely productive overs followed before it occurred to Farley Richardson that the fields he had set for his opening bowlers might not be appropriate. In the captain's opinion the fault lay with the bowlers rather than with himself. The team clearly needed some new fast bowlers. He would advise Cranley Nice that the criteria of company recruitment policy should be tweaked with that consideration in mind. For the moment Fred Ranger and Tom Amwell would have to be rested. Perhaps, Farley Richardson consoled himself, they might come back and do better against the Outcasts' tail. He entrusted the task of breaking the Pelham/Faulds partnership to one of the newer members of the side, Kris Vertz.

Austrian, with very little English, Kris Vertz was an unlikely person to be found in a village cricket side somewhere in England. He worked in the research laboratories of Nice Spice, had wandered down to the sports ground one spring day and joined in activities at the net. It had been reported to Farley Richardson that he had shown an astonishing ability to bowl a cricket ball with a high degree of accuracy (by village standards). He could even, it seemed, achieve late swing. His performance when put to further test was seen as all the more remarkable in light of his appearance. Although no more than thirty-five, he looked about twice that age with a very round bald head and piercing blue eyes. He had embraced cricket with enthusiasm. His one outing to date in match conditions had not conclusively tested his worth. Five overs had cost twenty-six runs, but he had taken one wicket. He was now to be given the opportunity to add to this record.

Farley Richardson was not as prescriptive in setting the field as he had been with the opening bowlers. This had nothing to do with any cricket nous he possessed, because he possessed very little cricket nous. Farley Richardson was in awe of scientists and was not comfortable in their presence. He felt particular unease in the presence of Kris Vertz. The penetrating blue eyes commanded co-operation not instruction. Accordingly the field-placing was a jointly conducted exercise. What emerged erred on the side of defence. If that was the intention, it was at least initially successful. Kris Vertz achieved a relatively accurate over from which no more than a couple of singles were taken.

Farley Richardson felt that it was too early for spin, but not too early for himself to join the attack. The sight of him preparing to bowl did not instil confidence in the rest of his team. They suppressed their doubts sufficiently well that Dean Faulds and David Pelham prepared themselves to avoid taking liberties until they had examined the new bowler. Farley Richardson set a very defensive field (he was not a complete fool), but that made no difference to his first ball which was a wide. The second might have been called a wide if Dean Faulds had not anticipated where it might pitch. With lightning footwork he reached it and slashed it backward of square to the boundary rope. Farley Richardson whirled his arms to convey the message that he had not yet loosened up and that the two previous balls were aberrations. His next delivery almost fooled Dean Faulds by being straight, but the next was short and inviting. The batsman needed no persuasion to accept the invitation and the ball was pulled one bounce over deep mid-wicket. Farley Richardson tried a faster ball which Dean Faulds missed. He tried another faster ball which hit the batsman on the

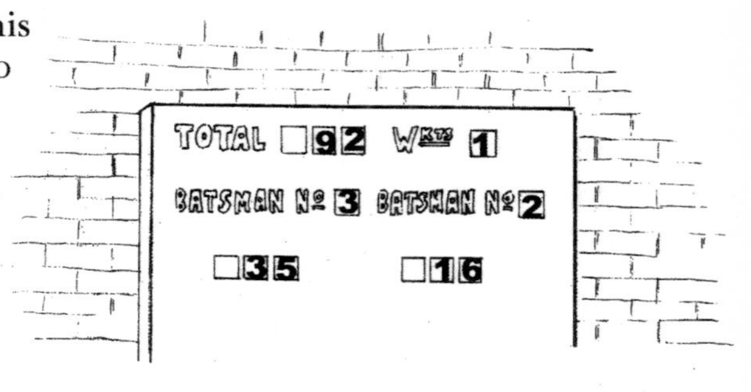

pads. Farley Richardson (to his disgust) was the only one to appeal. 'Not out', roared Syd Breakwell, who for once was right. The ball would have comfortably missed leg-stump. Farley Richardson found a leg-stump line again and this time was driven sweetly past the diving hand of mid-on for another boundary. Despite having twelve hit off it, Farley Richardson believed that it had not been a bad opening over. 'Nearly got him', he confided to Kris Vertz as he tossed him the ball. He was met by a cold blue stare.

Within the Northwood family conclave there was a stirring. Harry's father did not know a great deal about cricket, but he had seen enough to recognise that the batsmen were on top and against the array of bowlers so far seen were likely to remain on top. He calculated that a good hour might pass before his son came to the wicket. Harry had been deliberately vague about his place in the batting order, hinting (deceitfully) that it might be sixth or seventh – or even, when he sensed that there might be movement on his parents' part, eighth. Harry's mother knew less about cricket than her husband and was quite ready to fall in with his suggestion that they had time to take a look at Ranchmore House which was a (minor) historic building of (minor) note in the area. They would be back in good time to see Harry bat. Harry was liberated. In a trice Winston Jenkins was bearing down on him.

The two coaches struggled towards the Essex/Cambridgeshire border. The sense of struggle embraced vehicles and passengers alike. The coaches were old and ailing when purchased. Had their new owner spent more on mechanical overhaul than on painting the exteriors, it would have been a wiser investment, although even that was doubtful. The coaches shone and gleamed as they might have done in their heyday, but the trouble was that this particular marque of vehicle had never enjoyed what could truly be called a heyday. Only twenty had ever been built. It had been an ill-fated venture for an obscure manufacturing company, which had shortly afterwards gone bankrupt. Of the vehicles which had survived most could be found in the hands of travellers and three at least were parked engine-less on allotments where they acted as over-sized storage sheds. For a bus of the age and provenance of the Sleekway Express (optimistically styled Mark 1) it was an altogether more appropriate function than conveying Japanese tourists to Cambridge.

Undeterred by a series of failed career moves which had embraced among other things market gardening, office cleaning, body-building, female impersonation, computer servicing and building supplies, Roger Trysom's current reincarnation was as the proprietor of Culture Coachtours. A friend of his father had directed him to two coaches which were going cheap. In the understatement of the year he was advised that they would need 'a bit of doing up'. Ever the optimist, Roger Trysom had bought the advice and the vehicles. His budget had allowed for only a certain amount of doing up and he had put appearance before mechanical reliability. The outer paintwork had been complemented by some (necessary) re-upholstery, which had been undertaken by his mother. Her efforts, whilst painstaking, had fallen a little short of being wholly professional. The mechanical check-over had been left to 'a mate', who had said that the buses were as good as £500 could make them. Roger Trysom allowed himself to believe that he was on the threshold of a new career.

His small advertisement in an inexpensive travel journal, which, he had been told, circulated across the world, had produced some enquiries. They were exclusively from the Japanese. Had Roger Trysom questioned beyond the price of the advertisement for which he was paying this would not have surprised him. The journal to which he had entrusted his hopes of foreign business did indeed circulate across the world - right across the world, in Japan, and then only in certain quarters of that country. That was why he now found himself in charge of sixty geriatric Japanese visitors with an understanding of the English language, which ranged from limited to zero, but an increasing understanding of the travails of their journey.

Meanwhile David Pelham felt that his travails were behind him. There had been an uncomfortable period at the start of his innings, but now he had settled. The pitch seemed docile and the bowlers ordinary. With first Jon Palmer and then Dean Faulds hitting the cover off the ball, David Pelham could settle for the long view. This could be an opportunity to restore his all-rounder credentials. There was no need for any heroics. For all his baleful glares Kris Vertz caused David Pelham no problems as he added a gentle two and a quiet single to his score. He then prepared to take strike against Farley Richardson. If he had felt any disinclination to bowl again after the punishment he had received from Dean Faulds, Farley Richardson would have taken heart from the sight of David Pelham at the receiving end. Here, he believed, was the lesser of the two Outcasts. Although this was a view which he might hold in common with most of the Outcasts, it was to be of no significance in what followed.

Reaching out to a wide-ish ball, David Pelham steered it past the solitary slip and ran a nonchalant single. Dean Faulds took a moment or two longer to study the field settings than Farley Richardson had done in making them. The first ball he received was a wide down the leg side. With the next Farley Richardson managed to find a good length and direction. Dean Faulds patted the ball back to him. Not so the one which followed. This was struck with great force and the bowler kept his hands well away from it. He then pitched short and Dean Faulds lifted the ball over the inner ring of fielders and out of reach of the man patrolling the mid-wicket boundary. Farley Richardson veered to the leg side again and was rewarded with a ferocious pull. He smarted, deeply aware that sceptical eyes were rounding on him. Yet again it was short. Yet again it was on leg-stump. Yet again it was pulled by Dean Faulds. But the batsman had been careless. The big man, Ray Beckett, on the mid-wicket boundary, out of breath with his exertions and slow-moving at the best of times, had not regained the position in which Dean Faulds had mentally placed him. He was in position to take a straightforward catch. Farley Richardson's joy and Dean Faulds' fury were equal in their intensity. The batsman was three runs short of fifty and the Outcasts were 109-2.

An atmosphere of crisis was beginning to envelop the visitors. This had nothing to do with the score, but with the absence of refreshment of a suitable nature. Fourteen overs had passed without a pint being consumed. That this was a massive over-reaction to the events of the previous year had become the prevailing view in the Outcasts' dressing-room. The person to whom responsibility had been delegated to remedy this state of affairs, Harry Northwood, was in urgent consultation with his captain. Openly to carry back two large jugs of beer in full view of the co-licensee of the Pink Pedlar, Haydn Bliss, would be likely to have repercussions, the more serious of which would be an early inclusion of Harry Northwood on the list of barred people. This would have a negative effect on supplies. Desperate men can summon up great ingenuity. Within a few minutes it was arranged. What appeared to be a typical couple proudly propelling their baby in his push-chair left the ground through the pedestrian entrance. Its sole security guard had an entirely relaxed view about comings and goings, being more interested in a pile of magazines by the side of his stool. They were not about cricket.

Meanwhile Rashid Ali, who doubled as the Outcasts' wicket-keeper and legal adviser, had taken up station at the non-striker's end. Owing as much as anything to his own modesty, Rash had emerged late as one of the Outcasts' most reliable batsmen. Coincidentally he was the only member of the side who batted left-handed. His distinction as a left-hander was likely to be the most that could be remembered about him by the surviving members of last year's Doredell team, for his batting skills on that occasion had not been allowed to flourish. The current situation seemed made for him. A flat wicket and seemingly innocuous bowlers could be conditions conducive to a typical Rash, but not necessarily rash, onslaught. His friends in the pavilion settled down to watch him with as much anticipation as they awaited the overdue arrival of liquid refreshment.

David Pelham shared this sense of anticipation. It reinforced his determination to play a responsible anchor role and let Rashid Ali play his shots. There was no early evidence of his willingness to surrender the strike during the next over sent down by Kris Vertz. The Austrian seemed to be warming to his task although there was nothing warm in his demeanour. He made run-scoring difficult and when the only opportunity came off the fourth ball, Rashid Ali ensured that they ran two. It meant that at the beginning of the next over Rashid Ali would be facing Farley Richardson. After taking a wicket in his previous over there was never any doubt that the Doredell captain would continue.

To David Pelham's surprise Rashid Ali's response to a very ordinary delivery from Farley Richardson was to tuck it for one fine of the square leg umpire. Anxious to restore the strike to his partner, David Pelham quelled the temptation to lash a woefully short ball to the boundary, tapping it instead towards deep point for another single. If Farley Richardson had fielded better to his own bowling, Rashid Ali would not have been able to score a run off the third ball. David Pelham played a firm drive to a mid-off who had gone deep and Rashid Ali cut to third man. David Pelham then stunned the last ball of the over at his feet, not intending to run, but finding his partner hurtling towards him with a yell of 'yes'. With an answering yell of 'Christ' David Pelham took off in the opposite direction and the run was safely achieved.

The doting couple – in reality Sophie Crossley and Harry Northwood (now in line to be dubbed toy boy) – pushed the baby carriage. If Brian Sachin Crossley was a magnificent specimen of baby boy, so too was his conveyance. Constructed on the larger size of gross, the chariot had capacity for an ample-sized baby-cum-toddler and the many accessories needed to sustain an ample-sized baby-cum-toddler. To save the proud mother (or father) having to be burdened with another receptacle when shopping, this model of carriage also found space for a wire basket in which provisions could be placed. It was top of the range in all respects. On this special occasion, however, it had been stripped of everything, barring Brian Sachin, so that two large enamel jugs could be fixed in place and discreetly covered by a vinyl hood. Following a rough sketch map drawn by Winston Jenkins, the idyllic nuclear family arrived at its first port of call – the inconvenient store run by Mrs Iris Pearlhammer.

Winston Jenkins had not been able to remember whether Iris Pearlhammer was licensed to sell beer, wine and spirits. What he did vaguely recall from his conversation with her whilst standing in her shop a few months earlier was a shelf behind her on which were stacked cans of a well-known brand of stout. Before this point could be further investigated there was an interruption from Crossley Junior. He began to grizzle. Ever the caring mother, but also modern woman, Sophie Crossley extracted Brian Sachin from his harness and deposited him in the arms of a nonplussed Harry Northwood. 'Here you are, Dad', she said. 'Just nurse him a while. The practice will come in useful.' Leaving Harry no time to argue she departed with a giggle into the shop. Harry, appreciating that they were acting a part, felt that this was pushing verisimilitude too far especially as there was absolutely no one around to be deceived.

Winston Jenkins had been right. The cans of well-known stout were still there. They seemed to be the only form of alcoholic beverage on display. That they were on display at all represented a show of defiance on Iris Pearlhammer's part, for she had never bothered to go through the cumbersome procedure of acquiring a licence. That they were on display also showed Iris Pearlhammer's disinterest in the ambit and activities of Trading Standards officers. After asking for fifteen cans Sophie Crossley had received an old-fashioned look from Iris Pearlhammer which she had returned after noticing that the sell-by date had passed more than five years before. This in no way worried her as the purchase was not being made with consumption in mind. She, her temporary partner and son then made their way to their second destination whilst Iris Pearlhammer congratulated herself on another clearance of old stock. How right she had been, she told herself, to rescue it from that skip on the building site in Cambridge.

The batsmen were deep in conversation. 'What was all that about?', David Pelham demanded of his partner as he recovered from the scrambled run. And in a reference to Farley Richardson, 'I thought I was giving you the chance of blasting him to all corners.' Rashid Ali smiled. 'Patience, my friend, we still got six off the over.' 'It might only have been five', interrupted David Pelham, before his partner continued to explain his thinking. 'It would be a pity, my friend, to lose him too soon from the attack', said Rash with a dreamy look in his eyes. He need not have worried. After what he had thought to be a relatively tight over Farley Richardson had convinced himself that his bowling might hold the key to the match. In a sense it did (though not in the way he meant), but it was far from being the only factor in determining the outcome.

Despite his odd appearance and style Kris Vertz was putting in a respectable performance. There was nothing particularly threatening about his bowling. He was helped by bowling to a batsman in the form of David Pelham, who was trying to avoid risks. This allowed Kris Vertz to show an economy rate of less than three an over which contrasted sharply with the Outcasts' overall run-rate of more than seven an over. Kris Vertz's fourth over maintained the favourable balance. David Pelham was content with a neat deflection for two and a strike-stealing single. Boosted in confidence or not, Farley Richardson opened his next over with an appallingly wide delivery. The ball which followed was straighter, but short and wide. David Pelham, anchor-man or not, could not stop himself. He slashed it slightly uppishly, but in the end safely, for four. He thought he detected a slight shake of the head on the part of Rashid Ali as though his partner thought that such a shot might be premature. So he spared Farley Richardson's blushes by playing a couple of defensive shots before calling Rashid Ali for a leisurely single. Rash then managed to make a long-hop look spiteful by playing an over-elaborate defensive prod on the backfoot. He smiled in David Pelham's direction. The final ball of the over darted towards the leg side and Rashid Ali neatly helped it on its way. They ran three. Rash smiled again.

As Sophie Crossley and Harry Northwood, not forgetting Brian Sachin Crossley, approached the Pink Pedlar they were met by two tourist buses, one billowing black smoke from its rear and the other clouds of steam from under its bonnet. The vehicles ground agonisingly to a jerking halt adjacent to the pub's car park and disgorged a stream of elderly Japanese. Outside observers could not have begun to assess the degree of relief felt by these visitors as they emerged into the fresh sunlit air of Doredell. They had not set out in search of Doredell, but finding it was a joy they could never have anticipated when they left London earlier in the day. The joy was to be short-lived, but now they no longer cared whether they saw Cambridge. They made for the Pink Pedlar as if they had found their favourite tea-house. Doredell had taken on the mantle of an oasis of beauty in a journey of sorrow. It would all too soon cast it off.

In the year of their construction no one had thought to add air-conditioning, a WC or a hot drinks dispenser to these coaches. No one had thought of it since and certainly not Roger Trysom whose business was run on a shoestring and not a very long one at that. As the sun had beaten through the windows, the passengers found that they were unable to open them. At some point in their history they had been screwed shut. After more than an hour into the journey one man had desperately tried to loosen the screws with his nail file, but without success. Nor had the passengers had much to distract them from their increasing discomfort. The tour guides were Roger Trysom himself and an impecunious Japanese-American student called James Saito, who, being willing to try anything, had answered the former's advertisement. The tourists had been divided into two groups according to their ability to understand spoken English. By a misunderstanding Roger Trysom, who was familiar with the local sights and countryside, was with the group who understood nothing but Japanese whilst the bilingual James Saito, who had no clue where he was, accompanied those with the better grasp of English.

Roger Trysom's budget for the trip had envisaged lunch in a burger bar on the outskirts of Cambridge. He now realised that an itinerary which had taken in Dedham Vale and the Stour Valley had been too ambitious. It had always been ambitious with these particular coaches, but delays on the A12 and one or two steep gradients as they had finally headed west had placed on their engines a burden too great for their age and fitness. By the time the turning to Doredell was reached the age and fitness of the engines were not the only things about which the tour operator had to worry. There were clear signs of distress among the passengers, a distress not eased by his complete inability to understand what they were saying. When gestures became as sufficiently explicit as the emissions pouring from his vehicles he reluctantly signalled a change of course to his driver. His spur of the moment decision to turn off the main road - a decision he would come to regret – was prompted by a sign welcoming visitors to 'Historic Doredell' as a prefix to which a local artist had added the letters PRE. Judging that Cambridge might not now be an attainable destination, Roger Trysom hoped that an historic English village might offer some compensation. By the time the coaches came to a halt the tourists had greater priorities on their mind than sights of 'olde England'. One of the oldest passengers had already reminded himself that many years ago he had had a journey to Hawaii which had been more comfortable.

Harry Northwood was a quick-witted young man. Instantly he saw a way of turning this unexpected Japanese invasion to his advantage. Leaving Sophie Crossley with baby Brian Sachin in the pub's beer garden, Harry joined the stream of eager patrons entering the Pink Pedlar. As most of them were looking for the toilets before partaking of refreshment, Harry did not have to wait long to be served with six pints of Hoppenhall's Charger bitter. For added authenticity he had specified straight glasses. Nodding vaguely in the direction of the beer garden he had also requested a tray. Geraint Poppledown was too distracted by the sudden boost to his trade to question whether high quality real ale was the likely favoured beverage of a party of Japanese in his beer garden or whether coincidentally a party of real ale fanatics had decamped outside or whether the purchaser was eighteen. He was short-handed by virtue of his partner's absence at cricket. The licensee was not too distracted to note that Harry Northwood was a good-looking young man. So he was quite pleased rather than made suspicious by the young man's speedy reappearance to order six more pints.

Sophie Crossley had not been idle. Through an open window she had spotted someone in the pub's kitchen. A thought had immediately occurred to her. Moments later, armed with a tin-opener, she had set to work on the cans of stout, emptying their contents into a convenient nearby flowerbed. With equal care she had transferred the first six pints of Charger bitter into one of the jugs at the back of Brian Sachin's baby carriage. By the time another six pints had been added it was obvious to Sophie and Harry that they had capacity for perhaps four more pints. Harry was prepared to risk another trip to the bar, but when he put his head round the door he saw the Japanese standing four deep awaiting service from a thoroughly harassed Geraint Poppledown, who had to rely on the translation skills of James Saito to explain that marinated sea slug was not on the menu, not even as special dish of the day. Sophie therefore agreed: twelve pints in the jug were worth hundreds left in the cellar. They headed back to the sports ground with a judicious mix of speed and care to ensure that neither baby nor beer was spilled.

Kris Vertz's next over cost eight runs. This slippage in accuracy on the part of the austere Austrian scientist appeared to cause Farley Richardson more concern than his own next over being hit for nine. To everyone's surprise it was Kris Vertz who was taken off. True there had been one bad ball which Rashid Ali had smacked for four, but the other boundary had not been the fault of the bowler. The ball he had bowled would not have placed him in the ranks of Barnes or Bedser, but it had seamed and lifted. Rashid Ali had been obliged to hit it more defensively than aggressively and there would not even have been a single if the fielder had concentrated. Unfortunately the ball went through his fingers and an involuntary boundary was collected. The fielder was Farley Richardson. The subsequent removal of Kris Vertz from the attack caused him to evince the hint of a snarl in his captain's direction. By that time Farley Richardson had produced an over for which there were no excuses. The bowler somehow satisfied himself with the reflection that there had been no boundaries hit. That was largely because Doredell's other fielders had been more alert than their captain.

For the twenty-first over of the Outcasts' innings Farley Richardson's favours finally fell on a short, slightly plump, fresh-faced process worker. His name was Ed Fylder, who bowled off-spin – occasionally. He bowled regularly enough; it was the number of times he actually imparted spin that could be described as occasional. Having seen what he had seen Ed Fylder asked for a defensive field and Farley Richardson was not disposed to argue. Fresh from a further discussion with Rashid Ali, David Pelham gave the new bowler an encouraging start. With his eye now well in – his innings did not usually span twenty overs – David Pelham was not feeling in any trouble. In fact he was enjoying himself. Yet he was puzzled.

If an opinion pollster had been at work amongst the Japanese tourists who had now infested Doredell, their state of mind would have been quickly established as puzzled. Not all of them actually understood they were not in Cambridge. Some were still wandering round the village vainly looking for buildings which might correspond with pictures they had seen of Cambridge's famous colleges. A trickle of the more intrepid amongst them had discovered Iris Pearlhammer's shop. For a while they contented themselves writing sepia-coloured postcards of old Doredell, another welcome diminution of the storekeeper's old stock. The remainder of the Japanese, cutting their losses, had not stirred from the Pink Pedlar. Neither had Roger Trysom's coaches stirred from their place of rest outside the pub.

Too late Roger Trysom had found out that Doredell possessed no garage. In opting for the Essex side of the county boundary for what he supposed to be the benefit of his frustrated passengers, he now realised that the whole party was marooned in a facilities-challenged backwater. The nearest thing to a garage, he had learned from Geraint Poppledown, was in Hayste. This was not far as the crow was wont to fly, but it presented a challenge to Roger Trysom. He had yet to form a plan to meet it. Elsewhere various other plans were in various stages of execution.

It had taken David Pelham a while to recognise him, but some twenty overs into the match he realised that the rarely-employed leg-spinner who had done them so much damage last year was in fact on the field. That being the case it seemed strange that he had not been brought into the attack. Of course David Pelham did not know how rarely the leg-spinner had been employed under the old regime. It happened that the bowler was unlikely to commend himself to the new captain of Doredell cricket club. There were two reasons why he was out of favour. Both were utterly unconnected with his absence or otherwise of bowling skills. Adrian Wills had left the employment of Nice Spice of his own accord and then had the temerity to stand for the council in the forthcoming by-election in opposition to the candidate favoured by the company. He was lucky still to be in the side. The team was not so well endowed with talent that it could afford (as yet) to dispense with his consistent batting.

As he waited to see how Rashid Ali's plans for dealing with Farley Richardson unfolded, David Pelham surveyed the scene with contentment. From his perspective the contrast with last year was very marked indeed. Undoubtedly the spice company possessed a better ground with a better pitch than the previous home of the cricket club. In truth David Pelham was not in the best position to make such a qualitative judgement. His stay at the wicket had been of the briefest duration. He had also been very drunk. It was an altogether better gloss on the event to claim that he had been bamboozled by a viciously turning ball off an unplayable surface. After all some of his team-mates had not been in the best position to argue. They had been looking for a good excuse themselves.

Rashid Ali could scarcely conceal his delight that Farley Richardson was going to continue bowling. He sneaked a quick smile towards David Pelham and then made an elaborate fuss of playing out an over which cost no more than a wide. With real mischief in mind Rashid Ali had decided to play a little longer with the fish he had on his line. At the other end David Pelham could feel a rare half-century coming on. He was determined not to lose out. He therefore played Ed Fylder with care whilst advancing his score by four. This took the Outcasts past one hundred and fifty. With seventeen overs left (a forty-over match had been agreed) it was a good score.

The next fifteen minutes were a period in his life which Farley Richardson would be keen to forget. Thinking that he had by now done enough to set him up, Rashid Ali prepared to take Farley Richardson's bowling apart. The first two balls, which were reachable, were reached with alacrity and dispatched over square leg for six apiece. The third ball was fuller and Rashid Ali stroked it wide of mid-on. He was denied a boundary by some agile fielding on the part of Jim Flote. David Pelham took his cue, but not his chance. He swung mightily at a loose delivery from Farley Richardson and missed. Next ball he tried again. This time he connected. The ball did not go where he intended, but nevertheless it was a boundary which took him to the brink of the fifty mark. Farley Richardson's next offering was a full toss which was so tempting that David Pelham felt his mouth watering. He advanced expectantly towards it.

The twelve pints had not lasted long even if, for subterfuge, they had had to be decanted from the jug into redundant stout cans before consumption. There was impatience in the Outcasts' section of the pavilion for the pitcher to be taken to the well again. Harry Northwood looked anxiously at his watch, trying to calculate when his parents might return from their excursion to Ranchmore House. He did not relish the complication of being caught in transit between the cricket ground and the Pink Pedlar either on the arm of a woman and son or as an amateur drayman. Perhaps there was time. Urged on by his team-mates he located a willing Sophie. Brian Sachin was conveniently taking a nap in his carrycot in the high tech scorebox. Simon was content to look after him. Brian Sachin's place in the superior pushchair was taken by an extra jug which had been found in

the pavilion. It was discreetly covered as the expedition moved off. The question was whether the same trick could be pulled off a second time. With the unwitting co-operation of Doredell's Japanese visitors, it could.

The usual processes were not Andy Lizzard's preferred way of doing business. He was a man for direct action. The treatment handed out to Mildred Askern seemed to provide a heaven-sent opportunity. On the back of this grievance he reckoned that he could have the whole works unionised within days. Growing impatient with the company's internal appeals mechanism, Andy Lizzard believed that the moment must not be lost. Sidling alongside Mildred Askern, he suggested that she stepped outside to have a quick brew from the drinks dispenser in the porch. Leaving her to slake her thirst, he shot back into the department to let it be known that Mildred had walked off the job and deserved an immediate show of solidarity. Within a minute the place was empty. Skilfully Andy Lizzard had ensured that the departing workers filed out through the next-door department so that the cause of dissension should be more widely known. Sub-groups gradually formed. Andy Lizzard busied himself in maximising the contagion.

Oblivious of impending crisis where it mattered most Farley Richardson was celebrating. Sitting on the ground nursing an aching foot he might have been, but glowing with satisfaction he certainly was. David Pelham, perhaps over-anxious about reaching fifty and perhaps over-confident in his ability to dispatch Farley Richardson's low grade bowling, had swooped on the full toss and hit it smartly down the track. Nine times out of ten it would have been four. But not this time. By a bizarre fluke, Farley Richardson had slipped as he completed his follow-through leaving his foot extended in the path of the oncoming drive. The ball ricocheted back like a rifle shot to be retrieved by the wicket-keeper with David Pelham stranded in pursuit of a triumphant, but now stillborn, run. He was easily run out. Farley Richardson took this as a personal triumph. It was to be a cruelly false dawn.

A parched but resolute Winston Jenkins crossed with a parched and furious David Pelham. The first consignment of Hoppenhall's Charger bitter had not stretched to the captain of the side.

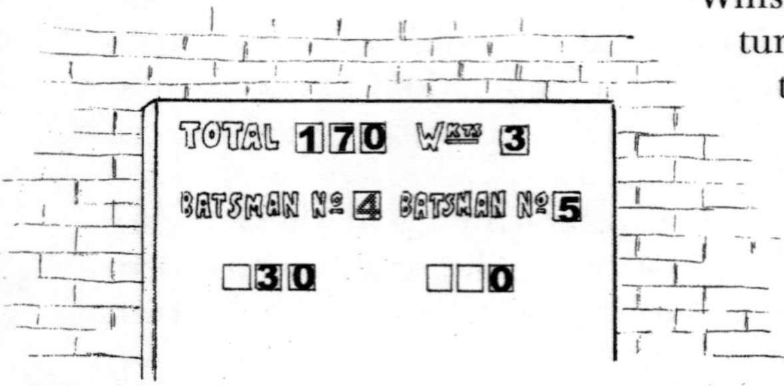

Winston's back had not been turned for long, but what he thought had been a filled stout can was, when he finally reached for it, empty. The faces of the men he was leading were either averted or inscrutable. In Winston's mind that decided it. He would bat next, ahead of Phil Cole and Harry Northwood. He would grab some of the action although he had been denied the beer. If David Pelham could score runs, Winston reasoned, then he himself should have a good chance. This looked to be a great day for batting – so long, he reminded himself at the last minute, as that leg-spinner was kept out of the way.

The Pink Pedlar had the appearance of being under Japanese occupation. Sophie Crossley took up station in the beer garden whilst Harry Northwood advanced on the bar. Snacks were still being served to disparate groups of Japanese visitors, but the earlier pressure had obviously eased. Emboldened, Harry asked for eight pints. Having conveyed them to the garden outside, Harry was soon back for another round. Geraint Poppledown now had time to be curious. After a moment or two he followed his thirsty customer. The sight that greeted him would forever be etched on his memory. Eight very elderly Japanese ladies sat at a table with empty pint glasses in front of them and serene smiles on their faces. Harry Northwood deftly removed the empties and replaced them with full glasses from his tray. Geraint Poppledown stared at this scene in bemusement, scratched his head and retreated indoors.

Swiftly the glasses were emptied into the jugs concealed in Brian Sachin's pushchair. Harry was on his way back to the bar. Sophie Crossley thanked James Saito whom she had nimbly recruited to help her create the scene to which Geraint Poppledown had been treated. A few words from the tour guide had assured and amused the Japanese matrons, who had merely been resting in anticipation of when they might be resuming their sightseeing tour. (This was a question to which there was as yet no ready answer,) With twenty-four pints on board Harry and Sophie began their return journey. This should have been the least stressful part of the operation. It wasn't.

Rashid Ali felt that he had another appointment with Farley Richardson, if, as he felt sure, the hapless captain of Doredell would bowl his final allotted over. The batsman had not yet faced Ed Fylder, but from what he had observed he did not think that the off-spinner was any great threat. And so it proved. Rashid Ali was able to do much as he pleased. A steady seven runs came from the over with Rashid Ali making sure that he gained the strike. He found that Farley Richardson was in no mood to shirk, as he saw it, further glory. Thus began an over which all who saw it would remember for a long time.

The number of spectators had increased to a respectable size for a sleepy afternoon on the Essex/Cambridgeshire border. No one slept. A terrible long-hop from Farley Richardson was lifted for six a long way over mid-wicket. A full toss followed, but this earned only four. The next ball was fairly straight and fairly close to a length. Rashid Ali took two steps down the pitch and drove it high for another six. With this magnificent shot he reached his fifty. It was greeted with respectful applause. At this point Farley Richardson must have lost his presence of mind. Trying to alter the angle of delivery, he bowled from wide of the stumps. The ball passed well wide of where both batsman and wicket-keeper were standing. Four extras resulted. Farley Richardson tried again, but overstepped the mark and was called in a career-threatening move by Rodney Carrington for no-balling. Rashid Ali swung it effortlessly for a bonus six. Farley Richardson made the mistake of re-pacing his run, ended up thoroughly confusing himself and was no-balled again. Another boundary followed. Thirty runs had accumulated, the Outcasts' score had gone past two hundred and the over still had half its legitimate span to come.

Farley Richardson could count. That was one of the things he did well. He could no longer fool himself. He felt all eyes upon him and he knew they were not rapt in admiration. He began to count the cost not just to the performance of Doredell cricket club, but to his own career. It was a fatal distraction at this juncture. The next ball was wide and signalled as such. Then at last he bowled a legal ball, but it was short and hammered square for another boundary. Short of patience (whether with himself or the batsman was neither here nor there) Farley Richardson tried a faster ball and was no-balled again for overstepping. Rashid Ali, eluding mid-on's stretched right hand, helped himself to a boundary. The bowler switched to a slower ball and saw it sail back over his head one bounce to the rope. One ball left. Farley Richardson tried to clear his head. Concentrating hard he strove for line and length. It was his best effort. Too bad that the batsman used his feet intelligently and drove higher and harder in his own best effort. The over ended. It had contained eleven deliveries and cost forty-nine runs. The crowd's enthusiasm by now had been kindled. Farley Richardson's most certainly had not. The applause and cheers were this time extremely disrespectful.

Ranchmore House had been a disappointment to Mr and Mrs Northwood. Most of its paintings of note were on loan to the National Gallery (of Botswana). The garden flowers had been ravaged by some as yet unidentified pest. The noted miniature railway was temporarily shut down whilst engineers dealt with a suspected case of gauge corner cracking. Even the cafeteria was on restricted service due to staff shortages. So there had not been much to see or do if your interest was not in firearms of which Ranchmore House boasted a large collection. This was not a major area of interest for the Northwoods, especially Mrs Northwood whose mind was in any case turning towards a sighting of her son in whites. After a perfunctory tour of the rooms they had left.

Mrs Northwood's renewed sighting of her son was not in whites, but unmistakably walking along the road deep in conversation with a young woman who was pushing an overlarge (Mrs Northwood's opinion) baby carriage. The car slid alongside. Harry was startled by his mother's greeting. What indeed was he doing here? Harry was pressured into some fast thinking. Like many of his generation (and probably generations through the ages) his relationship with his parents was based on the need-not-to-know principle. Hence they knew next-to-nothing about the Outcasts with whom Harry had been spending an increasing amount of his time. They were completely unaware of a scorer called Simon Crossley who had a wife and a baby. Without this foreknowledge, Harry could readily anticipate, his mother was capable of putting an entirely erroneous construction on his close proximity to this young woman and child.

Harry produced what was, for him, an unnatural torrent of words to drown his mother's nascent suspicions. The Northwoods learned more about the Outcasts in fifty-six seconds than they had previously gleaned in fifty-six weeks. It was mostly sanitised generality, but with particular emphasis on Simon, Sophie and the youngest Outcast of all. Harry overdid it. His mother began to get out of the car to submit the infant prodigy to closer inspection. Harry leaned heavily against the car to make this operation as difficult as possible whilst desperately racking his brains for another excuse or invention. Even halfway towards the pushchair the smell of hops and malt would have felled her. Harry was saved embarrassment by Sophie's inspiration and an entirely fortuitous event.

Having completed his permitted maximum number of overs Farley Richardson was also spared embarrassment – for the time being. Ed Fylder continued the bowling from the Doredell end with mixed emotions. Part of him reckoned that his captain was a total buffoon as a cricketer whilst another part of him reacted against the humiliation being heaped on the team. His resolve was stiffened. To the new batsman, Winston Jenkins, he sent down a respectable over conceding no more than a single off the last ball. Winston's relief to be off the mark was tempered slightly by ironic cheers and (empty) beer-can clinking by the rest of the team in the pavilion.

Despite the drubbing he had received Farley Richardson remained in an unforgiving mood towards Adrian Wills. His prejudice was further reinforced by the belief that, if his own bowling had been expensive, a leg-spinner on this wicket would fare worse. No one who knew was prepared to remind him what had happened when the Outcasts had last faced Doredell's rarely-employed leg-spinner. Admittedly there had been special factors at work.

The only other untried option was Jim Flote, who was Doredell's stock bowler, but was more safely defined as an opening batsman. He was not a stock bowler in the usual sense. He simply could not be relied on to reel off over after over at low cost. Jim Flote was in the category of bowler to be used when the captain could not think what else to do, and sometimes he was lucky. Farley Richardson was not by temperament someone who saw himself as not knowing what to do. For the moment he decided to give Fred Ranger another go even though the Outcasts' tail had not yet presented itself. It was a decision about which Winston Jenkins felt relaxed and optimistic.

Brian Sachin Crossley, by now gurgling happily on his playmat in the scorebox with a rubber dolphin, would have been surprised to know that he had had a very bad night and that on no account could his mother risk him being disturbed. Whether this improvisation would have warded off Mrs Northwood from taking 'just a peep' was never put to the test. With the matter still unresolved there was a whistle and a shout. A large breakdown recovery vehicle approached, its way blocked by the Northwoods' car. Harry's mother closed the car door again, forced to make do with Sophie's promise that she would bring the baby across the moment he woke. Her husband manoeuvred the car forward and prepared to do business with the Nice Spice security system. The consignment of ale was carried through the pedestrian entrance past an absorbed security guard and arrived ahead of the Northwoods by several minutes.

Even the most occasional watcher of cricket should have been able to derive some pleasure from the game so far. A scoring rate in excess of eight an over was pretty reasonable fare at any level of cricket. The fact that this amount of punishment was being handed out to the home team might have been expected to subdue spectators. In fact they had been quite animated. This was far from being a homogeneous crowd. Those who came from the next-door village of Hayste where there was no cricket club gave a kind of detached support to Doredell, but they felt free to cheer anything of note. Since the virtual acquisition of Doredell cricket club by Nice Spice, employees of the company felt obliged to cheer on the local side. However, there had also been a negative aspect to this development. People who had been made redundant no longer felt the same degree of allegiance, especially not towards members of the team most closely identified with their former employer. The taking apart of Farley Richardson had gone down really well with them. Equally there were people present who remembered the Outcasts' previous visit with disfavour bordering in some cases on disgust. So it was a crowd of disparate elements. And the Japanese had yet to put in an appearance.

After Farley Richardson's excruciating experience Fred Ranger

Iris Pearlhammer satisfied most of their needs either in Hayste or at some more distant but more delightful shopping mall. This had had a depressing effect on the number of retail outlets in Doredell unless the potential customer had an interest in antiques or pine furniture. It did not have to be an extensive interest to be quickly satisfied. None of the Japanese tourists mistakenly ferried to Doredell by Roger Trysom had travelled with the acquisition of pine furniture in mind. The owner of one of the antique shops had sold a nineteenth century wrought iron poker, but it was not clear whether the elderly Japanese purchaser, wearying of the excuses of the tour leader, had purchased it with a utilitarian or an offensive purpose in mind.

Another of the Japanese, who had once worked in the motor industry, had an eye (watery though it might now be) for detail. He took in the state in which the coaches had come to a halt and he took in the state of the Bilsdon brothers when they had later appeared on the scene. It did not take him long to work out that he and his companions would not be escaping Doredell at an early hour. Adventurous in spirit he had followed in the direction set by a trickle of local people. That was how he found the cricket match. He returned to the centre of the village as fast as his Zimmer frame would allow to acquaint his fellow tourists with the discovery of this strange English folk ritual. Apart from the ladies, who preferred to rest in the beer garden of the Pink Pedlar, most of the Japanese made their cautious way to the sports ground. By the time they arrived the tea interval had begun.

Before then the Outcasts' innings had proceeded for a while at a more sedate, but still satisfying pace. There was a combination of reasons for the change of tempo. No bowler on the Doredell side could be quite as awful as Farley Richardson. In the wake of their captain's dire performance, the other players had become more determined that their team should salvage some pride. They applied themselves with far greater determination than perhaps they had ever done. The eventual dismissal of Rashid Ali took the supercharge out of the Outcasts' batting. His replacement was not the naturally aggressive Harry Northwood, who was thought to be more important playing the role of drayman, but Phil Cole whose style in cricket parlance was to nudge and nurdle. That said, it remained a very good batting wicket and the bowlers, however hard they tried, were not in the penetrative or restrictive class of the greatest. But then their opponents were only the Outcasts. However, Farley Richardson had not yet made his last misjudgement.

Recollection of last year's fixture had also influenced the course of the innings. As Rashid Ali had prepared to face the thirtieth over of the innings which was to be bowled by Fred Ranger, his mind flickered back to how he had performed on the last occasion he had faced Doredell. He shuddered.

It had not been his greatest day. He had not been exactly drunk, but neither had he been fit. In Bill Blimp's mobile bar Rashid Ali had remained firmly on the lower deck. By Outcasts' standards he was a moderate consumer of ale, but he refrained from drinking any at all on that journey. Pleading a bad headache, he was reticent about the reason.

The previous evening Rashid Ali had been introduced into the exclusive ranks of a dining club which had been set up by some of his friends in the legal profession. The club went by the title of The Briefs, but nothing too serious was ever contemplated at its gatherings. Evenings when new members were introduced tended to be exceptionally hilarious. Certain rituals took place at which the name of the club provided more than the faintest hint. The amount of legal badinage exchanged was strictly in modest proportion to the quality of the fare which graced the table. Not wishing in any way to indicate a lack of appreciation of the honour he was being paid for admission to this company of respectable and respected solicitors, Rashid Ali had entered fully into the spirit of the festivities. After some well chosen vintage wines, spirit was not an inappropriate word to attach to the event. As he fumbled his way from the taxi to his front door Rashid Ali giggled at the silly thought that the club he had joined could well have been called The Shorts instead of The Briefs. In the morning he was no longer giggling.

It had required a supreme act of willpower on Rashid Ali's part to be on time for departure to Doredell the following day. The fact that he might not have been his usual eager and proficient self was betrayed not by his abstinence on the journey, but his insistence that Kevin Newton should keep wicket. The point could not be further argued as on arrival he had been found to be asleep – a deep sleep which neither light-hearted nor heavy-handed banter could disturb. It had not been part of Tim Jackson's game-

plan as twelfth man to do much more on the field than take out a sweater or a shin guard. He had imbibed on the journey accordingly.

What had finally awoken Rashid Ali was the noisy return to the double-decker of a couple of his team-mates who fancied a swift pint before tea at the end of Doredell's innings. Down to bat at four, Rash steeled himself to the task after a barrage of teasing. He had watched with contentment the opening stand of Alan Birch and Stewart Thorogood and thought that he might yet be spared. It was not to be and nor was it one of his more productive performances. After five limp singles he had been called for a sixth by a super-charged Ray Burrill. Rash's aching head and reluctant limbs had not been a match for a smart piece of fielding and a direct hit on the stumps.

Well, he thought, he had made up for that this year. He nonchalantly stroked Fred Ranger's second ball for two and followed it three balls later with a single. Winston Jenkins blocked the last ball of the over. He too was thinking. They had joked about him last year, but, as time passed, he had convinced himself that he had been a victim of exaggeration.

Winston had to admit to himself that he had taken full advantage of Bill Blimp's innovatory bar. He had probably consumed a little more than he had intended, but he put that down to the delay on the journey. The coach may have catered for input, but its lack of matching provision for output was a problem. Halfway across Hertfordshire there had been insistence on a comfort stop. The route they were following seemed bereft of public lavatories. It was not bereft of public houses. From a distance of three hundred yards Charlie Colson's eye for detail spotted the Suggistons' sign and that was why the double-decker had rolled into the car park of the Thirsty Thresher. It was a while before it rolled out again. With all respect to Bill Blimp for his initiative, Suggies at the Thirsty Thresher was better kept than the beer in the barrel on the top deck of a moving vehicle. Having tried two pints during the stopover and then another two pints on board, Winston Jenkins was absolutely clear on the point, but not, as it proved, about much else.

By the time he was called upon to bat, Winston Jenkins felt better, but that had been purely relative. He had walked to the wicket with what he had fondly imagined was a spring in his step. To an impartial observer his gait resembled more nearly the uncertain approach of a man who had been singled out to assist the on-stage magician. Winston's face had equally borne the expression of not being sure what was expected of him. His instincts told him to take guard and look around the field. What he saw first was Ray Burrill bearing down on him from the other end. With two boundaries to his name Ray was in a cheery mood, which was only partly alcohol-induced. He had a ready formula for ending the match and he was anxious to press it on his new partner. However, he had not anticipated the part to be played by Mostyn Winchope.

This year would be different, Winston Jenkins concluded, as he waited to see how Rashid Ali would deal with Ed Fylder. It turned out to be a case of how Ed Fylder would deal with Rashid Ali. The first delivery of the over did not make this apparent. It strayed towards the batsman's legs and was driven beautifully wide of mid-on for four. Thereafter the bowler seemed to find his line against the left-hander. With three well-flighted deliveries he got the ball to turn away from the bat and commanded respect from Rashid Ali. The next one also turned the other way. If this was a surprise to the bowler, he managed not to show it. However, it was a complete surprise to Rashid Ali who was comprehensively bowled.

It was an intense disappointment to Mr and Mrs Northwood not to see their son march out to the wicket at this point, the more so as he had now appeared in his whites. This was a stratagem on Harry's part. He had reconciled himself to the improbability of his having to bat at all in view of how well the team had done and in view of how thirsty the team was proving to be. Another expedition to the pub would be very difficult to execute especially as his mother had had her belated introduction to Brian Sachin Crossley and was coo-cooing with him on the grass adjacent to the scorebox. In these circumstances the baby carriage could not leave with or without its human cargo. By changing into his whites Harry reckoned that he could attract his mother's attention away from Brian Sachin in order to obtain a precious photograph. He hated having his picture taken, but it was a forfeit he was prepared to make always supposing, he thought bitterly, that there was any film left in his mother's camera after her prolonged session of baby worship.

Fortunately the bait was taken. Mrs Northwood moved towards the other end of the pavilion. Sophie Crossley swooped and took her son back into the scorebox to the pleasure of his father but the veiled hostility of his opposite number, hunched protectively over his electronic device as though the baby might knock it from his possession. The words, 'smile, dear, you look lovely', addressed to Harry by his mother made him glower all the more. He knew that the instruction would have been heard by other members of the team. The film allowed as many as six shots to be taken and Harry was forced to endure them all. The final indignity was when his father joined in the session demanding that his son should practise an attacking shot. When his mother was done Harry, boiling with embarrassment, retreated into the pavilion to be greeted with cries of 'you do look lovely, Harry dear' and loud kissing noises as he made his way to the changing-room. What he did for ale, Harry thought to himself, as he once again donned his civilian garb.

During this time there had been three overs of studious play which had advanced the Outcasts' score by eleven runs. The only boundary came when Tom Amwell was brought back into the attack. Told by his captain to be aggressive he dug one in short to Winston Jenkins. The batsman, who had been telling himself not to be aggressive, could not resist. Being therefore less than one hundred percent committed to the shot – nearly always fatal with the hook – Winston was lucky to escape. Having not got the carry, the ball was falling to earth in the vicinity of Adrian Wills. The fielder was late to attend to the matter as he appeared to be involved in an altercation with a spectator (an aggressive Flote supporter). Alerted finally to the approaching missile, he made a terrible hash of it. The ultimate indignity came when his sprawling effort knocked the ball against the boundary rope. This stroke – be it the batsman's or the fielder's – carried the Outcasts' score past the two hundred and fifty mark. There were six overs left.

Harry Northwood's father's interest in the fixture between the Outcasts and Doredell cricket club began to wane. He had made the detour out of a genuine desire to see Harry perform. With so little of the Outcasts' innings left the sight of his son changed out of his whites sent a clear signal that Harry was unlikely to be doing much batting. He did not bowl and so to stay on to watch him field did not hold out much attraction. Of greater interest now was their destination in Cambridge. Their host produced an outstanding home brew and Harry's father thought that a couple of early pints would be an excellent prelude to the evening's hospitality. This was not a consideration likely to weigh with Harry's mother, but she, knowing nothing about the finer points of cricket, found some compensation in the photographs she had taken even if her intelligence-gathering operation regarding Harry's friends was showing only a poor return. Nevertheless she acquiesced in the retreat from Doredell leaving Harry with the chilling warning: 'Never mind, dear, we'll try and get along to your next match.' Keeping nimbly downwind and avoiding a maternal embrace, Harry trusted that his by now beer-laden breath had gone undetected. Once again he was free but he had to move fast.

With only six overs left a similar thought was going through the minds of the batsmen. It was agreed between Winston Jenkins and Phil Cole that a score of three hundred ought to be their target. To have any chance of getting near it Winston would have to secure the majority of the strike. Big hitting was what he enjoyed, but he did not always achieve success when embarked on it. Phil Cole – perhaps defensively – pointed out that a run a ball would carry them close to three hundred, but then Winston reminded him of their limited bowling attack. This persuaded Phil Cole to buy into the riskier strategy. After all, he reasoned to himself, Winston was captain.

Harry Northwood and Sophie Crossley travelled at speed towards the Pink Pedlar, passing on the way a slow-moving Japanese procession coming towards them. Had a concerned citizen observed the pace at which the wheels of the deluxe baby carriage sped along the road, he or she might have been disposed to ring the NSPCC or Social Services to complain about behaviour prejudicial to the welfare of an infant. The concerned citizen would not have known that the baby with title to the deluxe vehicle was actually enjoying a high standard of welfare in a nearby cricket scorebox. Fortunately the concerned citizen must have been off duty for Harry and Sophie reached the pub without the intervention of anyone. Harry's first thought on encountering the Japanese advance towards the sports ground was to wonder whether his helpful cover might have disappeared. He was reassured to see the ladies where he had left them in the beer garden, still with empty beer glasses in front of them and contented smiles on their faces.

There was no contented smile on Harry Northwood's face when he found the pub door firmly shut. Affixed to it was a notice informing the thirsty and maybe exhausted wayfarer that the establishment would be open again 'in an hour'. Harry gave vent to an expression which his mother would not have liked. Ordinarily the pub would have been open all day, but Geraint Poppledown had still to adjust to his partner's penchant for playing cricket. The added factor of an exceptional volume of tourist trade had left Geraint, as he confessed later, 'quite stressed out'. Before taking to his bed for 'a spot of shut-eye' he had remembered to shout last orders. This expression had been obligingly translated by James Saito before he too disappeared. The empty glasses which Harry had now seen were not the ones he had previously left behind. Harry quailed at the thought of the disgruntled reception when he rejoined his team-mates empty-handed and ale-less.

The two tourist far-from-deluxe coaches had not disappeared. They were obstinately parked outside the Pink Pedlar. A lively discussion was taking place between Roger Trysom and the Bilsdon brothers. A truly independent audit of the situation would have demonstrated that there was no hope of a successful outcome where lack of expertise was pitted against time-expired mechanical engineering. What the Bilsdon brothers lacked in applicable practical knowledge of the internal combustion engine they made up for in commercial precociousness. The bill, they informed Roger Trysom, for their diligent but fruitless ministrations, together with weekend call-out charge, was £250. With neither his drivers nor James Saito in evidence to give him support the tour operator was losing the argument. He eventually persuaded the Bilsdons to accept £200 cash. By way of a consolatory remark Trevor Bilsdon said that the vehicles should fetch a lot more than that as scrap. His brother, Neil, was quick to remind him that removal costs would have to be deducted. It was not just the bloody coaches, Roger Trysom thought to himself, there was also the cost of removing the passengers from Doredell. He would need to hire a bus and he weighed up the possibility of a whip-round amongst the Japanese to help to defray the cost. He brightened: it could be passed off as a tip for the drivers.

Phil Cole prepared to face Ed Fylder who was about to commence his final over. Phil permitted himself a twirl of the bat Alec Stewart-style (although there, of course, the comparison ended). He was content with his assigned role in the remainder of the innings. He felt emboldened to take a more assertive role in field-setting before he bowled his next over, and consequently felt more comfortable than during his opening spell. He was quickly into a familiar rhythm and produced his most economical over to date. The cost was a mere four runs. Rashid Ali at last got back the strike, but against Ed Fylder he was not given the leeway offered by Farley Richardson. Nevertheless it was a docile pitch and Ed Fylder was not much more than a docile spinner. Rashid Ali was a good player of spin and an excellent player of docile spin. Yet he was tested by a determined effort at accuracy by the bowler. The outcome was three straightforward singles.

The breakdown recovery truck had finally located its quarry outside the Pink Pedlar. Roger Trysom was relieved, but his relief would be short-lived. He thought that he had been lucky to establish contact with a conveniently local garage which was operational on a Saturday afternoon. Yet it was precisely at this point that his luck ran out. The Bilsdon brothers were willing, keen, hard-working and incompetent. To be fair to them – which by now few people around Hayste were prepared to be – any capable mechanical engineer might have balked at the elderly coaches which Roger Trysom had brought to Doredell. However, the two brothers and the two coaches was a fatal combination. At first this was not apparent. The Bilsdon brothers exuded confidence – which the cognoscenti would have recognised as a warning sign – and Roger Trysom allowed himself a moment of optimism. It would not last much longer than that.

The Japanese tourists had begun to recognise the limitations of Doredell as one of Britain's historical gems. After the original Saxon settlement from which only the church had survived, the next significant development in the village had been in Elizabethan times – in 1968 to be precise. This was when the then rural council had been persuaded of the merits of a mixed development of 'tasteful country homes' to meet housing needs and support employment opportunities in this border area. The resulting forty-two houses and eight bungalows might with most accuracy be described as units of accommodation. There was nothing about them which smacked of taste or rural character. The few older houses of note would not detain the visitor long. Other diversions were sparse. Anyone who had access to transport or an aversion to felt the warm glow of approximately (it was difficult to be exact when drinking from cans) two pints of fine ale in his belly and warmed to the prospect of more to come. Phil did not mind having to play second fiddle whilst his muscular partner sought to lay about him. Phil was amused at the thought of holding on to his record. In three previous visits to Doredell he had yet to be dismissed. Admittedly, like any record, it needed close examination. On the first occasion he had not actually been called upon to bat. The next time he had gone to the wicket in Doredell it had been to face nine balls, a feat he had accomplished without a run to his name. This did not stop him pointing out that it was the obtrusion of his pad which had led to the accumulation of seven valuable leg-byes. And then there had been last year.

With many more than two pints of fine and Bill Blimp's not quite so fine ale in his belly, Phil Cole had answered the unexpected call. He had first had to be prised from the environs of the double-decker where, pint glass in hand, he had been engaged in a long drawn-out and increasingly argumentative discussion about the structure of English cricket with a foul-mouthed man who turned out to be the headteacher of a local primary school. It had then been necessary to insert Phil into his cricket gear and send him on his way. There had been no warm glow, more a leaden weight and a feeling of drowsiness. He had walked unsteadily to the receiving end and had not been his usual precise self in taking guard. He saw that it was a slow bowler; he had not seen what had gone before. What followed was not a pretty sight.

Three not out then; four not out now; within a trice five not out as Phil Cole dutifully dabbed Ed Fylder's first ball past the now solitary slip towards third man. The strike transferred to Winston Jenkins without obvious effect. Winston completely missed Ed Fylder's next delivery, but had kept one foot anchored in the crease. The ball which followed was too good to be slogged. Winston was forced to defend. It was another dot ball in the scorebook and the laptop. Almost apologetically Winston Jenkins ran a single on the fourth ball of the over. Phil Cole presented him with the strike again and off the last ball they scrambled a couple of runs. The yield from the over did not match the prescription of the batsmen. However, amidst the general carnage Ed Fylder could be proud of his spell of eight overs, one maiden, twenty-five runs and one wicket.

Tom Amwell had no similar claim to be pleased with himself. His six overs had already cost nearly twice as much as Ed Fylder's total allocation. His seventh over was not destined to improve matters. Again Phil Cole obliged by taking a sharp single off the first ball. Tom Amwell's pace and direction – especially his direction – were more to Winston Jenkins' liking. When the bowler pitched straight he kept Winston quiet, but the two balls which were twelve and eighteen inches outside off-stump were hit hard by Winston Jenkins for four apiece. He felt much better. Farley Richardson did not. As he called up the professorial Austrian to succeed Ed Fylder at the Doredell end a little maggot of uncertainty nibbled at his mind. His equanimity was not helped by another close encounter with the penetrative blue stare. That aside, Kris Vertz did not let him down, conceding no more than a couple of singles. The tally from the over was twice that amount as a result of fumbling behind the stumps which permitted the batsmen to steal a bye and a leg-bye.

In the Outcasts' changing-room Harry Northwood's return was greeted with the anticipated dismay. An emergency planning committee was immediately formed. A further beer delivery had been confidently expected ahead of the tea interval. Not usually troubled by niceties the Outcasts, in view of what had happened during the last visit to Doredell, had reckoned that it would not be very tactful for a large quantity of beer to be paraded through the pavilion whilst all the players were meant to be at tea. The unexpected presence of one of the licensees of the pub from which they were barred absolutely forbade it. Before they went into the field it looked now as if they would be a round or two light. Once out in the field supplies would inevitably be more difficult to arrange, the more especially if the operation had to be conducted in full view of Haydn Bliss. On the basis of Harry Northwood's report it seemed that the Pink Pedlar would not be open again before the second innings of the game had begun. Both the acquisition and consumption of the necessary refreshment would have to be rethought.

These were problems of which for the time being Winston Jenkins and Phil Cole knew nothing. Winston Jenkins was concentrating on how he might exact the most profit from Tom Amwell's final over. The bowler, chastened by what had befallen him to date, tried to summon up one last effort. The outcome was a moral draw. Tom Amwell's first ball was aimed far too much to the leg side and Winston Jenkins aimed to hit it much further in that direction. He missed.

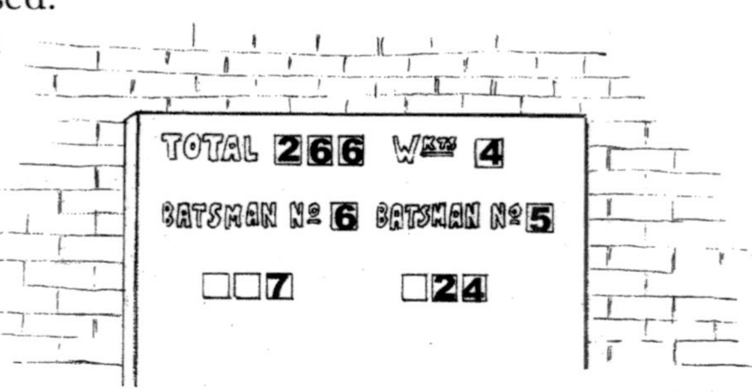

He connected with the second ball, which was better directed. The shot was not. It flew off the edge and over the head of short cover. The batsmen ran two. Winston was the undisputed victor in respect of the third delivery. Too short and too slow it was swung into the deep and beat two converging fielders to the boundary. Tom Amwell had a kind of revenge with his next ball. It was not a particularly good delivery and Winston Jenkins, his appetite now thoroughly whetted, went after it. It too sailed into the deep, but not with the same precision as its predecessor. The interest of the same two fielders was engaged. However, whilst airborne it was clear that it was likely to fall closer to the squarer of the two. No stranger to quick decision-making, Farley Richardson let cry a single word: 'Bliss!' This was not a reference to his state of mind either before or, as it turned out, after the event. The imprecision which had attended the shot, alas, attended its retrieval. With a series of movements which would have been instantly recognisable to anyone familiar with Act Two of Tchaikovsky's Swan Lake, Haydn Bliss tried to position himself under the falling projectile. It was a good try (some might have said a beautiful try), but it failed. In the final despairing lunge there were shades of a dying swan, although beauty and art were put to summary flight by the profanity of expression of the unsuccessful fielder.

Undeservedly Winston Jenkins had collected two more runs. The shot he played to Tom Amwell's next offering was far more orthodox, but earned him nothing. The over ended with a respectable delivery which was met with a respectable shot which enabled the batsman to run one and steal the bowling. It was as Kris Vertz strode menacingly forward to claim the ball to bowl the penultimate over that Farley Richardson suddenly understood his miscalculation. There were two overs to be played. Kris Vertz equally had two overs of his ration left, but he could not bowl at both ends. The captain spent the next over wondering quite where he had got it wrong. However, he did not intend to admit to his error. He would use Jim Flote to bowl the final over as if that had been the plan all along. This rationalisation was doomed to receive no endorsement in practice.

Farley Richardson should have been grateful to Kris Vertz, but he found it hard to warm to this strange man. He had the uneasy feeling that the boffin was contemptuous of his captain's cricketing prowess. This was outrageous, Farley Richardson told himself. The man was an Austrian. What did he know about cricket? The answer was that Kris Vertz knew sufficient to bowl a creditable thirty-ninth over from which no more than five runs were taken. Only three of those came off the bat. His mistakenly truncated ration of overs had cost twenty-four runs. Kris Vertz took his cap, gave Farley Richardson another prolonged stare and retreated to his presumed fielding position.

These scenes were watched by Ray Burrill with mounting frustration. He had been padded up for the last fourteen overs. He had seen what Rashid Ali could do on this wicket against these bowlers. He was confident that his own stroke-making would give the innings a late boost. What is more he had a new bat which he was itching to put to the test in match conditions. He had wandered out on to a grassy area adjacent to the pavilion and was practising the shots he craved the opportunity to play. A late cut here, a pull to mid-wicket there, not forgetting a cover drive at full stretch. It was then that he saw her.

She was laughing. She must have been watching him. She was young. She was shapely. She was fair. She was beautiful. Ray Burrill felt himself blushing. She approached. He noticed that she was carrying a small dog in her arms. It had a poorly paw. Thoughts of cricket went completely out of Ray Burrill's mind.

Jim Flote was both surprised and irritated to be invited to bowl the final over of the innings. He could not understand why Adrian Wills had not been asked to bowl his leg-breaks. Jim Flote remembered how effective they had been against the Outcasts the last time the sides had met. It was true, he recollected, that these occasional leg-breaks had never achieved such a degree of success either before or since, but a leg-spinner could often be a partnership breaker. On the other hand, if Adrian Wills could not find his length (another not uncommon attribute of leg-break bowlers) and was hit for plenty, it might not do him any good in front of watching members of the electorate they were in competition to serve. Jim Flote was annoyed that Farley Richardson had not read the situation that way. In a few moments he would be absolutely furious.

As far as Winston Jenkins could recall Jim Flote had not played a distinguished part in last year's game. He remembered that he had opened the batting and had not scored many. Winston's memory was hazier about whether Jim Flote had bowled against them. If he had, Winston was sure that it was without success. Alan Birch and Stewart Thorogood had been in no trouble at all until the introduction of the rarely-employed leg-spinner. So, Winston concluded, there should be nothing to fear in this final over. If Jim Flote was any good, he would have been on earlier, but then again the leg-spinner, who had been so effective against them, had been kept out of the attack. It was a mystery, which only the key to Farley Richardson's mind could unlock.

Jim Flote was given an ultra-defensive field and ran in off five paces. Winston Jenkins could not believe his luck. He was presented with a full toss which he hit back hard and high. Six runs. Jim Flote aimed to get his length right. He failed. Winston Jenkins crashed the ball just to the right of the bowler, but this time along the ground. The shot was rescued by Fred Ranger and earned only one. Phil Cole's first thought was to nudge a single and give the strike back to his big-hitting partner. When the ball coming towards him looked to be short and wide he had a second thought and allowed himself a liberty. It was a neat square drive which eluded the field. Phil Cole could not believe that he was being given a second offering. This time he did not get quite the same power into the shot and a fielder managed to intercept it before it reached the boundary. The batsmen ran three.

There was no doubt that the Outcasts would reach three hundred after all when Winston Jenkins launched himself ambitiously against a ball just too short of a good length and on leg-stump. It was an enormous pull over deep mid-wicket which earned another six. By this time Jim Flote was really hurting. With one ball left he wondered whether he cared. Part of him said that Farley Richardson deserved nothing better, but then again pride still played a part. Jim Flote counted to twenty and added ten more for good measure when Farley Richardson (of all people) called across, 'tighten it up, Jim'. At last he hit a length. It was hard to say whether the bowler or the batsman was more surprised. Winston Jenkins was on a roll. It was in any case the final ball of the innings. He was committed to swinging the bat and this he did – magnificently – across the line. The stumps were spread-eagled.

Nothing is more satisfying to a bowler than to hit the stumps. Jim Flote felt a modicum of pride return after what had otherwise been a gruelling experience. Even such momentary pleasure subsided when he overheard Farley Richardson boast to George Summermore, the wicket-keeper, that he thought he had made the right bowling change. As Jim Flote stamped off he realised that a lot would depend on his batting, not only if Doredell were to make a decent response to the Outcasts' total, but also if he was to retrieve some honour and credibility from this unpromising afternoon.

One question remained unanswered. If the fifth wicket had fallen earlier than the last ball of the innings, which of the Outcasts would have come in to bat? For sure it would not have been Ray Burrill; he was absent without leave. It would not have been Harry Northwood as he was unchanged and unprepared. Kevin Newton with his alter ego, Boris Wigmouth, was trying to keep the lowest possible profile. John Furness, emboldened by more than his fair share of Hoppenhall's Charger bitter, had finally persuaded himself that there was some unfinished business from last year to which he had to attend. Greg Roberts, determined to avoid the temptation of the aforesaid Hoppenhall's, had taken himself off to the more sober surroundings of the scorebox. Listed at number eleven in the batting order he was sure that he was by then surplus to requirements.

The players departed the field for tea. The Japanese tourists arrived in time to see an empty arena. They wondered about this special piece of English pageantry, but they were a patient people. Their patience was bolstered by fatigue. They did not relish the exertion of an immediate return to the centre of the village. They sank thankfully on to some available benches and decided to await developments. There would be several.

TEA INTERVAL

The tea to which the players were led – some with more enthusiasm than others – was of a very distinctive nature. It took place in what appeared to be a mess room behind the pavilion. Conviviality would have found it hard to impose itself on such stark surroundings. At some stage in its history the glass in its windows had been painted a bilious shade of green. This meant that even on the sunniest day artificial lighting was required, an unusual extravagance to be conceded on property controlled by Nice Spice. The dominant feature of the room was a bank of vending machines. Though little could be said in favour of the Formica-topped tables and plastic chairs, the vending machines were magnificent.

The thought occurred to Winston Jenkins that they were about to be asked to pay for their tea, an impression heightened when he heard a jingle of coins. However, these turned out to be tokens without which the vending machines would not disgorge their contents. The various edible items on offer were all hygienically packaged, even the inevitable slab of fruit cake. It required patience and a large number of tokens to assemble all the elements which the average cricketer would recognise as a decent match tea. Breaking into the wrappings of these items required strength and in some cases ingenuity. Anyone who wished to add mustard, salad dressing or ketchup to his fare needed particular perseverance.

The food was readily acknowledged to be plentiful in variety, but equally quickly, to be wanting in taste. The home-made teas provided in previous years in the cricket club's old headquarters might have lacked sophistication, but they had been well received by cricketers glad of a respite from their endeavours. Rough hewn slabs of ham and cheese between jagged slices of bread laced with injudicious layers of full-cream butter might have won no marks for finesse, but they had been full of taste, character and cholesterol. In the new venue those who chose sandwiches found thin strips of grey meat (or grey cheese) between slices of cardboard bread with thin smears of a 'very nearly but not quite' butter substitute. Under the old regime the tea itself had tasted better; the liquid which came out of the slick-looking dispenser was weak and antiseptic. As Jon Palmer, Phil Cole and David Pelham later averred, this was a description which applied equally to the orange juice, lemonade and spring vegetable soup.

So far as the Outcasts were concerned, tea in the mess room was not a feast over which to linger. In any case they needed time to resolve the beer crisis. They moved back to the pavilion, leaving out of politeness only their captain in conversation with members of the home team. It was not just politeness which had detained Winston Jenkins. There was curiosity too. Without reviving embarrassing memories of what had occurred last year, Winston wanted to tease out the latest information regarding the vicar, the umpire and the pub licensee who had all been prominent participants in the drama which had threatened to engulf the Outcasts. Whilst Haydn Bliss showed no disposition to engage in friendly chit-chat and stalked off in the wake of Jim Flote and Howard Tiller to get ready to bat (he was number three in the order) other members of the Doredell team seemed in easy-going mood. Several of them had not been witnesses to the goings-on of September last, but equally clearly were not in ignorance of them. 'Not everyone wanted to see you lot back here', explained Farley Richardson, trying not to wince as he took a draught of tea, 'but it was' (Farley Richardson nearly said company policy) 'our new president's wish to maintain' (Farley Richardson nearly said business as usual) 'the same fixture list.'

The vicar was someone who had very positively not wanted 'to see you lot back here'. This was a piece of news Winston Jenkins gleaned from Tom Amwell. The vicar apparently had made direct representations, but the views of the club's new president had prevailed. Cranley Nice was a secular man. The vicar had then tried to persuade individuals not to play in the match, but company influence and love of cricket had proved more powerful than the influence of the church. The vicar's last shot had been to use the parish magazine to urge his parishioners to boycott the game. He clearly had no idea of the customary fate of this publication after its retrieval from villagers' letterboxes.

The Reverend Andrews had been rather more aware of the stories which had circulated around the area in the wake of the September incident. It was understood by everyone (perfectly well) that the trouble had been caused by one of those loud-mouthed, uncouth men from London. The whole village knew (perfectly well) that the blond one obviously fancied himself as a ladies' man and chased anything in a skirt. The Reverend Andrews' parishioners accepted (perfectly well) that the sexual predator from London must have lured poor Mrs Andrews to the vicarage with his own vile purpose in mind. And yet, and yet. Some of those same people compared the age and appearance of the Reverend Andrews with the age and appearance of his wife. Fay Andrews was young, good-looking, vivacious and, of course, naïve. It would have been equally understood (perfectly well) if she had had certain needs. Thus had the intellectual discussion progressed. There was no doubt that hints of it had been detected by the vicar in the course of his pastoral care. Inwardly he had boiled. And he had boiled again when he heard that this disgraceful cricket team was to come to Doredell. And he fumed when he had been unable to prevent it. He did not know why he sensed another emotion – worry. Only one option had remained open to him. He had booked his wife and himself into a devotional retreat for the weekend. Durham was, he judged, far enough away.

Adrienne Palmer had spent most of the afternoon in Hayste where she had found an interesting collection of shops. They had included a pharmacy which had facilitated a purchase. To exit the sports ground directly towards the Cambridgeshire side had been a trouble-free exercise. Having penetrated the company's site through the goods delivery access point in Doredell, a visitor could walk relatively unimpeded through the main factory area and out into Hayste. The return journey as a pedestrian was also straightforward. The security guards were satisfied with Adrienne's assurance that she was coming back to watch the cricket. It struck her as a glaring loophole unless one assumed that the industrial espionage practitioner or saboteur was unlikely to be conversant with cricket's seeming priority over the integrity of the spice works.

Like the Japanese Adrienne Palmer came upon a deserted pitch.

She rejoined her friends in the pavilion where crisis talks had resumed. Being acquainted with the nature of the problem, Adrienne announced to general surprise and pleasure that she might have an answer. Enlisting the help of Sophie Crossley who was asked to bring along Brian Sachin as a vital accessory to the scheme, Adrienne Palmer set off again for Hayste. This time it was necessary to travel by car. The Crossley estate was employed for this purpose and it passed through the Essex gate without so much as a glance from the employees of Stopp Security Systems.

The Outcasts had indicated that their preference was for the tea interval to be longer rather than shorter. The day was bright and Farley Richardson had been prepared to indulge them. The request had been made not out of a desire to linger over any actual tea that the home team would provide (and how percipient they told themselves they had been in that regard). The thought had been that in the discreet cover of the changing room they might have disposed of a couple of pints before taking the field (and how lacking in percipience that was proving to be). With time pressing Harry Northwood was pressed to resume his gofer role. He was sent off at speed to Iris Pearlhammer's shop, the nearest, but not necessarily most likely emporium, to acquire four vessels for drinking purposes. They had to be opaque and as close to pint size as he could manage. The empty cans of stout, far from ideal with their jagged edges, had finally been deemed to have passed their use-by date.

John Furness had still not returned to the fold. When he left it John felt that the quantity of Hoppenhall's Charger bitter he had consumed had given him Dutch courage for the mission on which he had finally resolved to go. By the time he had walked as far as the main street of Hayste – not very far – his courage had begun to ebb. To reach his intended destination he had to pass the Red Barrel. In keeping with the strong views of the Outcasts on keg beer and the establishments which insisted on purveying them to the exclusion of all others, John Furness would normally have crossed the street to avoid being seen in the proximity of such a wretched tavern. On this occasion he could not believe his eyes. Perched on the pavement outside the door of the pub was a display sign. It informed the passing public that this week's guest bitter was Mandam's Special. John Furness knew his beers. You could not have been an Outcast for five years without having gained an encyclopaedic knowledge of every brewery and its range of products. Turning up the collar of his tracksuit top and looking furtively around him, John Furness decided to investigate.

Regarding the fate of Mostyn Winchope, Winston Jenkins could only sympathise – with Mostyn's former employers. He remembered that pointing finger. More out of politeness than interest Winston asked what the ex-security guard and ex-umpire was doing now. He gathered that Mostyn still lived in the village, relying on his pension and the fruits of a case he had taken to an industrial tribunal after dismissal. Winston had not recalled the proceedings, which had apparently been given sensationalised treatment on television and in the tabloids. Backed by his union and a publicity agent, Mostyn Winchope had enjoyed a handsome windfall. The award from the tribunal had been modest, but an exaggerated version of the case and alleged associated hardships highlighted by the publicity agent had brought a greater financial harvest. With only a twinge of embarrassment he had succumbed to an invitation to become an honorary vice-president of the Eastern Region Deaf Society. As some of his acquaintances acidly observed, Mostyn Winchope had never in their presence failed to respond to the offer of a drink however quietly it had been spoken.

The interior of the Red Barrel was more congenial than John Furness, a man of abiding prejudice against pubs associated with gaseous beers, had expected. It was not ritzy and glitzy whilst at the same time not a typical old-style village pub. The place was divided roughly evenly into a public bar and a saloon. John Furness opted for the former and instantly knew that he had made the right choice. It had the right feel of a public bar about it with darts and bar billiards available. More importantly, John could not mistake a barrel of Mandam's sitting on the bar counter. It was not of a size to satisfy a regiment, but John reckoned that there should be sufficient to pep him up and send him determinedly towards the completion of his mission.

Meanwhile Harry Northwood had successfully completed the mission with which he had been entrusted. He had entered Iris Pearlhammer's shop with a light step, but his mood had quickly changed when confronted by a steely-eyed glare from its owner. At first sight of her new customer Iris Pearlhammer had become instantly alert. She had preconceived ideas about modern youth, especially one dressed as Harry was. Iris Pearlhammer was put in mind of mischief if not villainy. At the same time Harry was not obviously carrying a sawn-off shotgun; nor could she see any suspicious bulge in his pocket. Not yet rejecting the possibility of his carrying a knife somewhere on his person, Iris Pearlhammer edged nearer to a point where the heavy-based frying-pan was in reach. Her suspicions began to fade when her customer spoke. He was polite, he smiled and his accent reflected education. Perhaps after all he was not a criminal lout. Nor, it seemed to her, would someone bent on armed robbery have such a contrived request.

Iris Pearlhammer assured Harry Northwood that she had various things which might satisfy his requirements. Could he be more specific? Gradually she teased out of him the exact use to which the vaguely described receptacles would be put. Still keeping half an eye on the young man in case he should make a dash for the door with a box of firelighters or a packet of soap powder (shop-lifting had not been eliminated from her thoughts), Iris Pearlhammer began to rummage amongst some cartons kept on a shelf beneath the counter. After one or two failed attempts, in which some quite unsuitable objects had been placed on the counter, Iris Pearlhammer finally employed two eyes on the job and produced in triumph what she could see at once brought joy to her customer's face. He paid what she asked and departed with six rather than four, having been told by Iris Pearlhammer unblushingly and untruthfully that they were a set. She had also said, as she took his £10 note, that they normally sold for £15. After the door shut she relaxed and smiled, glad to see the back of the last of the ceramic mugs commemorating some distant royal wedding which she had picked up as a job lot in a car boot sale for fifty pence.

The first pint had gone down swiftly, but John Furness lingered over the second. This was unexpected joy, but it was joy of another kind he was seeking. He knew that he could not put off much longer his visit to the garden centre. Hayste had a large and impressive one which John Furness had first seen mentioned in a trade journal, *The Central Gardener*. Working his way up (hopefully) the family business, John was keen to embrace new ideas.

Taking time off from the match in September, John had made his way to the Hayste Garden Centre and that was when he had seen her. In her blue uniform with the orange collar she had been a vision. John Furness struggled to overcome his shyness with women. How to make acquaintance? In the middle of a cricket match he could hardly buy a plant. She had been on duty behind an enquiry desk and eventually he had found a moment when she was not occupied with another customer to say to her that he 'ran' a garden centre himself and how impressed he was with this one. She had smiled – John's temperature had soared – and said 'how nice'. But then someone with actual money to spend had asked to purchase a set of garden furniture and she had moved away from casual chit-chat to a more profitable conversation. In those few moments John Furness's heart had been completely captured.

Another twenty minutes or so mooching round the garden centre had given him no plausible excuse to renew contact, but time enough to note some of the innovatory features of the place. He had made some notes. Passing the enquiry counter again on his way out, John had managed to flash a smile in the direction of its busy custodian and note that her name, according to a badge attached to her chest or bosom, was Fern. Back at the family firm he had sought to renew the fleeting relationship. Several telephone calls to Hayste asking to speak to Fern had earned him the information first that she was Miss Sadler and secondly some answers to some fatuous questions that he had succeeded in putting to the young lady herself. It was from an entirely unexpected direction that a vital new fact emerged.

'Doredell?', John Furness's father had queried when his son had casually mentioned the nightmare cricket match. 'That's close to where the Sadlers have one of their garden centres. You should take a look at it.' 'Oh God!', John thought, 'She was one of the family.' What an ass he had been! Thereafter he had tried a different tack. Now it was an exchange between equals. Subtly, he hoped, altering the pitch of his voice, he attempted to do business with Miss Sadler about particular ranges of product which perhaps his company could share with hers. Their affairs prospered and on the back of them he and Miss Sadler increasingly engaged in pleasantries. But it had really gone no further than that. John had not been able to manufacture any natural excuse to travel to Hayste until at the Sink and Plumber he had seen his chance.

John Furness jolted himself back to his present situation. Was he man or was he mouse? Something had to be done. There was after all a cricket match at which his presence was required. The barrel of Mandam's was clearly not exhausted, but John felt that he had to be on his way in one direction or another. Having come so far he decided that he must plunge into the garden centre. He was taken aback by what he saw when he reconnoitred the enquiry desk. There was the object of his desire cradling an infant with a degree of intimacy which allowed no doubt in his mind that she was the mother. Another staff member – clearly the father – was in doting attendance. A totally sober John Furness might have looked for explanations other than the obvious. However, his lack of natural confidence and sobriety led on John's part to a melancholy conclusion. He retreated in dismay in the direction in which he knew he would be wanted – the cricket match arena.

Winston Jenkins had gently brought the conversation round to the subject of Haydn Bliss. He took a bit of stick from one or two of the Doredell team who could remember all too well the embarrassing scene in the Pink Pedlar. Winston hastily explained in carefully crafted language (bearing in mind the not too distant presence of Boris Wigmouth) that they had excluded from their team this year those Outcasts who might in any way have caused offence on the last visit. Winston apologised once again and stressed how grateful they were to be asked to play again in Doredell. His demeanour was such that the mood relaxed. Winston sensed that, short of peace, at least an armistice had been established. More of what had happened in Doredell over the intervening months was explained to him. The emergence of the ballet dancer-cum-publican as cricketer was just one of the things he learnt.

Andy Lizzard was not a happy man. He thought that the blue touch paper had been lit and he had been waiting for the conflagration to start. Yet things had not progressed as fast as he had hoped. These East Anglian people, he told himself, were hard to motivate. In his old stomping ground the whole of Merseyside, let alone a single factory, would have been at a standstill by now on the strength of such blatant victimisation of a worker. Andy Lizzard had two lieutenants helping him to stoke the fires. Both were Scottish lads who were always ready for a scrap with the bosses just as in their leisure time they enjoyed a scrap on the terraces. Despite their efforts it seemed that the flames needed a little more petrol if the desired objective was to be achieved. Into the rumour chain he inserted the suggestion that the company's intention was to abolish tea-breaks altogether. That helped.

Adrienne Palmer and Sophie Crossley spent longer in the garden centre than they had anticipated. There were two reasons for the extended visit. They suffered an onset of uncertainty over the object they had come to purchase and were further delayed by Brian Sachin's need for a nappy change. They were in the midst of a discussion about the former with a pleasant young lady called Fern when the latter need erupted. What had led them to the garden centre had been Adrienne's thought that an ornamental plant pot would be a suitable vessel to hold a generous quantity of beer. However, when she had seen it, Sophie Crossley had disagreed. She pointed out that its porous finish might lead to an alien taste being imparted to the precious ale. They had debated the possibility of a plastic water barrel, but Adrienne had judged that this was too large an object to fit into her car. Various other, smaller objects had been considered, but rejected.

It was this indecision which had brought them to the enquiry counter where Fern Sadler brimmed over with resource. Sophie Crossley could use the office if she wished to change her young son. Gratefully Sophie shot out to the car to fetch the necessary apparatus whilst Adrienne was directed towards the DIY section of the garden centre where she would find at £5.99 a polypropylene funtub much in demand at pre-schools, playgroups and reception classes. With cling film across the top, Fern added, it should do very well and inexpensively for the purpose which had been explained to her. Meanwhile Fern Sadler, aided by a passing member of staff, comforted an increasingly uncomfortable and irate Brian Sachin. Thus was explained the tableau to which John Furness had been witness.

It was a timbered property of some vintage to which Ray Burrill was led (none too reluctantly) by his new acquaintance cradling her young border collie. More than his professional instincts had been aroused. The young vet felt a complete fraud. He knew that he could have completed his diagnosis there and then at the sports ground, but that might have cut short his dalliance with the attractive client in distress. It had been unprofessional of him not to dispel the lady's query at once. Yet he had sensed that there might be more mileage in the encounter and so he had allowed himself to procrastinate. Yes, he had said sagely, it probably would be better if he could take a good look at the animal in proper conditions in which the dog would be familiar and comfortable and in which he, Ray, was quite keen himself to gain familiarity and comfort. He freed himself from the encumbrance of his pads, but not on reflection his abdominal protector, and was on his way with a spring in his step.

Having achieved entry into the home of the border collie puppy and this exciting young lady, Ray Burrill overcame the ailment with a gush of veterinary jargon which seemed to satisfy patient and owner alike. He then lapsed into a gush of sycophantic praise for the house wherein he was now situated with, he had to admit, a glow of pleasure. Would he like a drink? Yes, he would very much like a drink. He hoped that the beer on his breath was not too evident. Would he like a beer? No, thought Ray, harking back to his lager days, not the kind of beer which came in a can from the fridge. A glass of orange would be fine, he heard himself answering. Where was this going, he wondered and hoped. She fixed him with admiring eyes and said that it must be wonderful to be a vet always helping sick animals. Ray, whose final qualification was of only recent vintage, assured her that it was, well, just wonderful. They were closer together now. She smiled. Ray was in two minds whether his right arm should be reaching for the glass of orange juice or doing something more ambitious. Her smile grew wider. Ray was encouraged and smiled his as yet most professional smile. It was then that the dog bit him.

As he wandered glumly away from the garden centre, John Furness half thought of drowning his sorrows with another stopover at the Red Barrel. Two things dissuaded him. Checking his watch, he realised that he must be getting dangerously close to missing the resumption of the match. Secondly, as he gazed longingly at the notice outside the pub which exhorted knowledgeable beer drinkers to try Mandam's finest, the barman he had met earlier came outside and chalked on the board the dread words, 'sorry sold out' (without punctuation). That settled it. John Furness quickened his step and rejoined his team-mates amongst whom was a protesting Tim Jackson.

Had he chosen the escapist option, John Furness would surely have homed in on the public bar. He would not therefore have seen the three men plotting at a table in the saloon bar and drinking, from the barman's point-of-view, disconcertingly little. He perhaps might have recognised one at best. There were two older men and a youth. They had been there an hour. One round had been purchased and still not fully consumed. If the bar had not been quiet, the barman would have been fussing over them by now. He was tempted to ask for proof of age of the young man in front of whom stood an unfinished pint of strong ale. The three men had their heads together. Between them lay a lap-top computer, the property of Mostyn Winchope's nephew. Uncle Mostyn understood barely a word of what was being said by his nephew, but he was pleased to be part of the conspiracy. Billy Gorman was planning his revenge.

The closure of the Pink Pedlar, apart from putting the Outcasts at risk of severe deprivation, had also upset tour operator Roger Trysom. He had gloomily come to the conclusion that he had to summon up a vehicle from somewhere or risk Doredell becoming a

Japanese colony. Working from a dog-eared notebook, in which his inked entries were partly fading, he had made nine calls to coach companies. To three there had been no reply and three were wrong numbers as a consequence of his being unable to decipher the correct figures in his notes; in the other cases there had been no available coaches. Before he could embark on a tenth call, the battery of his mobile phone expired. He had no means of recharging it. He had been deserted by James Saito and also by his two coach drivers who had come to the conclusion that any further driving to be done that day would not have to be done by them. They had gone off in search of a drink and an early lift home. Alternative mobile phones had gone with them. The ladies from the land of electronic gadgetry who sat serenely in the beer garden had none to offer him, even if they had understood Roger Trysom's question.

Temporarily denied access to the pay phone in the comfortable interior of the pub, Roger Trysom tramped towards the public phone box. By what passed for a village green in Doredell there nestled the traditional red structure beloved of rural communities. Of its ilk it was a gem. For their part local residents ensured that it was regularly swept. They had even secured permission from the phone company to paint it. The red paint shone in the sunlight. In many respects it was pristine. Its lack of glass might have been seen as a disadvantage, but this had helped to dispel the odour of stale urine. The box was well stocked with directories covering, Roger Trysom noted, a wide area. What was missing was the raison d'être of the whole thing – a telephone instrument. A politely-worded message from the phone company informed the disappointed client that a state of the art system would shortly be installed. The yellowing card on which it was printed contradicted the promise. Promises of a different kind were made on a series of smaller cards with which the kiosk was festooned. Roger Trysom mused on the degree of interest in the area in massage and some very special forms of physiotherapy before cursing the telephone company and stomping off back towards the Pink Pedlar. Momentarily it had crossed his mind to knock on someone's door and ask to use their phone. After reading the advertisements in the kiosk he decided against it, unsure what he might find behind some of those doors.

Geraint Poppledown let out an entirely involuntary scream. Lying spread-eagled on the king-sized bed in the pub's master bedroom he had dozed fitfully. Various images had flitted through his mind, not all as pleasurable as he would have liked. His episodic dreams acquired a distinctly oriental flavour. At one moment he was being pushed into a crowded subway train in Tokyo, then he was kneeling before a Samurai swordsman, next he was pulling endless pints in a bar packed with young Japanese in military uniform shouting angry abuse at him; and finally he opened his eyes and found himself staring into an unmistakably Japanese face. It took around two seconds for the scream to emerge. Geraint Poppledown

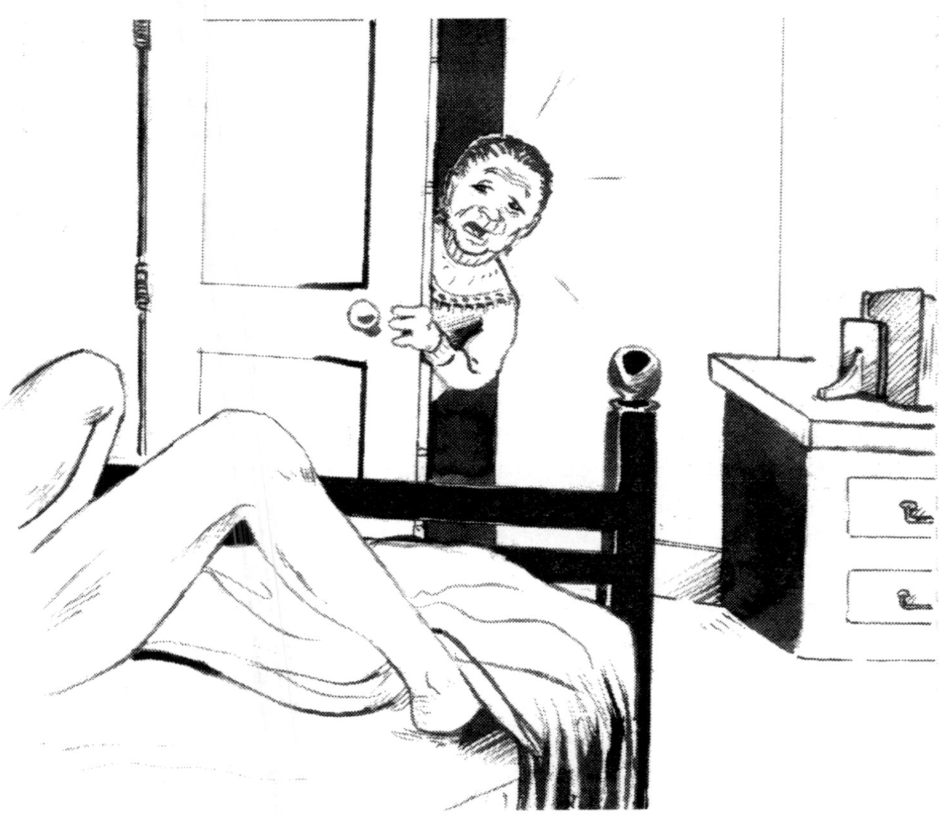

could not be sure whether its cause was the live Japanese presence or the realisation of the full frontal nudity he was presenting to a woman.

For all the experience she had packed into her eighty-two years, this was a first for Mrs. Fujirama. Never before had she entered a man's bedroom let alone one occupied by a Caucasian male in a state of undress. That was not the way things had been done in her country. Even so she had shown more sang-froid than her unwitting host. After entering the room (the last door she had tried) Mrs Fujirama reproached herself that perhaps she had gazed a little too long at Geraint Poppledown's well-proportioned physique. However, relief had triumphed over remorse. She knew that she could now expect to get out of this place and rejoin her travelling companions. At least she would be able to do so once Geraint Poppledown had made up his mind how to overcome his nakedness. Mrs Fujirama's continuing presence and unrelenting gaze prolonged his indecision.

It could have been the squid in the Japanese restaurant in the Rising Sun Hotel in Bayswater the previous evening or the Doredell special beef, mushroom and ale pie which she had adventurously chosen at the Pink Pedlar, but whatever the cause the outcome had been a prolonged occupation by Mrs Fujirama of a cubicle in the ladies' toilet zone at the back of the pub. For a ladies' rest-room in a country pub it was exceptionally well-appointed. This was a tribute to the artistic talent of Haydn Bliss. It was doubtful whether the state of the decoration, the quality of the accessories or the style of the decor had made any impact on the Japanese visitor. On the way in her state of health was such that she did not dally to appreciate her surroundings. On her way out some considerable time later, she was also in a hurry, fearing, with all too justified prescience, that she might have been left behind. She had wandered round the deserted pub with a growing sense of despair. All exits were blocked by locked doors, the keys to which were not to be found by the casual searcher. The defunct coaches obscured the view from the windows and so Mrs Fujirama could not attract the attention of passers-by - had there been any. Slumped for a while in a chair intoning a prayer to her private god, she was disturbed by a creak. It suddenly occurred to her that there might be life above her. That was how she came to make her sensational discovery.

It should have been a simple decision, but Geraint Poppledown was ridiculously embarrassed. The clothes which he had discarded lay by the side of the bed. What would have been simple and straightforward – to have swathed himself in his gown - was made difficult and complicated because Mrs Fujirama was blocking his route to the ensuite bathroom. To dress himself would not only take more time, but also add to his awkwardness in that the Japanese lady would become privy to his taste in underwear which was of a minimalist, even suggestive nature. But there seemed to be no alternative. Thoroughly hot and bothered, Geraint Poppledown fumbled and stumbled to restore his respectability. His next objective was to expel this oriental voyeur from his premises, little appreciating how much this was a shared desire.

Swiftly and silently Geraint Poppledown opened the pub's front door and Roger Trysom, who had been negligently leaning against it, fell inside, knocking Mrs Fujirama over in the process. The lady did not know whether she was about to be raped or robbed, but she displayed considerable resilience for one of her years. As Geraint Poppledown hauled Roger Trysom to his feet, Mrs Fujirama picked herself up and rushed, relatively speaking, from the hostelry with unintelligible cries. In the process she knocked into an approaching pair of ladies, causing them to drop the bright red tub they were carrying.

Adrienne Palmer and Sophie Crossley had not had much time to think of a plausible reason as to why they should want a polypropylene funtub to be filled with prime ale. There did not seem to be much plausibility in representing themselves to the publican as local housewives going into the production of beer shampoo or steak, mushroom and ale pie. It was needed for a party, they finally and weakly explained. They were fortunate in finding him numbed into an unquestioning mood. As Sophie was encumbered by Brian Sachin, Geraint Poppledown even assisted in the transfer of the laden tub into the back of the estate car where the cling film was carefully applied. The main part of the mission had seemingly been accomplished, but it has been truly said that there can be many a slip twixt tub and lip.

As the Outcasts began to reassemble, there was no sign of either beer or Ray Burrill. Tim Jackson, who had counted on a leisurely afternoon with no more exertion than was required by use of the phone to complete social arrangements for the evening, and by use of his pocket radio to collect racing results, was peeved to find himself obliged to take the field. Winston Jenkins did not feel good about it either as this made him another bowler light. To have to rely on Greg Roberts with his occasional allsorts as fifth bowler was risky enough, but promotion to fourth looked to be courting disaster.

Winston Jenkins could not have known how much at that moment his originally intended fourth bowler desperately wanted to be taking the field with the rest of the Outcasts. Instead Ray Burrill was gazing down the barrel of a gun held not many inches away from his head.

As he surveyed the scene, Farley Richardson could sense at once that there was something wrong. Discounting the Japanese contingent there was an abnormally large number of spectators ringing the ground. Cricket might be enjoying a revival, but surely not to this extent. Even before his production manager had arrived breathless at the pavilion, Farley Richardson had noticed the predominance of company overalls. There were production workers who should have been producing, packaging workers who should have been packaging and maintenance workers who should have been maintaining. None of them should have been watching cricket in the middle of a Saturday afternoon. Uttering a strangled cry, Farley Richardson departed, running.

Having dispensed an unusually large quantity of beer, the publican had turned his attention to his other premature customer. But Roger Trysom had not come to buy even so much as a box of matches: he needed a phone and some advice. Geraint Poppledown was not well versed in bus operators, local or national. However, there was a name stuck at the back of his mind for no reason that he could recall. Had he not kept a card? A brief search yielded a smeared and thumb-marked business card. Geraint Poppledown seemed to remember that they had a double-decker.

The previous customers of the Pink Pedlar were proceeding cautiously along the narrow road between the pub and the factory goods entrance. At no more than 20 mph it was still a shock to come round a bend and face a heavy goods vehicle of juggernaut proportions which had just made its exit from the spice works (the last consignment to do so for a while). Sophie Crossley instinctively braked. There was no risk of collision, but catastrophe of a different kind could not be averted. The cling film was no barrier to such stress. A tidal wave of Hoppenhall's Charger bitter slopped over the back seat, drenching the unfortunate infant strapped to it in his baby seat.

At the opposite end of the site no such obstacle impeded the smooth entrance of Cranley Spice's executive limousine. Even allowing for the darkly tinted glass it was what he could not see which alarmed Cranley Nice. There was not a sign of any work being done. From the security guard at the gate who had saluted (very laxly, Cranley Nice had thought) he had not seen another operative during the progress of his executive limousine towards his executive office. Until. It was then that a movement caught Cranley Nice's eye. Emerging from a building down an avenue to his right (Cranley Nice's eye for detail did not extend to knowing that it was a lavatory) was James Saito. Cold fear gripped Cranley Nice. He had a paranoid fear of the Japanese. A deserted site, a Japanese stranger marching through it; this could mean only one thing. Takeover.

As the umpires left the shelter of the pavilion on their way to the middle, they were accompanied, first, by a screech and a crackle and, secondly, by an unseen voice which uttered a hollow sound just distinguishable as 'remember on Thursday, vote Wills; Wills for Widdle on Thursday'.

It was an altogether inauspicious background to the commencement of the second innings of the match.

SECOND INNINGS

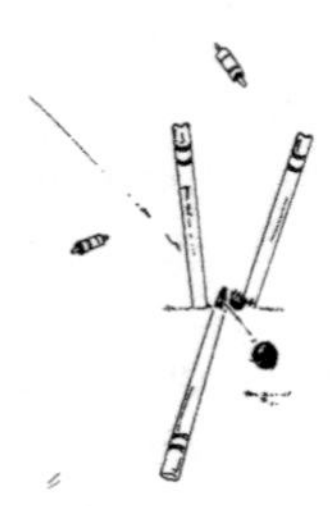

Apart from the sudden burst of amplified electioneering, Syd Breakwell and Rodney Corrington were not aware of anything untoward as they approached the stumps to put the bails in place. They were not a matching couple. What might have been described during Syd's career in the force as a burly figure had now to be admitted as stout. From behind he looked almost twice as wide in his short white coat as the tall, slim and much more youthful spice salesman beside him, whose long, tailored white coat was ruined only by the company logo on front and back. The contrast was completed by Syd's familiar white trilby-style hat, which made him look like some kind of hygiene inspector, and Rodney's baseball cap, again adorned front and back with the company logo.

Personally, however, the two umpires had hit it off. Having given up on the mess room at an early stage, they had both settled for bottles of water and taken them outside where they had found a couple of convenient deckchairs. Lounging in these, Rodney Corrington had given his partner a potted résumé of his career since they had last met while Syd Breakwell had offered a sanitised account of the uneven progress of the Outcasts Cricket Club. It was when Syd referred to the previous visit to Doredell that Rodney Corrington sat up and took particular interest, for none of the previous history of the fixture had ever been conveyed to him. Sensing that he had an audience, Syd quickly made up for the lack.

As he stepped back to admire his handiwork and confirm that the bails were perfectly level, Syd Breakwell chuckled. It had certainly been from his point of view a more relaxed tea interval than he had experienced when he had last stood in an Outcasts' match in the village. Memory of that occasion almost provoked Syd into sniffing the lapel of his white coat to ensure that it bore no lingering bovine odour, but he recovered himself in time. With a final chuckle he turned to await the players. The Japanese contingent in the crowd had begun to show interest when the two white-coated figures had entered the playing arena. Such a scene had a faint familiarity for them. There was expectation of some kind of physical contest between the two of them, notwithstanding the unequal physique of the two men. Anticipation quickly became confusion and ultimately disappointment when eleven others came on to the field followed mysteriously by two additional men wearing helmets and carrying sticks. Anyone knowing the Outcasts and aware that the opening bowlers on this occasion would be Winston Jenkins and Phil Cole would have shared the sense of mystery that the batsmen were bothering to wear helmets. Battle, but not in the Japanese sense, was about to begin.

Bearing in mind the Outcasts' drastically depleted bowling resources, the wild idea had flitted through Winston Jenkins's mind that he should use a ploy once applied by New Zealand, and ask Greg Roberts to open the bowling. The arguments in favour of this had appeared to be one, getting the worst out of the way at the beginning, and two, possibly taking their opponents by surprise. The argument against, which very quickly asserted itself, was the full recollection of Greg's record as a bowler. True, he had not recently been given a long spell in which he might have settled down and established a rhythm, but recent opening overs which had cost twelve, nineteen, twenty-two and sixteen had had a pretty negative effect on his colleagues and on Greg himself.

Six overs into Doredell's innings Winston Jenkins was being forced to question the wisdom of orthodoxy. He and Phil Cole were supposed to be the pace bowlers of the side or at least the nearest to pace which this particular side could offer or at the very least an experienced pair. None of this was borne out by the evidence of the scoreboard which showed the home team off to a flying start. The fifty was up and no wicket was down. Sarcastic comments were heard all around.

The scoring had not been evenly shared between the two batsmen. Jim Flote had been by far the more aggressive of the openers. It was hard to say whether this was just one of those good days when on a true wicket a batsman was able to ride his luck and get away with an uninhibited innings, whether he was determined to wash out the memory of his bowling performance or whether Jim Flote had been goaded into an uncharacteristic display by the insistent derogatory prompting of the invisible loudspeaker which continued to invade proceedings. Only the Japanese spectators believed that the urgings from outside the ground were an integral part of what was happening on it.

Jim Flote had passed forty whilst his partner was still in single figures. Howard Tiller appeared a composed, compact batsman, unworried by the frenetic pace being set by his partner. He was equally undistracted by the electioneering being practised from beyond the boundary. Howard Tiller might have been in a world of his own. Unbeknown to anyone, that was exactly where he was. He could not have been happier that Jim Flote was taking charge of the innings. Playing second fiddle enabled his mind to wander to his garden. Howard Tiller might have been the head gardener on the factory site, but it was his own garden at home which was occupying his thoughts.

Howard Tiller loved gardening with a passion which bordered on fanaticism. It had been his passport to respectability. He had learned his gardening and his cricket in the same place – a gaol in the north-east of England. As a young man Howard had been caught up in a vortex of crime. His offences were always petty and nearly always fruitless, but rather like the person addicted to the National Lottery he maintained his nefarious habits in the belief that one day he would get his break. And in a sense the day came. It was the day when Howard Tiller met Judge Edward Dellworth.

The meeting took place in a peculiar set of circumstances, all of which related to the judge. Edward Dellworth was something of a talking point on the Northern Circuit. For several years he had been an unremarkable but diligent lawyer, earning enough for respectability but insufficient to shake off anonymity. When a vacancy on the bench had to be filled political correctness was in the air, but, of course, unspoken. It was Edward Dellworth's advantage at this critical moment that he was one quarter West Indian. This made him a candidate who satisfied both sides of the argument. Once elevated Judge Dellworth had surprised the legal community. At the outset his appointment had not unnaturally attracted mild interest from the press. This seemed to have the effect on the new judge that a first taste of alcohol has been known to have on a teetotaller. He quickly became transformed into a full-blooded media personality. Such was his impact that in a popularity poll undertaken by a national radio station he had come joint fifth with an eighteen-year-old fledgling county cricketer who had scored a hundred off the touring Bangladeshi cricket team and a sensation by removing his clothes for the centre-fold of a glossy magazine.

In his courtrooms, Judge Dellworth dispensed justice with a style bordering on sassiness and without always one hundred percent adherence to the letter of the law. Despite his freewheeling approach (often accompanied by pithy homilies which were food and drink to the media industry), Edward Dellworth's judgements were rarely appealed. Criminals and police alike seemed either content with the trial outcomes or unwilling to provoke public outrage by appearing to gainsay a judge who had quickly acquired folklore status.

It was Howard Tiller's fate to meet Judge Dellworth (he in the dock, the judge on the bench) on a morning when the latter was not feeling his best. Edward Dellworth's previous day had not been a good one. He had played a wretched round of golf when his ball found every ornamental pool of water with which the course was liberally endowed. In the clubhouse he had eaten a prawn sandwich with miserable repercussions. Tuning into teletext on his return home he found that on the third day of a four-day county championship match played at Old Trafford, Yorkshire had been humiliated by Lancashire. Sufficiently recovered (from the prawn sandwich, not the cricket result) for an evening of bridge, he had been partnered by his wife's sister whose erratic calling had robbed the occasion of any meaningful intellectual test. At nine forty-five his village suffered its fourth power-cut of the year and the household went to bed in darkness, the judge vowing that he would have his revenge if ever the chairman of the electricity board appeared before him on a motoring or any other offence. However, overhanging his whole day and still dogging his mind on the morrow were serious doubts about the wisdom of his having recorded early on the Sunday morning a cameo role in a spoof television documentary.

Howard Tiller could not deny that he had been involved in the robbery for which he was on trial, but it had truly been a bit part. He had been employed in a purely diversionary role. Disguised as an elderly, blind man his job had been to dally on a pedestrian crossing to delay the police pursuit of the getaway van. There had not been much to say about the thoroughly unpleasant villains who had carried out the robbery. Judge Dellworth had contented himself with meting out maximum sentences with minimum comment.

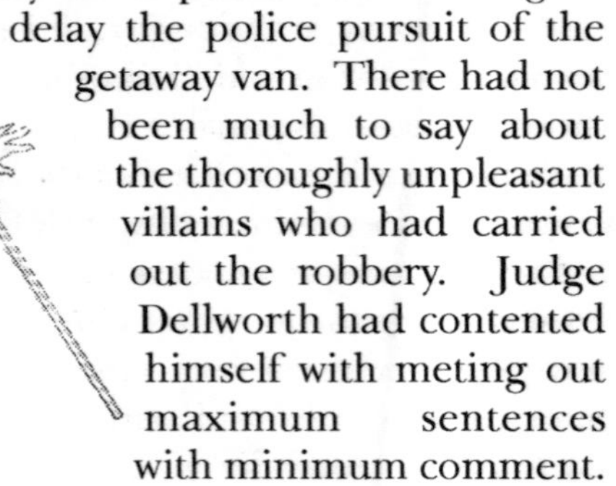

When it came to Howard Tiller the judge saw a different man altogether. He noted his record and recognised a petty wrongdoer in a pathetic rut. A combination of impatience and zeal persuaded him to read the riot act and the whole of Howard Tiller's unworthy life to date was paraded before the court. Then, as if carried away by his own oratory, he reached a climax which was a prison sentence. Both its imposition and severity were a surprise to Howard Tiller, the prosecution, the police and even by the time of the court's adjournment to the judge himself.

Although deeply flawed in law, the judge's assessment and impulsive decision proved to be brilliant. The shock to Howard Tiller's system could not have been more salutary. His solicitor would doubtless have advised an appeal, but this advice was not available as coincidentally he had just been sent down for embezzling clients' funds. So Howard Tiller found himself incarcerated in a prison governed by a man who had a touching belief in the curative effects of gardening and cricket. Under this far-sighted and benevolent regime Howard Tiller had prospered. His reform had been completed by his approval on release for a gardening role at the spice factory whose previous owners had co-operated fully with the concept of rehabilitation.

During the tea interval Howard Tiller had had a telephone conversation with his partner which had contained items of exciting and disturbing news. Their consignment of bedding plants had been delivered, prompting in Howard's mind artistic thoughts as to their deployment. The only thing to mar his musing was his partner's promise that she might make a start on the planting. Call him selfish but Howard did not have the fullest confidence in the greenness of his partner's fingers. If he had not been concentrating so intensely on antirrhinums, pansies and polyanthuses in harmonising or contrasting colours he might have heard Jim Flote's call earlier than he did.

Having decided that a change of bowling was essential, Winston Jenkins would have liked to have been able to call on Ray Burrill, who could purvey off-cutters as well as off-spinners. At that moment his first choice would dearly have liked to have been available to answer the call; at that moment it even occurred to Ray Burrill that he might not live to bowl another over. He had problems. The dog bite had been but the first of them. No doubt the animal, endearingly called Lambkins, had been protecting his mistress from physical assault (that much was right, Ray Burrill ruefully admitted to himself), but his pre-emptive bite had admitted no room for discrimination as to the friendliness or otherwise of the visitor's intentions.

Ray Burrill had sunk to the floor with a yell, which he had the presence of mind to replace with groans lest his manliness was compromised. Commendably he had managed to suppress the words which the shock might so easily have provoked. Lambkins had been expelled from the kitchen into the adjoining utility room which was his usual home. In a role reversal his mistress then tackled the patient, who was wriggling around on the kitchen floor his clenched teeth defending what was left of his dignity. Rolling up the trouser leg was not an option, Ray having invested in a tailored, tapered pair. She reached for a pair of scissors. Ray screamed 'no'. The tailored, tapered garment had not come cheap. 'Then there's only one alternative', she said with a smile which in other circumstances Ray would have found profoundly stimulating. She unlaced his boots and pulled off his trousers. With a bowl of hot water and some antiseptic ointment she squatted at his feet and began to attend to his wound. Treatment had not advanced very far before the kitchen door opened again and this time it had not been Lambkins.

In retrospect Ray Burrill could understand that the scene which confronted the newcomer was capable of more than one interpretation. He was nevertheless aggrieved that the possibility of innocent explanation had apparently been set aside with the same lack of full and careful consideration shown by Lambkins. This was evident from the presence of a shotgun being waved dangerously close to his head by someone who was prepared to use words which a short while earlier Ray himself had stoically avoided. This show of anger perhaps was understandable in the father of the young lady. The situation was not helped by an unfortunate coincidence. The two men were not strangers.

The fall of Doredell's first wicket came as a great relief to Winston Jenkins, but he could hardly congratulate himself on engineering it. His choice of bowler had been heavily restricted by circumstances and a run-out could not really be credited to his selection of David Pelham in place of himself at the Doredell end. What was to the bowler's credit was that he found an accurate line from the start. This was not something which could be guaranteed as Winston Jenkins reminded himself. Last year's match against Doredell had been a case in point. This time at least David Pelham had the advantage of being (almost) sober. It was not an advantage which would persist.

Jim Flote played the first few balls from David Pelham warily, but it did not take batsman or bowler long to realise that the ball was unlikely to misbehave on such a placid strip. If David Pelham could get no turn, at least he kept it straight and on a good length. Presented with no obvious opportunity for boundary shots, Jim Flote felt that the tactic must be to keep the score ticking over. After four monotonous forward defensive strokes he clipped the next ball to mid-wicket and called his partner for what should have been a comfortable single. He was far too committed before realising that Howard Tiller had barely stirred. There was no going back. Belatedly Howard Tiller recognised that too. Expelling thoughts of bedding plants and colours and patterns from his mind he launched himself down the pitch. Even though the mid-wicket fielder, John Furness (who also had had other things on his mind), had fumbled, his return to the wicket-keeper arrived comfortably ahead of Howard Tiller.

The muddle in the middle was matched in the pavilion. Farley Richardson's sudden departure on other duties had left a vacuum. No instructions had been left as to who should bat first wicket down. Some captains write out a batting order and pin it up for all to see (and dispute). Others make it up as they go along so that they can more easily adapt to changes of circumstance. Farley Richardson belonged to the latter school, but the effectiveness of this approach depends crucially on the presence of the captain or at least his attendance at audible distance. On this occasion neither condition was met. Nor did the position of vice-captain have any place in Farley Richardson's approach to leadership. He was resolutely against the existence of any alternative power-base. Adrian Wills and Ray Beckett, both padded up, might have continued their 'after you – no, after you' routine for several more minutes if someone had not called out, 'It's Bliss'. And it was. The unseen but intermittently vocal section of the public championing Adrian Wills was thereby kept waiting.

Despite the affinity between cricket and the arts being well-known, there was less appreciation of how far ballet schools or occasional games of rugby bred good batsmen. However, first impressions did not confirm the Outcasts' prejudice that Haydn Bliss would be a pushover. He took guard from Rodney Corrington in a manner which suggested that he was no stranger to the crease. He then studied the field before bending over his bat. He met the last ball of the over with a similarly good-looking defensive shot as the ones previously employed by Jim Flote. David Pelham had brought relief to his captain by achieving a maiden over. The respite would only be temporary.

A mopping-up operation had been carried out in the Crossley estate car. The shrieks of Brian Sachin Crossley had quite quickly given way to gurgles. Having got over the kind of shock which he associated with bath time, Brian Sachin, like millions before him, had found Hoppenhall's Charger bitter to his taste. There was every sign that he would walk in his father's footsteps. By the time Sophie had extricated herself from the driving seat and entered the rear compartment she had found only a look of utter contentment on her baby's face. He seemed reluctant to be parted from the beer-sodden clothes he had been wearing. Some rudimentary clearing-up inside the car still left an overpowering smell of hops. Sophie could foresee that this might not play well with the officious security guards of Nice Spice. It was Adrienne Palmer who had the brainwave. When the estate car finally approached the gate, Sophie Crossley flashed both her sweetest smile and Brian Sachin's dirtiest nappy at the security guard. She gestured towards her son and said there was a bit of an emergency. Conveniently Brian Sachin began to yell, indicating perhaps that he was ready for another drop of that tasty new drink to which he had been introduced. The guard really did not want to know (or smell) any more and the makeshift brewery tanker was waved on its way.

For want of any better idea and in the belief that the Greg Roberts's experience could be held back a little longer, Winston Jenkins decided to switch himself to the Hayste end in place of Phil Cole. Sometimes, he told himself, that kind of thing worked if only by creating uncertainty in the minds of the batsmen. For Winston Jenkins at Doredell that kind of thing did not work. The pitch was playing no worse at one end than the other. Winston Jenkins's bowling in his fourth over was little different from what he had purveyed during the first three. The batsman on strike was equally no different and Jim Flote felt on form. Assisted by Winston Jenkins's lack of direction Jim Flote played shots all round the wicket. Eight runs came from the over. So did Jim Flote's half-century. Dutifully the Japanese joined in the applause.

Up to this point David Pelham was feeling fairly pleased with himself. He had been the second highest scorer in his side's innings and he had just contributed the first maiden over bowled in this innings. He aspired to do better still to compensate for his unfortunate performance on the last occasion the two teams had met. He was now bowling to Haydn Bliss who was an unknown quantity. David Pelham managed to maintain both line and length and would have recorded a second maiden over if the batsman had not nicked him between first slip and keeper for four. As if mesmerised by the metronomic sequence of five forward prods neither Rashid Ali nor Jon Palmer had so much as quivered as the ball sped past them. Boris Wigmouth at third man had been similarly transfixed.

Winston Jenkins persevered, but there was nothing in his fifth over to add weight to the theory that as a bowler gets into his rhythm, his performance improves. Jim Flote and Haydn Bliss shared the honours in advancing the score by ten. Winston told himself that Greg Roberts would undoubtedly have gone for more, but it was cold comfort. He and the rest of the team brightened when Sophie and Adrienne were observed placing receptacles of refreshment at key points around the boundary. This was cold comfort in a much more acceptable form. David Pelham had to pull himself away from the boundary to bowl before a receptacle had been placed in his sector of the field. This enhanced the prospect of another over of tolerable respectability.

It was unusual for Bill Blimp, the proprietor of Executive Sporting Coachways, to be in his office on a Saturday afternoon. This was meant to be the time of maximum deployment of his fleet. In an ideal, profitable world Bill Blimp would have expected to be out on the road himself. But his world was far from ideal and barely profitable. Due to the imposition of ever higher standards of coach maintenance, which Bill Blimp ascribed to idiotic bureaucracy and stifling red tape, Executive Sporting Coachways had found it difficult to sustain the affordable service for which many sports clubs were (just) grateful. Finding vehicles which to him were affordable had not proved an easy exercise. To advertise openly for a bus which was within the law, but only just was not a straightforward task. Bill Blimp, being unfamiliar with the art of coded language, had had to rely on word of mouth.

Rebuilding the fleet was proving a slow process. Bill Blimp had even been forced to wonder whether the double-decker had been the wisest acquisition. Moodily he glared at it across the depot yard. What a bloody awful afternoon! What the hell was he doing there? It did not take long to remind himself of the answer: Mrs Blimp. Scenting that her husband might not be fully engaged in his usual gainful employment, Mrs Blimp had produced a list of the things which he could do to help her. None of them held the slightest attraction and he had bolted to the depot on the excuse that he was expecting a most important, if not life-changing, phone call. When the phone did in fact ring he hesitated, his first guilty thought being that his wife was checking up on him. Roger Trysom had almost given up hope of a reply by the time Bill Blimp lifted the receiver. Little did he realise how a few seconds separated him from a further chapter of humiliation and disaster.

These twin fates had also seemed to be beckoning Farley Richardson as he rushed from the playing area of the factory site to the supposed working area. He had pushed his way through the rows of employees shouting remarks which were not drawn from any basic textbook of industrial relations. His admonitions served only to inflame the situation. In the background Andy Lizzard could at last afford to smile. Farley Richardson's entry into the fray had acted as a pair of bellows on spluttering embers. Farley Richardson commandeered the production manager's office and called a council of war of all his available managerial staff. The last to arrive, unaware of the exact purpose of the meeting, announced himself cheerily with the words, 'I see Mr Nice is here'. The colour drained from Farley Richardson's face until it was paler than the clothes he was wearing. Immediately changing tack he told his production manager, 'you'll have to get this sorted and be bloody well quick about it'. And for the second time that afternoon he departed, running.

David Pelham felt reasonably satisfied with life after his first two overs, but reckoned he would have felt better still with a generous slurp of ale inside him. He was bowling again to Haydn Bliss who remained an unknown quantity with the bat. David Pelham maintained his accuracy and was pleased with himself when he tossed one a little higher and beat the batsman in the flight. There was no chance of a stumping because Haydn Bliss had kept his back foot firmly anchored. Rashid Ali shouted approval from behind the stumps. David Pelham followed up with his faster ball which was not so well directed. Nevertheless it surprised the batsman, eluded the bat which came down in a hurry, struck the pad and went towards fine leg to add an extra to the score. The last ball of the over to Jim Flote was not David Pelham's best. It was short of a length, but not wide enough to cut. Jim Flote was undeterred, got a top edge and saw the anguish on David Pelham's face as the ball looped just above the outstretched hand of Jon Palmer at slip before being athletically retrieved. For the bowler the only consolations were a maiden over and the sight of a mug of bitter now within convenient reach at the boundary.

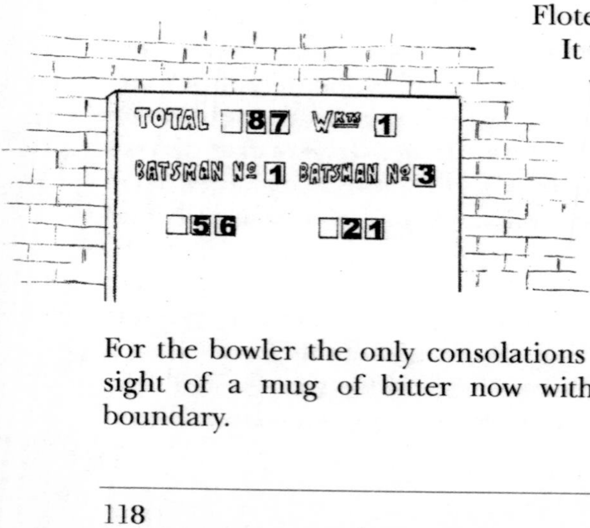

As David Pelham strode towards what he judged to be his well-deserved refreshment he reflected that he was in better shape than when he had taken part in last year's match. His first three overs then had certainly cost more than four runs. Still, it had been a very different situation.

After the opening blast of Colin Banks had reduced them to fifteen for three wickets, Doredell had staged a recovery. Stewart Thorogood had managed an over or two more than Colin Banks and secured a fourth wicket in the process. He then complained of stomach cramps (no prizes for guessing the underlying cause) and the twelfth man had had to be pressed into service. Thereafter some unusual pace from Winston Jenkins and the military medium of Phil Cole had, to put it kindly, lacked penetration. So spin had been summoned. Neither Ray Burrill nor David Pelham had been in any condition to supply it. In David Pelham's case the only thing spinning was his head.

All that a change of bowlers achieved was a change of pace. Spin as such was imperceptible. Yet it is said that batsmen have to work harder to get their runs against slow bowlers. That is exactly what Doredell's fifth wicket pair did. The increase in the scoring rate was masked by the fortuitous fall of a fifth wicket to a delivery from Ray Burrill which, if Syd Breakwell had been alert, should have been called a no-ball. This had led Alan Birch into the error of persisting a little longer with the Burrill/Pelham combination. By this time David Pelham had bowled three overs at a cost of thirty-one runs and had vomited (discreetly) twice. In the circumstances to be accorded a fourth over was an extraordinary act of faith – or desperation – on the part of his captain, but it had paid off.

A draught of Hoppenhall's Charger bitter reinforced Winston Jenkins's mind if not his body. Charge in is what he did from the Hayste end of the ground. He could not be faulted for enthusiasm or for his determination to lead from the front. The fruits of his labour had to be more sternly assessed. Haydn Bliss, his eye by now adjusted to conditions, scored three elegant boundaries with a flourish which would not have been out of place at Covent Garden (where Haydn Bliss had never been quite good enough to appear). Winston Jenkins tossed the ball almost in relief to David Pelham for a fourth over which was to prove not as fortunate as the one granted by Alan Birch last year. Winston Jenkins cursed his own efforts and for good measure cursed the absence of Ray Burrill.

The ears of the vet of recent vintage should have been burning. Instead it was his cheeks. In a flash Ray Burrill learned one of the lessons of life: be careful about how you treat people because you never know when you are going to meet them again. It had been a night of celebration. And why not? After years of study and diligent work (well, most of the time) he had qualified as a veterinary surgeon. He and his fellow erstwhile students had had a few drinks before they descended on the restaurant which one of their number had selected as the centrepiece of the evening's entertainment. It was a Greek taverna in Islington. Apart from its good and reasonably-priced food (it had not yet become fashionable) it had been chosen on the basis that its boisterous atmosphere might more easily absorb a celebratory party. It also helped that the owner, Mitsos Deflopolous, was on good terms with the father of one of Ray's companions and was prepared to offer good terms in respect of the bill.

The party had proceeded in increasingly convivial fashion to the point at which the actual taste of retsina was no longer noticeable. Meanwhile the revellers had become aware of a couple sitting at a nearby table. The term 'nearby' was relative, because Mitsos Deflopolous had created a cordon sanitaire between the young vets and other patrons. For no particular reason, Ray and his friends had begun to speculate about the relationship between the man and the woman. They certainly did not give the impression of being husband and wife. Although the couple appeared to sense that they were being discussed the situation might not have deteriorated without a wholly extraneous factor: the ringing of the man's mobile phone.

Users of mobile phones in confined quarters fall into two categories: the discreet and the plain noisy. Ray's neighbour in the taverna belonged to the latter group. His conversation with someone in Melbourne was loud, long and disputatious. Within minutes this had led him to initiate a call to Bombay, a connection made at the fourth attempt, by which time his irritation and volume had increased. What he heard he seemed not to like and he embarked on a series of further calls. By the time he reached Auckland he was at full throttle. Even his companion was showing distinct signs of disapproval.

Two of Ray Burrill's friends decided to take out their mobile phones and conducted loud but fake calls. This had absolutely no effect in shaming their neighbour into silence. Emboldened by drink they came up with another idea. A co-conspirator was required. The pale young man waiting on their table was summoned. How much were his wages? Really! Only that? Would he perhaps be interested in a bonus? At a tenner apiece from each of them he became very interested. What had their loud-talking neighbour ordered? Moussaka. Perfect! A short while later the waiter appeared at the couple's table with two plates and a dish containing the chef's special moussaka. The waiter winked at Ray and Ray smiled invitingly at the waiter. By this time someone in Toronto was being harangued. He or she was among the first to hear the agonised scream as the tureen of moussaka was deftly deposited into the caller's lap.

The members of Ray's party agreed afterwards that the follow-up performance of the young waiter was itself worth the money. Overflowing with apparent remorse, the waiter could not stop apologising as he fussed around with cloths and water. The scalded diner, telephone instantly abandoned, was assured that never in the waiter's seven-year career had anything of this nature ever before occurred. Mitsos Deflopolus dramatically called an ambulance and more diplomatically made noises (quickly) about compensation. The episode came to an end with the man being escorted away without either his trousers or his dinner companion. Ray Burrill was not sure, but he thought that the lady cast a little smile of thanksgiving in the direction of his table as she left.

The memory of that smile came back to Ray Burrill as he lay (now his turn to be trouser-less) in a strange kitchen in a village on the border of Essex and Cambridgeshire. Had she spotted the conspiracy? Had she, in a later moment of reconciliation, shared her suspicions with her dinner companion? If so Ray's situation was doubly perilous. Fortunately the daughter did the talking. She had easily charmed Ray Burrill and she was no less effective in sweet-talking her father. Restored to his trousers Ray looked more cricketer than hooligan and the transformation appeared to blur the man's memory. Having put his gun away he had continued to stare at Ray asking, 'haven't I seen you somewhere before?' Evidently for the moment he could not answer his own question and Ray had no intention of assisting him. Anxious to put some distance between himself and the father, Ray beat as hasty a retreat as he could. The whole episode would have been written off as a disaster if the daughter had not said as he left, 'perhaps I'll see you later'.

In David Pelham's case the strategically-placed mug may have refreshed the inner man, but outward appearances were not favourable. Jim Flote and Haydn Bliss took advantage of a lull in the external political commentary to build their partnership. The bowler's length and direction showed signs of wavering as the pressure built. Thirteen runs came from the over with the batsmen sharing the spoils. With a final neat single Jim Flote hoisted the Doredell total to exactly one hundred and pinched the strike. The home team was one third of the way towards its target with about one third of the overs gone. Had he been abreast of the situation no doubt the Doredell captain would have been pleased, but after two minutes in Cranley Nice's office Farley Richardson did not think that he was abreast of any situation.

Despite the short distance between production manager's office and the suite occupied by Cranley Nice, Farley Richardson managed to consider and reject at least half a dozen explanations for the idleness of the factory. As he entered Cranley Nice's office he decided to opt for a downright lie. Farley Richardson surprised even himself with the wealth of detail with which he was able to embellish the justification for his decision to hold a fire drill. What seemed extraordinary was the ease of its acceptance by Cranley Nice whose attention seemed to be directed elsewhere. 'What about the Japanese?', he demanded to know. Farley Richardson had a vague notion at the back of his mind that a party of Japanese visitors was inexplicably watching the cricket. Thus there followed an exchange which was entirely at cross-purposes. It finally ended with Farley Richardson giving Cranley Nice the emphatic promise that any trace of Japanese presence on his property would be expunged within the hour. He then speedily departed, muttering about the need to get a report on how the fire drill had gone.

Another change of bowling brought another wicket. However, there was no causal connection between the two events. Having conceded thirty runs from three overs in his second spell, Winston Jenkins thought that he should give way to Phil Cole. Although it had not worked for him he decided to repeat the tactic of giving Phil Cole the other end from which to bowl. He then had another thought. David Pelham could switch as well. To effect this double change Winston reckoned that he might dispose of one of the overs which Greg Roberts would have to bowl. He knew that in pursuance of his wager Greg Roberts was stone cold sober, but experience taught that this could not be expected to have any bearing on the quality of his bowling output. His sense of foreboding was borne out when Greg opened with two wides. He improved on this with a long-hop which Jim Flote struck far into the deep, but not entirely clear of the extremely defensive field on which Winston had insisted.

There looked to be two certain runs and Jim Flote was set on three. The first was successfully completed. Jim Flote had passed Haydn Bliss on the second before the incident occurred. When Jim turned to test whether the third run was on, he was confronted by the sight of his partner stranded in mid-wicket. Halfway through the second run Haydn Bliss had lost his shoe. He might have made his ground if he had not decided to retrieve it. Jim Flote could only watch the unfolding situation in amazement. An excited Harry Northwood had thrown the ball vigorously from the deep - too vigorously for any hope of Greg Roberts being able to gather it. Four overthrows were prevented by Dean Faulds who flung himself at the ball. He too failed to gather it, but it cannoned off his recumbent body and by pure luck rolled towards the stumps where the bowler gave it a helping hand before impact. Haydn Bliss only narrowly failed to ground the shoe in his hand.

As if sensing the fall of the wicket the loudspeaker outside resumed its public service announcements. 'We want Wills', came the relentless voice. And Wills it was who appeared. He had held a long discussion with Ray Beckett about the strategic situation regarding the match. He had explained that as Doredell were up with the pace his own more orthodox style might better complement the stroke-making of Jim Flote. He could help to anchor the innings. Ray Beckett's big hitting would be more useful in the final run-chase. Adrian Wills continued to dredge up reasons as to why he should go in next. In the end they tossed for it.

Having lost the argument but won the toss, Adrian resolved on a display of studious batting. When facing Greg Roberts this would be quite a challenge. But Adrian Wills had been given no time for thought. Jim Flote, who had remained at the striker's end, instead of thumping a full toss for four patted the ball down in front of him and charged down the pitch for a single. Adrian Wills was taken unawares. So too were bowler and wicket-keeper. The run was achieved. Greg Roberts was flattered by the ultra-defensive response of Adrian Wills to the assortment of deliveries which the remainder of the over comprised. Winston Jenkins was not fooled into thinking that an economy rate of four runs an over could be maintained. He decided that the pleasure of Greg Roberts's second over could be deferred.

In view of what had happened in his first three overs Phil Cole did not step back into the breach with any relish. With sixty-four runs to his credit Jim Flote looked well set. Nor had Adrian Wills fooled him by treating Greg Roberts with such exaggerated respect. Something was afoot and Phil Cole did not reckon that he would be a beneficiary of it. An over of three frenetic singles later Phil and his captain were pleasantly surprised. If the batsmen wanted to employ this tactic, it was no skin off the Outcasts' nose. Strangely David Pelham's return over was treated in much the same way. His first ball, which was pitched woefully short, was pushed rather than pulled by Jim Flote, earning one when a boundary seemed to be on offer. When Adrian Wills placed the next ball to the right, but only just to the right, of cover point's right hand he found himself answering his partner's call for what was a risky run. Jim Flote drove the third ball in the same direction and was again the caller, changing his mind when Adrian Wills was almost halfway down the pitch. His success in scrambling back to safety was assisted by the fact that the fielder, Greg Roberts, was statistically unlikely to return the ball accurately twice in succession. The over ended with another rushed single after Jim Flote angled the ball towards an advancing third man and set Adrian Wills a tough race against the arm of Harry Northwood. Something was indeed afoot and Rashid Ali was the first of the Outcasts to see it.

Other quite distinct features of the occasion struck Ray Burrill as he limped back on to the ground. Firstly, there were more spectators than the Outcasts usually expected to see at their matches. Secondly, the game had seemingly attracted the attention of a large number of Japanese visitors. Thirdly, the company's employees had turned out in force to watch the game. But it was not merely the number of people which had caught Ray's attention; it was the partisanship they showed. He now noticed for the first time the strange contrasts of allegiance. The Outcasts had supporters from Hayste and detractors from Doredell. So did Doredell cricket club. Permeating the support for both teams another element was at work: some in the crowd backed Flote in the by-election whilst others favoured Wills. Even amongst the non-eligible voters from the Cambridgeshire side of the border there was sympathy for the company man on the one hand, but on the other a liking for the man who had defied management and put up in opposition. Overall the crowd had become very noisy, but not so noisy that the loudspeaker's encouragement of the Wills cause could not be unheard. Apart from the sheer number and make-up of the spectators, none of these undercurrents was immediately comprehensible to the late returning Outcast as he passed through them on to the field of play.

Ray Burrill's reappearance was noticed first by Tim Jackson, the involuntary twelfth man, who was skulking at the boundary's edge wondering when the mug of ale would be replenished. Tim was warm in his greeting of the missing player. 'You bastard, where the hell have you been? Don't you know that I'm trying to get the socials sorted?' Ray Burrill did know and set out to placate his friend with a sanitised but still lurid account of what had befallen him. Their discussion was sufficiently prolonged for Winston Jenkins to pick out his missing bowler. He was on his way across to him when he spotted the limp. The nightmare scenario of Greg Roberts as fourth bowler was re-enacted in his mind. Anxiety showed in his hailing of Ray. 'You bastard, where the hell have you been? For Christ's sake what have you done to yourself?' (This is an edited version of Winston's welcome.) Continuation of the innings could no longer be held up. A deal was struck. Ray would get further attention to his leg, but must relieve Tim Jackson on the field within twenty minutes. Winston Jenkins was left to ponder whether he could count on a fifth bowler or not.

In the meantime the captain had also had to digest the intelligence he had received from Rashid Ali. If it was correct that Jim Flote was deliberately trying to run out his rival, Adrian Wills, how could this best be facilitated? Rash suggested that the fielding needed to sharpen up a notch. Winston Jenkins wondered instead whether the fielding should aim to look slacker (a much easier option in Outcasts' cricket) in order to instil the belief in the batsmen that easy runs were there to be taken. Word was put out and Winston Jenkins spoke, in particular, to the two best fielders, Harry Northwood and a still grumbling Tim Jackson, moving them into key positions. It was scarcely a plan, more a matter of waiting on events.

An event off the field preceded any event of significance on it. A squad of security officers descended on the hapless Japanese visitors and indicated that they should leave. This had to be done more by gesture than by word which was mutually satisfactory as the security guards, like many of the Japanese, had only a poor understanding of the English language. The physical treatment was nevertheless brusque. This was politely excused by the Japanese on the assumption that there was a need to hurry to board their coaches. They were to be cruelly disillusioned. On reaching the Pink Pedlar they clambered aboard the vehicles and sat there for ten minutes in stifling heat before they were noticed by Roger Trysom. Knowing that Bill Blimp's relief bus was some way off, Roger Trysom had the humanity to realise that his customers could not remain on the coaches. Knowing that Geraint Poppledown was listening, he cried out: 'What on earth can I do with them now?' The publican, pointing to a notice affixed to the wall by the side of the bar, had a suggestion.

The responsibility for bowling the ball which would engineer the run-out fell to Phil Cole. This was quite a challenge to a bowler who could not always guarantee getting right even such basics as line and length and whose radar was by now beginning to be affected by the extent of his refreshment. The auguries were not good. Successful execution correspondingly came as an almighty relief. The over did not begin well. Phil's direction erred too much to leg and, trying a different tactic, Jim Flote clipped him between deep mid-wicket and long-on with a view to running three (or, as he thought to himself with a grim smile, only two and a half). A non-contrived piece of sloppy fielding by David Pelham allowed the third run to be completed almost at the walk.

Phil Cole then produced a full toss wide of off stump. Adrian Wills could pick his spot and, notwithstanding his self-imposed discipline, did. He was tempted to add a single when he half-drove in the direction of Tim Jackson at cover and wished he had done when the fielder made only a lethargic lunge at the ball and let it through his legs. He had stopped Jim Flote in his tracks with a stentorian 'no'. Phil Cole strove to repeat the delivery and Adrian Wills again found Tim Jackson wanting, but caution had prevailed. Why worry, the batsman thought, there's bound to be another four ball in a minute. But it was not a four ball; rather it was a three card trick. To his credit Phil Cole produced another tempting delivery outside off stump. It was met by Adrian Wills with a well-timed, firm drive and a massive 'yes' as he took off down the wicket. He heard rather than saw the stumps shattered. Tim Jackson had leapt on the ball like a panther and in one movement had gathered and thrown. The Outcasts had got their third wicket.

This was not information reflected by the electronic scoreboard. In fact the figures on the board bore absolutely no relation to the state of the innings. Spectators were expected to believe that Doredell had scored seven hundred and eleven runs for the loss of thirty wickets. The last man had been dismissed for two hundred and sixty-nine and the last wicket had fallen when the score was one. Outside the scorebox and from an inconspicuous vantage point the conspiratorial trio looked on with satisfaction. Mostyn Winchope and Billy Gorman were the most impressed by what they saw. They had found it hard to believe when Mostyn Winchope's nephew had told them what might be possible. Now they had proof of the power of the computer and the insidiousness of software. They sat back to enjoy such further tricks as could be performed for their benefit.

Inside the scorebox the mood was very different. Doredell's scorer, Robert Vine, pressed the keys on his laptop in vain. All he could get on his screen was a jumble of nonsensical numbers. The realisation that what he was looking at would also be what the outside world would be seeing was not instantaneous. It took a bellow from Syd Breakwell ('Come along now, scorer, what's to do?') to wake him to the full awfulness of his situation. 'Just a little technical difficulty', he called back defensively, 'I'll have it sorted in a moment.' However, his usual confidence must have been lacking when he added, desperately turning towards Simon Crossley, 'Do you know anything about McAfee?'

In the adjoining pavilion first aid was being administered. Had Ray Burrill's relationship with Lambkins, the border collie, been maintained on a professional basis the recently-qualified vet would doubtless in due time have had an opportunity to examine and admire the fine set of teeth the animal possessed. As it was, his appreciation of the canine molars had been achieved in both premature and painful fashion. Lambkins' owner had been denied time to bathe, anoint and bind the unwelcome wound by the unwelcome appearance of her father. Sophie Crossley and Adrienne Palmer, pausing from their beer distribution duties, had found all the necessary items in a well-stocked glass-fronted box decorated with a red cross. Fortunately they had claimed it from its position on the wall moments before it might have been struck and shattered by the flying bat of the recently-dismissed player. Unfortunately another member of the team had wholly innocently found himself in the line of flight. The makeshift nurses found Haydn Bliss an altogether more distressed patient.

No batsman is at his best in the immediate aftermath of his dismissal. Naturally there is disappointment, perhaps at an opportunity foregone or a display of imperfect technique or even a foolish stroke. Disappointment can turn to anger when the batsman has been run out, because often this represents muddle between himself and his partner. It is worse when the dismissed man feels that his partner is to blame. The mood cannot be expected to improve, if, as in this particular case, the trudge back to the pavilion is accompanied by a derogatory commentary. The man on the loudspeaker was extremely well informed. By the time the departing batsman got out of earshot he had been taunted repeatedly as a loser. It was small wonder therefore that the bat left his hand in a savage act of violence which was no respecter of persons and objects in the way. Jim Flote was no better for realising how easily he had been out-tricked.

Ray Beckett had had no intention of allowing further debate about his place in the batting order. He was on his way to join Adrian Wills at the wicket before Jim Flote had taken more than a dozen steps of his forlorn but furious return journey. Realising that this was no occasion for an exchange of confidences, Ray Beckett had given his exiting team-mate a noticeably wide berth. Nor did he have anything to say to Adrian Wills. He already knew how he intended to play. His skills gave him little choice. In any case he felt that this was his moment of destiny when he could emphatically announce himself to his new side. If Doredell was to be sure of reaching such a large total, his broad bat and his heavyweight muscle would be essential. Adrian Wills could prod and poke if he wanted, but in Ray Beckett's opinion a rumbustious innings was needed. From what he had so far seen of the visitors' bowling attack he was confident he could supply it. Within a minute he had taken guard, surveyed the field and swatted the final ball of Phil Cole's over to the boundary. Ray Beckett smirked at Adrian Wills. His day had come.

Farley Richardson returned to the production manager's office to find that his colleague had indeed been 'bloody well quick about it'. A solution to the industrial dispute had been found. It owed absolutely nothing to the production manager although with everything short of a direct boast he claimed the credit for it. Farley Richardson would have done exactly the same in reporting to Cranley Nice until he reminded himself that his boss might still be in ignorance of the strike. The peace formula had been the brainchild of the assistant human resources manager – to the minor annoyance of the chief human resources manager.

Following the Nice Spice take-over, Ashley Bright had been seconded from head office to bolster the personnel function at the former Fingerbarrows works. He was a keen, clever and ambitious young man. It would later emerge that he was a promising leg-break bowler, but for the moment he had kept this talent to himself. Being recently married he had other preoccupations at the weekend. Attending emergency meetings on a Saturday afternoon was not one of them. Ashley Bright had an attribute which was not shared by anyone else attending the meeting in the production manager's office nor indeed by Farley Richardson who had deserted it. Ashley Bright had read books on the psychology of labour relations – indeed one of them had been written by his father. His theoretical knowledge (fortunately) had been backed up by acute observation during his first few weeks as assistant human resources manager. His plan to end the stoppage contained two elements: one positive, the other negative. The prime need was to placate Mildred Askern, who was a sympathetic figure, whilst identifying another 'victim', who was not. The production manager repeated for the benefit of Farley Richardson and without a blush what he (or rather Ashley Bright) had in mind.

For a while Ray Beckett marched with destiny. However, it was not an endless journey. It had a stuttering kind of start. After his first massive blow the left-hander was made to wait the best part of two overs before he got the strike again. Either David Pelham bowled a steady over to Adrian Wills or the batsman treated it with excessive respect. Two runs were scored off the first ball and a scrambled leg-bye off the last. Phil Cole's next over was far from steady and Ray Beckett's impatience grew as Adrian Wills seemed to make heavy weather of it. Finally he took a single off the fifth ball. Ray Beckett smacked his lips in anticipation, gave his bat a twirl and drove the final ball back over Phil Cole's head one bounce for four.

None of these changes in the score could be shown by the scoreboard which seemed to be in the grip of a digital snowstorm. Following Simon Crossley's admission that he knew nothing about McAfee or any other virus protection system, Robert Vine had tried every expedient, but could find no way of bringing order to the read-out. From the security of his pencil and paper system, Simon Crossley was obliged to convey the score at the end of each over by the time-honoured Doredell method of shouting. His counterpart continued to fiddle and fuss, resisting too long the thought that a virus could have penetrated his system. Had the realisation come sooner, he might have closed down the equipment and isolated the scoreboard. Much grievous embarrassment would have been spared.

Roger Trysom stared at the notice in the bar of the Pink Pedlar. He had never heard of Longbirch Hall or the maze which was its only surviving feature. Geraint Poppledown explained the background. Some people made a career out of acquiring a run-down property, restoring it, selling (at a handsome profit) and moving on to another. Jack Jamieson had developed a variant of this procedure. He specialised in buying large properties, burning them down, claiming the insurance and moving on. His nemesis was Longbirch Hall which lay on the outskirts of Doredell. For a well-practised pyrotechnician he might perhaps be adjudged a trifle reckless to have reduced the place to a smouldering ruin within fourteen hours of completion of the purchase. In fact fate had played a trick on him. Hard-pressed though he was at the time to satisfy the avaricious demands of the second Mrs Jamieson in her divorce settlement, he would have waited at least three weeks or until he could have persuaded the soon-to-be-ex Mrs Jamieson to spend the night there before contriving a conflagration. The exercise of his professional judgement was frustrated by an electrical fault in the central heating boiler. The destruction of his property was thereby taken out of his hands. Linked with six previous fires which had marred his foray into country living, the loss of Longbirch Hall finally gave rise to police suspicion. All of this had resulted in Jack Jamieson going to prison for a very long time and the second Mrs Jamieson having to re-charge her financial batteries by becoming the third wife of a wealthy industrialist.

The maze situated on the edge of the estate had not been at risk. Its upkeep was assured by a bequest from a previous owner of the hall which was administered by a small trust. The resources available to the trust sufficed only for the basic maintenance of the maze and the operation of a tiny tea-room-cum-souvenir shop operated haphazardly by volunteers. What the resources did not permit was much by way of publicity. The maze was advertised only within a very localised area. Roger Trysom was one of millions who did not know of its existence. There was now an opportunity to reduce that number by a few score if the Japanese tourists felt fit enough to cover three-quarters of a mile on foot. As a means of killing time until Bill Blimp's arrival it was worth a try. It proved by a wide margin to be over-kill.

Despite a show of impatience over his (so far) unexplained disappearance, Winston Jenkins was hugely relieved when at last Ray Burrill trod warily on to the field. His relief was a little less huge when Ray expressed doubt about bowling, citing his painful leg. When he put weight on it during his bowling action, he said, he was likely to suffer some discomfort. To Winston's disbelieving expression, he responded with the worry that his accuracy could be affected. Winston suggested that a couple of pints – he indicated the pots currently being refreshed by Tim Jackson – would probably deaden the pain. In truth Ray Burrill's unusual display of reluctance to bowl owed more at that stage to depression than pain. The balm and bandaging applied to his leg by Adrienne and Sophie had medically deadened the pain. Ray was out of sorts with himself for two quite different reasons. Being bitten by a border collie made him wonder for the first time whether he was truly cut out for a career caring for animals. Had the last few years been wasted? And then there was his new female acquaintance of whom he was deeply enamoured. What chance did he have in that direction when she learnt that he was the type of man who had caused piping hot moussaka to be tipped into her father's lap? Ask any bowler: it was not the best frame of mind in which to be turning in a competent performance. In this instance, however, Winston Jenkins was a beggar as well as a captain, as he was certainly not endowed with much choice. That left Ray Burrill with even less and so willy-nilly he found himself bowling the twentieth over, though insisting on his slower style.

In their ways both Winston Jenkins and Ray Burrill were correct. Unless Ray was brought on to bowl at this stage of the innings – each bowler being restricted to eight overs – Winston would be in danger of not being able to juggle his attack (the very word made him grimace) without calling on a sixth person, who by definition could only be worse than Greg Roberts. Winston left himself with a measure of flexibility by using Ray without further delay. That at least was the theory. It was not given much of a boost on the evidence of Ray's first over. Ray was plainly not at his best, bowling with a stilted action and a pained expression. Even Adrian Wills, supposedly in a self-appointed anchor role, could not stop himself from gorging on a diet of ill-directed balls wide of the stumps on either side and keeping to no constant length. But for two smart pieces of fielding, one heroic and one accidental (Greg Roberts could not get his hand out of the way in time), Adrian Wills would have notched up his score by more than three boundaries and the single which stole the strike.

Ray Burrill gave Winston Jenkins a meaningful look and sought a fielding position close to a flask of ale. A feeling of vindication was matched by a sense of shame mixed with a dash of self-pity. He had to admit that after the first couple of balls he could hardly claim that he was crippled. It was more the experience of the last couple of hours which had prevented him from applying himself properly to the job in hand. He realised that he was letting down his comrades. Once more he felt self-pity. But as the next over progressed he found the antidote in several draughts of Hoppenhall's Charger bitter, a well-known source of comfort to the despairing cricketer.

Mildred Askern had remained largely unaware of the extent to which her grievance had been blown out of all proportion. Finding deserted the usual areas which she frequented, Mildred in her innocence came to the conclusion that there actually was a fire drill taking place. She had not heard a siren, but she put that down to trouble with her hearing. Her next problem was trying to remember which was the safe area where her department was meant to gather. She had wandered about the site without success and finally decided she could do no better than wait outside the packaging department with another cup of tea. If she could not find them, she reasoned, they would come looking for her.

The person who found her was Farley Richardson, ever anxious to ingratiate himself if opportunity could be found. He had a message to impart. Mildred Askern was to remain in the packaging department, but with a new and important assignment. As a new marketing ploy and with an eye on the Christmas trade, Nice Spice were about to launch a gift pack made up of small quantities of a range of their products. Putting together this selection of spices in their presentation box was a fiddly and time-consuming job requiring much patience and, of course, great experience. Farley Richardson laid heavy emphasis on experience. Mildred would be able to work at her own pace at a special table where she would be in sight and earshot of all her friends and fellow-workers. All this was put over with a dose of sickly charm and Mildred Askern was persuaded. On enquiry she was assured that the fire drill (Farley Richardson gave her a strange look) was complete and she could now go home. With equal relief Farley Richardson set off back to the cricket murmuring to himself 'and after Christmas, redundancy'.

On the field of play Winston Jenkins was weighing his options. There seemed to be no getting round the fact that, if the innings was going to run its course, seven of the remaining overs would have to be bowled by Greg Roberts. The only thing in Greg's favour, he kept on reminding himself, was that he had not had a drink. Others, including himself Winston Jenkins had to admit, were in various distances of being able to make that claim. With a reservoir of Hoppenhall's Charger bitter so close at hand no one – again Winston Jenkins included himself – was likely to get more sober. He could see David Pelham in the act of refreshing himself and Phil Cole had just set down what was now an empty receptacle close to the third man position. It remained questionable whether Greg Roberts without liquor could bowl a better over than his team-mates who were increasingly with it. What finally swayed the issue in Winston Jenkins' mind was the need to swallow up another over of Greg's allocation: he persuaded himself that the odd one here and there could almost be secreted into the sequence. Even if this removed any chance of Greg settling into a spell, it would equally deny the batsmen too much familiarity with the bowler's output. Even as he threw the ball to Greg, Winston knew that this was a desperately implausible theory.

Having secured alternative transport for his Japanese clients and having glimpsed a means of keeping them diverted until it arrived, Roger Trysom's morale was further boosted by the return of James Saito. He greeted him with a show of enthusiasm which subsided only partially with the realisation that his co-guide and interpreter was severely the worse for wear. Roger Trysom's assessment of his situation bore similarities to that made by Winston Jenkins in relation to Greg Roberts. What it boiled down to was acceptance that a drunk Japanese speaker was more use to him at that moment than any amount of sober companions totally unfamiliar with the Japanese language. However, as he conveyed to James that the Japanese visitors needed to be prised from the coaches, and as James sought to pass this message to them, Roger Trysom realised that the advantage he had gained was marginal at best. The elderly Japanese began to descend from the first bus, but it was obvious that James Saito's exhortation had deteriorated in clarity by the time he was repeating it in the second bus. It was sight rather than sound which caused enlightenment when someone noticed that their colleagues from the first coach were grouping outside.

Despite his cloudy mind and slurred speech, James Saito had managed to get across two messages. The first was 'walk' which was bad, the other was 'tea-room' which was good. What persuaded the Japanese tourists to suppose that what they would find at the end of their walk was anything like the kind of tea-room which they might have imagined, no one would ever know. However, the mental picture of a tea-room was strong and they allowed themselves to follow Roger Trysom's energetic beckoning, embarking on what for them at that stage of the afternoon was the equivalent of a mini-marathon. Roger himself felt cheered, strengthened in his belief that he was regaining control of the situation. Before long he would be shockingly disillusioned.

The transport element of his recovery package was en route. This should have been a welcome factor. However, it was not, by virtue of Bill Blimp being at the wheel of the rescuing double-decker. As a coach operator, Bill Blimp had a disadvantage beyond the standard of the vehicles he provided. He had a hopeless sense of direction. It was not a handicap to which he admitted. When Roger Trysom had described his whereabouts, Bill Blimp's reaction had been full of assurance. Roger Trysom had been left with the clear impression that not only did Bill Blimp know exactly where Doredell was, but that he had actually been there on a number of occasions (which was quite untrue). It was not surprising therefore that Bill Blimp's first culpable mistake had been to select the wrong route out of London. This error was compounded by the second, which was not to have at hand a map of suitable scale to show the existence of either Doredell or Hayste. The third mistake, which was less culpable only for being consequential, lay in the choice of road to take him in the more north-westerly direction necessary to reach the Cambridgeshire border; within two miles Bill Blimp found himself in procession behind a funfair making its slow and deliberate journey towards its next engagement. There was no chance of overtaking.

Greg Roberts's second over of the innings had not been the disaster which Winston Jenkins had half-expected. Adrian Wills, who was on strike, had had no extended experience of Greg's bowling. Greg had not been called upon to bowl in the fixture last year and in any case Adrian Wills's stay at the crease had been, he remembered, nasty, brutish and short. From the few balls he had seen so far in this match he did not believe that Greg Roberts could be as bad a bowler as he might have appeared. Being instinctively cautious Adrian Wills decided to give him the benefit of the doubt. Having seen his first delivery, nice, docile and full, met by a correct, forward defensive push, Greg Roberts had a spurt of confidence. This inspired him to send down what for him were four deliveries of tolerably good length (some kind of record) which confirmed Adrian Wills in his caution. He did, however, wake himself from his apparent torpor by leg-glancing the last ball of the over for a single.

Ray Burrill, his pain both physical and mental now partly anaesthetised by high quality real ale, was determined to improve his performance. Adrian Wills was equally determined that he should not. Ray Burrill, however, had a capacity beyond that of Greg Roberts to bowl well. That Adrian Wills should doubt it lay in his recollection of Ray Burrill's ragged performance last year. Led on by Tom and Nigel Redman, Ray's pre-match preparation had not been ideal. His troubles had begun not in the saloon bar on the upper deck of Bill Blimp's flagship, but on the previous evening.

The brothers Redman had been spending their last day unencumbered by their mother's health demands. She was due to touch down at Heathrow the following morning. Tom and Nigel were determined that they would have a good night out before duty called. Shortly before the appointed closing time Ray Burrill had wandered into their bookshop in search of a volume on swine fever which he needed to assist his studies. It had therefore been with the worthiest intentions that Ray Burrill had innocently placed himself in the way of temptation. Without realising quite what he was in for, Ray was easily persuaded that there was a more agreeable way of spending the evening than absorbing Professor Arkin Salzheimer's theories on porcine diseases.

A few doors along from the Redman family bookshop was a recently opened oyster bar. It was to this establishment that Ray Burrill's downfall could be traced. In the matter of oysters he was a virgin. Nor was he well advanced in acquiring a taste for the black stout which the Redman brothers insisted was the proper accompaniment. Their stay in the oyster bar was extended so that Ray's tutelage could be properly accomplished. The trio then made their way to a tumbledown hostelry called the Beggar's Tent where it was clear that Tom and Nigel Redman were not unknown. This could be judged by the greeting which they received from the man behind the bar – 'Mother not back yet?' An array of fine ales was on offer. It was Tom who laid down the plan (or challenge). They would work their way through the card from the lowest specific gravity to the highest. It was at the 4.2% level that Ray Burrill finally quelled the pangs of conscience which reminded him how much he still needed to know about swine fever.

When the strongest ale had finally been drained amidst much self-congratulation, Tom proposed that they should now go back down the scale. Nigel disagreed. He was hungry. Ray cast his vote for a respite from drink and that was how they found themselves in the Temple of Eastern Promise which was within five minutes easy staggering distance from the Beggar's Tent. In an Indian restaurant Ray Burrill felt he was on safer ground. He was still out-paced by the Redmans who exhibited a desire to go through the card much as they had done in the pub. Not willing to drink Indian beer (designated along with lager as 'fizzy pop') or wine with curry, they had confined themselves to water whilst eating. At around ten to eleven, Nigel Redman pronounced himself in need of a beer and they adjourned to the Beggar's Tent in time to hear the landlord call last orders. Ray told himself he only had to manage just one more round. He was wrong. Once the general public was excluded it was clear that the relationship between the landlord and the Redman brothers was not one of mere acquaintance. There was true bonhomie, a bonhomie which was demonstrated well into the early hours. Ray Burrill could not remember how he got home. He could remember the ghastly wakeful hours he spent until it was time to collect his bag and join his fellow Outcasts for the trip to Doredell. To take one wicket for thirty-five runs was, in Ray's opinion, a creditable achievement in the circumstances – even if he had been able to bowl only two overs.

Ray Burrill winced at these recollections as he prepared to bowl to Adrian Wills. He winced once again when he got one to turn inducing a false shot from the batsman and a poor attempt at a catch from an optimistically-placed slip fielder. Adrian Wills luckily came by four runs, chastised himself and treated the remaining five balls of the over with more respect than they deserved. They were straight enough, but there was not a hint of any more spin. For his part Ray Beckett was condemned to watch. Between overs he gave vent to his impatience. The gist of what he had to say was that the pace had to be upped and that he, given the opportunity (Ray Beckett put some emphasis on those words) was the man to up it. Especially, he added, if they (he jerked his finger vaguely in the direction of Winston Jenkins who was in deep conversation with Rashid Ali) are daft enough to give that chap at the other end another over.

Giving Greg Roberts another over was precisely the outcome of the discussion. The previous one had gone far better than Winston

Jenkins had anticipated. That was why he had pondered the risk of getting another of Greg's allocation out of the way. The gamble did not pay off in quite the manner Winston had reckoned. The first ball tested the goodwill of the umpire too far. Rodney Corrington signalled a wide in the direction of the scorers and at the behest of neither of them the word 'wicked' flashed up on the board. The next delivery was not illegitimate, but it was ill-advised. Seeing the half volley Ray Beckett drove it hard towards the deep extra cover boundary. Had he picked a spot not much more than a foot or two either side of Harry Northwood he would have got his four runs. As it was, Harry had time to put down the beer he was drinking and field the ball. Ray Beckett had to be satisfied with three and dissatisfied with the fact that Adrian Wills was back on strike.

Greg Roberts would have conceded another wide if Adrian Wills had not stretched and tapped the ball just past point for a single. Ray Beckett would have been wise to have let the next one go as it might have been deemed a wide. Instead he flailed at it, but his full power was not in the shot. Ray Burrill had to give chase. Hampered by a now aching leg his coverage of the ground was laboured. The batsmen ran four after which it was a moot point whether Ray Beckett or Ray Burrill was breathing harder. Perhaps the exertion affected the batsman's next shot. A full toss which Ray Beckett intended to hit skimming past the bowler went in that direction but high in the air. Dean Faulds had time to circle the ball, get a good look at it and spill the catch; the batsmen had time to run three even at what for Ray Beckett was now a reduced pace.

There was no rest for the weary. Adrian Wills pulled a short, wide delivery from Greg Roberts towards square leg. This happened to be a part of the field which was well populated as Sophie Crossley had just re-filled the beer flasks on that side of the ground and fielders were edging towards them. The ball was recovered before it could cross the boundary and another three runs accrued. For a moment Ray Beckett leant on his bat hoping that Greg Roberts was not over-eager for more punishment, but Greg, anxious to finish this horrid over, was already at his bowling mark. Ray Beckett heaved himself into position and pushed rather than struck the ball just behind point. 'Come one', his partner shouted. It was a seductive call. Ray Beckett knew that he wanted to keep the strike. He set off.

Farley Richardson had not gone far before Cranley Nice fell into step with him. The owner of Nice Spice was now in a better frame of mind. His chosen method for relieving stress was to watch videos of English batsmen flaying Australian bowlers to all corners. Of necessity there was not much variety available to him. His particular favourites had been spliced together in a wonderfully biased collection. It included Brearley and Amiss at The Oval, Gooch and Gower at Lord's, Botham and Dilley at Headingley, Botham at Old Trafford in the same year, Hussain and Thorpe at Edgbaston and Michael Vaughan at Sydney. Together with perusal of last month's sales figures the effect on Cranley Nice had been uplifting. He had decided that he was ready for some live cricket.

In trying to answer Cranley Nice's queries about the state of the game Farley Richardson was at a disadvantage. The one hard piece of information in his possession was that the opposing team had scored three hundred and four runs for the loss of five wickets. He could not expect this on its own to be well received by Cranley Nice. Having been diverted from the match by other events, which would also be bad news to Cranley Nice if he became aware of them, Farley Richardson did not know whether the home team's response was making the Outcasts' score seem plenty or puny. He had a ready-made excuse to hand in respect of the fire drill which he had been supervising, but as this was total fiction he did not wish to place heavy reliance on it. He was forced to obfuscate whilst trying as they drew nearer to the sports ground to get a grip on the score. A glance at the scoreboard might normally have been expected to inform him. Had he known that Doredell were one hundred and sixty-two for three wickets in the twenty-third over, he would have been able to tell a good story to his companion. At this moment the scoreboard yielded no such information.

'You idiot', suddenly cried Cranley Nice. Farley Richardson's first reaction was that this remark was directed towards him. It was perhaps an understandable mistake as these were the first and third of four words currently displayed on the scoreboard, the others being a particularly vulgar epithet and his own name. But Cranley Nice's eyes were not focused on the scoreboard; they had gone directly to the action in the middle where Ray Beckett had failed to complete the journey on which he had embarked. Adrian Wills suffered a change of heart and sent his partner back. The screeching of Ray Beckett's internal braking mechanism was almost audible. The start of his return journey was not immediate and he fell three feet short when the wicket was broken. Realisation dawned on Farley Richardson, but he had more to worry about than the idiocy of Ray Beckett's running between wickets. He had to steer Cranley Nice out of eye-line with the scoreboard before discovering why this calumny was being perpetrated. This also meant skirting the large body of company employees whom his boss could not fail to notice. He took Cranley Nice's arm and embarked on this perilous path whilst agreeing that it had never been a run and that he would speak to the man. Out of the corner of his eye he noticed that the message on the scoreboard had changed to something equally offensive. Irrespective of the fall of the wicket the crowd seemed well amused.

Winston Jenkins weighed up the over which had just passed. Fifteen runs had been conceded, but a wicket had been taken even if this had occurred without any positive input from the bowler (who was nevertheless cavorting around with pleasure). Winston Jenkins had to accept that, if they could take the remaining wickets for fifteen runs apiece, they would win. He therefore decided to allow himself a thin margin of satisfaction. He did not have to worry about who was to bowl the next over and nor was there any doubt about who would receive the first ball as the batsmen had in the end failed to cross. Winston Jenkins placed reliance on Ray Burrill warming to his task. Uncertainty lingered over the identity of the batsman who would partner Adrian Wills. Farley Richardson had not yet reached the pavilion to resume command. He would have known that George Summermore, Doredell's wicket-keeper, was next man in. Inside the pavilion neither Ed Fylder nor Kris Vertz, both padded up, would have argued that George Summermore was the right man to go in next. Unfortunately the wicket-keeper was missing anyway. The immediate environs were searched without a sighting. Kris Vertz was the first to react and was halfway to the wicket before George Summermore ambled back into the pavilion with the pack of wafer biscuits he had obtained from a machine in the mess room. He would not have much time in which to eat them.

Adrian Wills had not expected to see Kris Vertz advancing towards him. He too had assumed that George Summermore would be joining him or even Farley Richardson. Kris Vertz was a mixed blessing. His complete lack of any track record as a batsman meant that he had to be rated worse than George, but very likely better than Farley. Of necessity judgement was postponed. Off the second ball of Ray Burrill's over, Adrian Wills called Kris Vertz for what should have been a routine single. The Austrian responded with alacrity, enthusiasm and no mean turn of speed. Two-thirds of the way down the wicket the straps of his old-fashioned pads became loose and one pad lodged in the flap of the other causing his feet to go from under him. Such was his momentum that he slid another yard or so on his stomach, but was still tantalisingly short when Rashid Ali removed the bails.

The party of Japanese visitors had by now lost any lingering appearance of a group of people engaged on a cultural outing. The weary procession bore the look of a column of refugees. Roger Trysom allowed himself the dark thought that, had they been genuinely fleeing persecution, they might have been moving faster. Eventually to Roger Trysom's relief and, he had to admit, surprise (a couple of old boys with Zimmer frames had had to be constantly chivvied) they reached the maze. It was a remarkable creation which had been kept in a very good state of repair by an enthusiastic but amateur landscape gardener whose dedication to his task had not been curbed by the budget available to him.

The adjacent tea-room, by contrast, might not have lacked love, but its very appearance cried out that it had lacked its fair share of resources for maintenance purposes. Shack would have been a flattering description for the wooden structure with its cracked windows and peeling green paint. It occurred to Roger Trysom that there was very probably asbestos in the roof, but he decided not to complicate an already tense situation by voicing his fears aloud. Such was the fragility of the volunteer roster that the tea-room could not always be guaranteed to be open. But their luck (they thought) was in; it was clearly open. The luck lasted only as far as the encounter with the lady on duty. Connie Stillmarch, spinster of the parish, was not by nature suited to a job which involved meeting the general public. Her interpersonal skills did not improve when the members of the public in question were Japanese. Neither the tea-room's seating capacity nor Connie Stillmarch's state of preparedness was equal to the sudden descent of such a large group of customers. From the pot which she kept on the go when she was in charge of the premises she was able to fill no more than three of the assorted and chipped mugs which had come from a cupboard marked 'china'. They were a far cry from the dainty receptacles which the Japanese associated with tea-rooms. Some sat down in exhaustion, others in despair, whilst the more hardy thought, having reached it, they would investigate the maze. James Saito slid away with them, not out of any duty of care, but to get away from Roger Trysom's baleful glances.

If Cranley Nice had to notice anything, it was marginally better from Farley Richardson's point of view that it was the presence of employees away from their work stations and not the stream of abuse against the company which scrolled across the scoreboard. For the former he had a ready-made explanation; for the latter he did not. Obligingly Cranley Nice, after roaring 'bloody fool' in the direction of the now retreating figure of Kris Vertz, asked Farley Richardson why he was allowing his employees to watch cricket in the firm's time. He was told that after an 'extremely successful' fire practice during which people had been 'extremely co-operative' there had been so little time left before the end of the shift that he had thought it 'extremely good for labour relations' to let them stay on to support the home team. Cushioned by the good sales figures he had digested earlier and inclined to be tolerant of those who supported cricket, Cranley Nice let the matter rest. In the haste with which Farley Richardson was propelling him towards the sanctuary of the pavilion he did not have time to notice that his employees were not one hundred percent supportive of the local side.

Ashley Bright, the assistant human resources manager at Nice Spice, had done a good job. With a couple of well-briefed managerial colleagues he had moved amongst the crowd of striking employees with a tale of outrageous spin. Having first passed on the good news that Mildred Askern was variously fine, happy, over the moon and keen to be back at work, the boot was put into Andy Lizzard with a vengeance. There was no dishonour which could not be heaped on him; no crime with which he could not be associated; no perversion of which he could be excused; and no infectious or contagious disease which he was not harbouring. Additionally, and this counted heavily with loyal employees, it was hinted that Andy Lizzard was a saboteur implanted in Nice Spice by a rival company. When finally they were told that they had the rest of the day off, the deal was clinched and the dispute was at an end. Some drifted away whilst the more discerning stayed to watch the cricket. They were supplemented by others who thought that there was a good laugh to be had.

Another gale of crowd laughter (apart from the cheer which had accompanied the demise of Kris Vertz) alerted Farley Richardson to the likelihood of another infamous slogan on the scoreboard. Ignoring the need to get ready to bat, Farley Richardson moved decisively in the direction of the scorers. He found a completely calm Simon Crossley and a totally distraught Robert Vine. Simon Crossley, reliant on traditional materials to record events, had no worries. By contrast Robert Vine was the victim of perverted technology and in fear of losing his job. His assiduously acquired computer skills had not equipped him to battle with an electronic invasion. Farley Richardson, who was within touching distance of IT illiteracy, had no time for niceties. He tore out every cable he could see. A groan from the crowd outside told him that he had succeeded in his purpose. Then he demanded of Robert Vine what the hapless scorer could not provide: an explanation. His final words as he stormed out were to advise Robert Vine to get some paper and pencils.

George Summermore was by now taking guard. He had not hurried to the wicket and had still been munching the last of the wafer biscuits as he asked Syd Breakwell for middle and leg. A spray of crumbs gushed forward as he spoke. George Summermore was a solid if unspectacular batsman, a description of which he gave early proof as he played out the rest of Ray Burrill's over. At first he gave Ray a circumspect examination before punching the last ball for a solid couple of runs. Only then did he consult with Adrian Wills about how they were going to set about acquiring the remaining one hundred and forty-one runs at an asking rate which was now close to nine an over.

Winston Jenkins had had the space of an over in which to reflect. Two consecutive overs from Greg Roberts, he concluded, amounted to too long a spell. He still had high hopes of Ray Burrill, but he

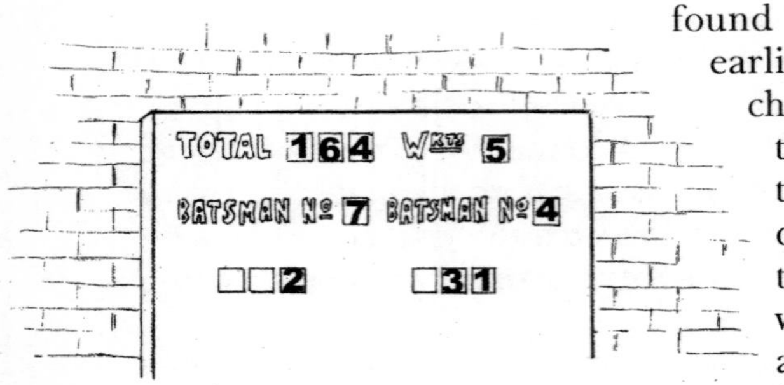

found himself reverting to his earlier thought that constant changing of bowlers gave him the best chance of confusing their opponents. So he decided to recall Phil Cole at the Doredell end. It took a while to attract Phil's attention as, beer container in hand, he was engrossed in conversation with Tim Jackson, who also had a mobile phone clamped to his ear. Delicate negotiations were being undertaken in relation to the evening's entertainment. Phil Cole had some difficulty in recognising his captain's summons and he was halfway back to the middle before realising that he was still carrying the flask of ale. Hurriedly he put it out of harm's way but felt decidedly bloated after marking out his run and preparing to bowl. He was not long in providing public evidence of how he felt.

Pace bowlers – a category to which Phil Cole had only tenuous claim – are often expected to produce a loosener when starting the fresh over of a spell. But not six looseners. The miracle was that the over did not cost him more than ten runs. A harsher umpire than Rodney Corrington would not have been criticised if three of the deliveries had been called wide. Had they been wide of the leg stump, Phil Cole would not have got away with it. However, extra width outside off stump leaves more scope for doubt and the doubt in Rodney Corrington's mind was created by the ease with which Adrian Wills had nimbly got across and punched the first, third and fifth deliveries for good runs. The fact that he failed to connect with the second, fourth and sixth (by some distance) proved to be of no avail. Phil Cole was glad that he had only one over left. It was a feeling shared by his captain.

After the twenty-sixth over of the innings Winston Jenkins wished that he had been consistent with the approach which had previously commended itself to him. Instead of substituting himself or David Pelham for Ray Burrill at the Hayste end, he faltered. Ray, Winston Jenkins reasoned to himself, had after a poor start bowled two economical overs. He looked to be settling into a steady rhythm. Perhaps he could apply pressure at one end which would push up the asking rate beyond Doredell's capacity. Unfortunately for the captain's calculations, reason and rhythm did not come into it. They were supplanted by romance and remorse.

Ray Burrill was about to turn at the end of his run when a flash of colour caught his eye. It was her. Those bright yellow jeans she had been wearing could not be mistaken. She waved. He wobbled. There was a pause – until Ray Burrill realised that she was not the only one staring at him. Collecting himself (or so he thought) he trotted in to bowl. Something was pounding. It was either his heart or his guts, in which a third draught of Hoppenhall's Charger bitter was now residing. The first ball did him credit with no one, except the batsman. George Summermore's eyes lit on the slow long-hop with much the same intensity as moments earlier Ray Burrill's eyes had lit on the object of his affection. Going down on one knee the batsman scooped the ball effortlessly over square leg for six. Ray Burrill compensated with a brisk full toss which went down the leg side, escaping George Summermore's swinging bat, but not the attention of Syd Breakwell, who majestically signalled a wide. Ray's next ball avoided the censure of the umpire, but it was short of a good length and inviting. George Summermore accepted the invitation, slamming the ball over a solitary fielder, who was wondering why in these circumstances he was so close to the wicket, and sending it one bounce towards the boundary between long-on and deep mid-wicket. He would have earned his second boundary had the ball's passage not been interrupted by the prone figure of Boris Wigmouth. His alter ego, Kevin Newton, had made a move (with the primary intention of getting out of the ball's way), but had slipped on a patch of grass made wet by an earlier, careless spillage of ale. Greg Roberts rescued the ball and two runs were saved. Kevin Newton was not particularly amused to see Ray Burrill clap his hands above his head in silent appreciation.

His mind in a whirl, Ray Burrill did not know how he managed to send down a respectable off-break which equally surprised George Summermore and struck him on the pad. Both Rashid Ali and Ray Burrill appealed. In the bowler's case this came out as a high-pitched screech. The sound hung embarrassingly in the air until it was cut short by a roared 'not out' from Syd Breakwell, who would in fact have benefited from video evidence. At that point Ray Burrill might have recovered his poise and his confidence. It was not to be. As he reached his bowling-mark he spotted the girl's father walking towards her. From the expression on his face Ray Burrill feared that he had remembered their previous acquaintance. He bowled two more attempted off-breaks which were despatched to the boundary, first on one side of the wicket and then the other. The final ball was driven hard and straight. Amazingly the stroke earned no runs, being fielded brilliantly (he modestly allowed this description to stand) by the bowler. In truth, brilliance had not come into it. Ray Burrill had made no conscious effort to save runs. His instinctive concern had been to save himself. Without his hands in the path of the ball, it would have struck his leg in the area made tender by the attentions of Lambkins, the border collie. Now another part of him hurt.

The minor road which had become the north-west passage to Doredell and Hayste was completely blocked. At the wheel of his double-decker Bill Blimp fumed. His company would never be in line for any accolades, but Bill Blimp did believe in good time-keeping – well, at least for a new client. First impressions counted. If the coach turned up on time, its actual condition might be overlooked. Still at this point believing that Roger Trysom could be a lucrative new client, Bill Blimp was anxious not to be too late into Doredell. To be brought to a halt in the middle of nowhere was maddening. However, he was shortly to be reminded of the force of the old saying that it is an ill wind that blows nobody any good.

In the inquest which had followed the over, Ray Burrill was full of apology, but too embarrassed to offer any kind of rational explanation for his lapse – although the truth would be dragged from him later. Winston Jenkins, who a few minutes before had been flirting with the idea of allowing Ray Burrill to bowl his eight overs off the reel, was forced to think again. Unfortunately for the captain thinking again did not get round the problem that five more overs from Greg Roberts could not be postponed indefinitely. He had thought of slipping another one in next at the Doredell end in succession to Phil Cole, but Phil's performance in his most recent over caused another re-think. An additional batch of looseners was not what Winston wanted, but should he let Phil Cole bowl his eighth over there and then in the hope that by now he was loosened up? A pronounced clearing of the throat and a meaningful look at his watch by Umpire Corrington standing at the Doredell end brought Winston Jenkins' review to a precipitate end.

The evidence of the over which followed showed that Phil Cole had indeed loosened up, but in mind as well as body. Feeling that one last effort was required before he could fully relax (and drink more ale), Phil adopted a high risk strategy. Instead of concentrating on putting the ball on the spot he hoped that the condition of the ball might allow him some reverse swing. It might have done, had Phil not lacked the proficiency to find the right line. In fairness he got the first ball to swing, but it went from outside off stump towards leg without any unconventional deviation. Adrian Wills had to do no more than help it on its way and the batsmen ran three. The next ball was a leg stump full toss without a hint of movement. George Summermore drilled it past the bowler and was peeved when Jon Palmer pulled off an acrobatic stop which confined the stroke to a single. Unwisely encouraged, Phil Cole aimed for leg stump again, found no reverse swing a third time and saw Adrian Wills produce a fine on-drive which reached the boundary before a fielder moved. The fourth ball of the over almost obtained a wicket. Over-correcting, Phil Cole produced a short ball which put the batsman in two minds. There was a change of pace which momentarily confused Adrian Wills. When he finally decided he should crash it over the deep mid-wicket boundary he got it on the shoulder of the bat and succeeded only in chipping the ball over the head of Harry Northwood, well above the reach of his flailing arms. This took Doredell to two hundred, and put George Summermore back on strike. Like the bowler he tried too hard, missing a straight ball outside his off stump. He did not miss the next one, but his timing was faulty and he had to be content with two.

Cranley Nice's feelings were mollified. Farley Richardson had brought him up-to-date with the score. Memory of the two appalling run-outs he had witnessed began to fade. He was persuaded that his team (for that is how he regarded it) could score one hundred and three runs off thirteen overs, especially if these overs were bowled by the kind of players he had seen in action. His confidence restored, he decided to move on. He did not favour Adrian Wills, who had dared to oppose Jim Flote in the local government by-election, and preferred to be absent from the ground when, as looked probable, the player got his fifty. Cranley's timing could not have been better.

Andy Lizzard was not in fact the sharpest knife in the box when it came to plotting a strategy for industrial action and union recognition. Having a certain degree of contempt for the docility of East Anglian workers, he was pleased when his exploitation of Mildred Askern's distress had seemingly had the desired effect. He had convinced himself that bull-headed management as represented by Farley Richardson would react badly and thus play into his hands. Leaving the situation to ferment he had retired with his henchmen to the pub in Hayste – a welcome bonus for being on strike. He had underestimated the distaste of the old Fingerbarrows workforce for militancy and he had reckoned without the advanced techniques of industrial relations strategy as practised by Ashley Bright.

By the time he returned to the sports ground, Andy Lizzard's brain was clouded. The greeting he received from one of his fellow workers was not what he had been expecting. 'You bastard', was a polite version of what a fitter from the main engineering workshop said to him. Words did not go unmatched by action. The man lunged towards Andy Lizzard in a threatening manner. 'Mess with my wife, would you?', snarled the fitter. Much like an interviewer on the Today programme, he did not wait for an answer. His hands closed round Andy Lizzard's throat much as politicians have dreamt of doing to interviewers on the selfsame programme. Some of the workforce instinctively moved to save Andy Lizzard's life whilst others recognised in his co-conspirators the thieves, thugs and fraudsters so artfully suggested by Ashley Bright and his managerial co-conspirators. What began as a minor disturbance threatened, blow by blow and insult by insult, to develop into a fully-fledged affray. Had he remained conscious throughout to appreciate it, Andy Lizzard would have noted that there were limits to the docility of East Anglian workers.

That anything untoward was happening off the field had gone unnoticed by the players as the twenty-eighth over began. Ray Burrill's plea to bowl it had been turned down by Winston Jenkins although not without misgivings – the principal one being the necessary alternative of Greg Roberts. The captain was more accommodating to Ray's supplementary request that he be allowed to field as far away from the boundary as possible. Even though when setting a field for a bowler like Greg Roberts this was quite difficult to achieve, Winston Jenkins pointed Ray to mid-off. It was a deeper mid-off position than Ray ideally would have liked, but he felt that it gave him some protection from the brooding presence of the girl's father.

Probably the exact point at which the minor disturbance actually became a fully-fledged affray was marked by a high-pitched, curdling shriek when someone's kick landed in a part of Andy Lizzard's anatomy which was not protected in the same way as that of the batsmen on the pitch. Greg Roberts had made by his standards a good start to the over. He had bowled two balls, neither of which had been struck to the boundary. Intent on reaching his half century for which he needed one more run, Adrian Wills pushed forward to the first delivery and tickled it round the corner for what he thought was the required single. Having already raised his cap, he was mortified to see Umpire Breakwell executing an elaborate pirouette to announce a leg-bye. 'Off the boot, I fancy', Syd explained, on seeing the surprise on Adrian Wills' face. The next ball had given the strike back to the near half-centurion as George Summermore did no more than push the ball in the direction of Ray Burrill. What followed could not have been predicted by the batsmen, the bowler or the fielding captain.

The vehicle carrying the ghost train had developed not one puncture, but two. As it lay second in the funfair procession, the whole cavalcade had halted behind it. The interruption to its journey took place on the very threshold of its destination: the village of Furzegard. In fact the lead vehicle had come to a stop alongside a sign which announced that Furzegard welcomed considerate drivers, a message which would have been a touch more welcoming if the word 'considerate' had been correctly spelt. However, not everyone in Furzegard was in welcoming mood. Funfairs by their nature tend to have both supporters and detractors. Normally Wayne Surplis would have been pleased to see its arrival but, alas, the situation in the Surplis household was far from normal. Wayne, the ten-year-old scourge of the village, had unwisely (and uncharacteristically) perpetrated one of his outrages within the curtilage of the family property. The Surplises, who had hitherto defended their son against all comers on the grounds that he was nothing more than a high-spirited, fun-loving, young lad, could no longer see the joke. A tin of black paint and the weekly wash had not gone well together. Wayne's punishment was that he was barred from attending the funfair. The high-spirited, fun-loving, but utterly obnoxious young lad had vented his anger by scattering tacks in the road.

The indirect beneficiary was Bill Blimp, who brought his mobile bar into operation. Those not actively involved in locating a second suitable spare tyre were glad of the opportunity for refreshment. Bill Blimp did a roaring trade. Such a good time was had by all that he failed to appreciate that his last and thirstiest customers were the very ghost train people whose repairs had been completed. Eventually the procession was persuaded to move on to cover the remaining fifty yards to the entrance of the field where the entertainment was due to be sited. It was as well that the field lay on the south side of what the highway engineers were pleased to call the village gateway. Few if any of the funfair vehicles would have been able to pass through this artificial constriction of the road. The Blimp double-decker only just made it.

The third ball of Greg Roberts's fourth over was again a pleasant surprise to the fielding side. A harsh judge would have called it a full toss, but arguably it was a near yorker. Greg Roberts had tried to bowl it a little faster and had been lucky not to lose direction in the process. He succeeded in taking the batsman unawares. Adrian Wills was able to do little more than stun the ball which rolled slowly forward. It would do. Calling clearly and firmly he embarked upon the run which this time would surely bring him his fifty. His partner was prompt in his response. To turn their heads in the direction of Andy Lizzard's piteous cry was pure instinct. It was more of a gasp than a cry when their two bodies met mid-pitch. There was no time for warning and no chance of avoidance. They both fell backwards, heads pointing in the direction whence they had come. For a moment nothing happened. Most pairs of eyes on the field were trained on the action off it – except one pair. Rashid Ali's gaze, in strict adherence to good practice, had never left the batsmen. The ball had come to rest by Greg Roberts' left foot, a circumstance which had to be drawn to his attention by a bellow from the wicket-keeper. Greg, retrieving the ball, made as if to break the wicket at the bowler's end. Another bellow from Rashid Ali forestalled this action. Still without any obvious signs of recovery on the part of the batsmen, there was time for the ball to be looped back to the wicket-keeper. The scalp which the Outcasts wanted belonged to Adrian Wills. The batsmen had not crossed, they had impacted. To ensure that there was no doubt over the identity of the dismissed batsman, Rash and Reg solicitously helped a shaken George Summermore to the sanctuary of the crease at the bowler's end. When finally the dazed Adrian Wills rose to his feet an apologetic Rodney Corrington came over from square leg to impart the bad news.

Connie Stillmarch had reluctantly cast aside the knitting with which she had hoped to fill her allotted time at the tea-room. If this interruption had put in peril the deadline for the completion of the shapeless bottle green pullover on which she was embarked, her nephew with the forthcoming birthday would at least be one to rejoice. Last year's red creation had gone to a needy scarecrow. Not without a grumbling commentary, Connie Stillmarch re-filled the ancient kettle and placed it on the ancient stove. Out of the cupboard she took a stock of mugs even more unsightly than those already on view. Obviously feeling that some of these had collected too much grime to be set out as they were, she complained that she had not been looking forward to an afternoon of washing up. Nevertheless she plunged them in a sink, sloshed them around in water and proceeded to wipe them with a tea towel which looked to Roger Trysom as if it had been used for cleaning floors. (This surmise was spot-on as, lacking a duster, Connie Stillmarch had had a flick round the cabin with the only cloth to hand.) The Japanese tourists who had been close enough to witness these preparations lost their appetite completely and decided that they too would try the maze.

As a tour leader Roger Trysom should have tried to jolly along those of his charges who, oblivious of its hygiene standards, remained in the tea-room. The only diversion whilst the water boiled was a collection of ancient-looking picture postcards of the now burnt Longbirch Hall, three wooden toast racks, two wooden egg cups and a colouring book. Whilst the items were embossed with a peeling image of the old house, the colouring book had no connection whatever with the area having been left behind a year ago by a seven-year-old schoolgirl. It was the first item to be purchased, Mrs Kuramochi having a great grand-daughter of much the same age. The souvenir-starved visitors swallowed up the other gifts sensing perhaps their rarity value. In that respect they were not wrong. Few Japanese homes would have their like.

A good tour leader would also have been wise to have made closer and fuller enquiries about the maze before allowing his guests to be let loose within it. Roger Trysom had been told by Geraint Poppledown that the Longbirch Maze was one of the most famous in England and was a must see. The publican's enthusiasm had fallen short of indicating that it was a must enter. Had his conversation with a harassed Roger Trysom gone that way, he might have referred to its density and complexity. However, the conversation had not gone that way. It had concentrated instead on the maze's beauty and upkeep. In any case, each entrant to the maze had been handed a map to assist them if their spirit of adventure (already weakened by the afternoon's experience) failed. The map was being used for the first time having just been reprinted in full-colour form. Roger Trysom was satisfied that nothing could go wrong. Too easily satisfied, as it turned out.

Meanwhile Bill Blimp was drawing nearer to Doredell, Cranley Nice to the centre of the village and Farley Richardson to the wicket. None of these would make quite the explosive contribution to events which would be achieved by the driver of a silver sports car which was fast approaching Doredell.

As he waited for the resumption of play, Winston Jenkins, who had decided that he would bowl the next over from the Doredell end, began loosening up exercises. There was a natural pause in proceedings while both batsmen recovered their breath and their poise. In the case of Adrian Wills the latter was the harder to regain. Contrary to the spirit of cricket he was not at first disposed to accept the umpire's verdict. He himself sought to invoke that spirit as a reason for the accident not to be the cause of his dismissal. He found Syd Breakwell completely adamant and a rather less certain Rodney Corrington in concurrence. The members of the home team, who had initially rushed out to administer first-aid to the stricken batsmen, found themselves finally escorting a disappointed Adrian Wills from the scene. Leaving the dispute to sort itself out and confident that it would do so to the Outcasts' advantage, Winston Jenkins had tried out a practice run with a view to resorting to what he, if no one else, regarded as his faster style of bowling.

Waiting to emerge from the pavilion (he had not rushed out as part of the mercy mission), Farley Richardson had observed not only the slow recovery of his players, but also the activities of his opposite number. He had never actually seen Winston Jenkins bowl. Without consulting anyone who had, he fell into the easy trap of thinking that anyone of Caribbean appearance and physique, and particularly someone who was marking out an extravagantly long run, was likely to be fast and dangerous. The extended delay in cajoling and in the end coercing Adrian Wills from the pitch gave Farley Richardson ample time to prepare. The batsman who set out – slowly and deliberately – to join George Summermore had the appearance of Michelin man.

Had Farley Richardson been preparing himself to face Lillee and Thomson or Ambrose and Walsh, he would still have cut an absurd figure. When in fact he was taking guard against Greg Roberts of the Outcasts Cricket Club his precautions were carrying farce to new levels. Farley Richardson bulged from every part of his anatomy. He had obviously acquired shapes and styles of protective padding not available to the average cricketer. Even his helmet looked as though it might have been designed by NASA. The hilarity which accompanied the batsman's appearance seemed to have swung the psychological balance in the bowler's favour. Presented with a target which seemed almost twice as wide as the stumps, Greg Roberts managed to find it. Of three straight up and down deliveries which another batsman might have milked, Farley Richardson got a bat on two, but runs from none. The third struck a distended thigh in a position which not even Syd Breakwell at his most erratic could have interpreted as being in line. Thus Greg Roberts concluded what was for him a most successful over: one run conceded (the leg-bye did not count) and a wicket, albeit indirectly, taken.

The atmosphere inside the sports ground had altered. The transformation was hard to define beyond the quelling of the disturbance amongst the company employees. This had finally been brought about by the arrival of the security guards, who may not have had the intellectual capacity to be effective in the job for which they had principally been hired, but could terminate a brawl in quick order. So hubbub had given way to quiet on one side of the ground where the only people left were those with a genuine interest in cricket and/or in Farley Richardson's humiliation. The sense of grand theatre had diminished. The supporters of Adrian Wills, council candidate, had gone quiet on his dismissal. So too had the unseen, distant loudspeaker, which signed off with the defiant and faintly biblical message: 'Wills will return and be returned'. Less noticeably the hacker and his paymasters had retreated and were even now back in their local pub celebrating the mayhem they had caused with the scoreboard. Those who were left had other battles with which to concern themselves. In some cases the most important was sobriety.

Although the funtub had spilled some of its precious contents when the near-accident took place, the loss of beer had not in fact been too significant. This had worrying consequences for the captain of the fielding side. Winston Jenkins had been as grateful as the next man for the ready availability of the excellent brew, but he was beginning to see that the continuous re-charging of the discreet receptacles around the boundary edge was exacting a price in terms of the liveliness of his team. The supply of Hoppenhall's Charger bitter seemed to be reserving its most marked effect for what remained of the Outcasts' bowling strength. There were the exceptions of Greg Roberts and, Winston Jenkins tried to persuade himself, himself. David Pelham had not bowled since the eighteenth over and had used the interval of the last ten to take on what was probably an injudicious amount of ale. Even when trying to exercise restraint, David Pelham could usually (and certainly in Charlie Colson's absence) be expected to top the consumption league. However, the eagerness with which Ray Burrill had indulged in the available refreshment had puzzled his captain as he finally marked out his longer run and prepared to bowl to George Summermore.

Observing that Winston Jenkins was about to use his long run, most of the Outcasts concluded that he had given up on the game.

They knew that their captain was not a genuinely fast bowler and that his only known attempts had ended in tears. Equally, it was evident to those who did not have to do the bowling that those who did, did not pose such a threat that one hundred and one runs off twelve overs presented any kind of difficulty to the home side even if it had only four wickets left to fall. Probably it was as well to get the whole thing over as quickly as possible and get on with such various pleasures as the night might hold. Doredell would be victorious and their victory might help to eliminate any remaining ill-will which had survived from the Outcasts' previous visit. That was the downbeat mood in which the Outcasts began the twenty-ninth over. By its end things were different.

Cursing at what he regarded as its total inaccessibility, Bill Blimp at last steered his double-decker bus into the long, winding central street which ran through Doredell. He had been told by Roger Trysom that their meeting-point would be the village pub. As it turned out this was a fortuitous choice, for at the moment he chose to arrive Bill Blimp could not have proceeded further than the Pink Pedlar. The road was obstructed by two coaches and a low-loader. This over-sized recovery vehicle had been parked alongside the coaches by the Bilsdon brothers, who were only now giving thought to the exact means of lifting or otherwise propelling the one on to the other. Whilst they did so the street was effectively closed to traffic.

Of Trysom and tourists there was no sign. For the moment this was not a matter of concern to Bill Blimp. His eyes feasted on the coaches. In their telephone conversation, Roger Trysom had said no more than that his tour buses had broken down. He had said nothing about how broken they had been adjudged to be. Bill Blimp looked at them and reckoned that they would be perfect to replenish his fleet. He already envisaged them as 'Spirit of England' and 'Sportsman of the Shires'. Might their owner, Bill Blimp wondered, be prepared to sell them? Leaping from the cab of his double-decker he put this very question to the Bilsdon brothers who looked at each other for inspiration. Limited though they might be in both mechanical skills and intellectual rigour, they could recognise an opportunity when they saw it. The first and wise thing they had to do was to avoid the admission that they had come to cart the buses away for scrap. The second imperative was to explain away the presence of the low-loader in a manner which did not betray their opinion that the coaches were a complete liability. Thirdly they had to keep talking and find out what might be on offer whilst remaining ambiguous about their relationship with the owner. All this represented a considerable challenge to the Bilsdon brothers, but profit was the spur.

What no Outcast could have predicted was that Winston Jenkins striving for pace could actually provide it. Not all the Outcasts had seen at first hand their current captain's previous attempts to bowl at speed off a long run, but accounts had circulated. If ever the mood at an Outcasts' gathering was in danger of being depressed, it could quickly be brightened by one of the team retelling the story of a Winston Jenkins express over. This whole folklore was threatened by Winston's first delivery. It was an absolute fizzer of which many more illustrious bowlers would have been proud. Whenever he was asked about it afterwards, George Summermore could not be drawn on whether he actually saw it. Certainly there was no danger of his bat coming even within visiting range of a ball which swung late and screamed past his off stump. Not to be impolite to his team-mate, Rashid Ali behind the stumps had retreated from where he would normally have stood for Winston Jenkins, but by no more than a foot. So he had no chance. The ball fizzed all the way to the boundary and four byes were conceded. The delivery may have cost the Outcasts four runs, but it still earned them a wicket.

George Summermore was as shaken as he had been by the recent collision. By temperament he was a phlegmatic, rather solemn man as befitted his profession. It was not the speed of the ball which had momentarily discomforted him, but surprise at its source. He remembered last year's fixture against the Outcasts.

After some good fast bowling from Colin Banks which had claimed three wickets, the black player had been called on as first change. Under instruction from his captain to press home the early advantage, Winston Jenkins had interpreted this as a need for all-out speed. To mixed feelings from those of his fellow team members whose minds were still able to be engaged in the game (one of them was heard to cry out 'Oh, no!') Winston had marked out his long run. The spell had proved to be short. The two overs were not especially expensive, but they began the recovery of the Doredell innings which was so emphatically completed by the bowling of David Pelham and Ray Burrill.

As Winston Jenkins had striven to emulate Courtney Walsh let alone Colin Banks, the ball had been sprayed all over the place. Syd Breakwell, who had been standing at square leg, was soon sitting and in need of first-aid after one thunderbolt had found his ample midriff like a heat-seeking missile. Winston Jenkins had been lucky not to be more heavily punished. The batsmen were too busy laughing to effect a serious demolition job. But it was his captain who saw the end of the joke first. Even Winston at normal pace had been rejected in favour of spin. Consolation was achieved and pride restored when finally Winston in conventional mode was seen as a safer bet than Burrill and Pelham, who had turned out to be more a staggering than a spinning duo. It was not, however, the end of his embarrassment.

It was the absence of true speed and for that matter true direction which George Summermore recalled. What he wondered on the slender but startling evidence of that first ball was whether Winston Jenkins, chastened by the humiliation of last year's performance, had acquired some new technique. There was no time to pursue these musings. He had to settle down over his bat and await the next delivery. What George Summermore did not know was that the bowler was as puzzled as he was by the snorter of a ball he had just produced. Winston Jenkins was not sure whether to be pleased or sorry. The doubt related to his ability to reproduce the feat. It would have helped if he had known how he had managed it. Commendably he refused to let excitement go to his head. Uncertain that he could combine speed and accuracy a second time in succession, he wisely opted for the latter.

The ball which came from Winston Jenkins's hand proved to be a slow full toss which fortunately for the bowler George Summermore treated as a cunning slower ball in the wake of the previous jaffa. Instead therefore of treating it on its merits and despatching it to a distant part of the field, George Summermore, like the bowler, took the cautious option. A gentle push into the vacant cover area was accompanied by a command to his captain to 'come one'. Two theories competed to explain why Farley

Richardson failed to make it. His more savage critics reckoned that, having seen what he had seen, he had no appetite to discover whether Winston Jenkins's first or second ball was the more representative of what he could expect to face if he had the strike. Those of a more generous disposition sorrowfully but sniggeringly pointed out that Farley Richardson was so impeded by his protective equipment that he might as well have embarked on the four hundred metres for all the chance he had of covering twenty-two yards before Harry Northwood running a similar distance had gathered the ball and returned it to Rashid Ali's gloves. As he lumbered back to the pavilion, Farley Richardson was painfully aware that not only the Outcasts were celebrating the seventh wicket to fall. He did not even have the consolatory thought that he could boot George Summermore out of a job for making such a crass error.

Ray Burrill was glad to find refuge in the huddle which Winston Jenkins decided to convene. Winston had hit on this idea having suddenly remembered that it was increasingly used by teams to convey a sense of added determination. If ever a side needed some added determination it was the wilting Outcasts in the late afternoon of that match in Doredell. The general and essentially platitudinous urging of Winston Jenkins could not restore the pre-match alertness (a relative term in respect of the Outcasts) of the players nor cancel the sense of anticipation of the evening's entertainment which was beginning to creep up on some of them. Even if a modicum of team spirit was generated it was countered by the dampening realisation that what their remaining effort amounted to was ten balls of Winston Jenkins, two overs of a visibly swaying David Pelham, four overs of a distracted Ray Burrill and undeniably four overs from Greg Roberts. Some huddle.

Yet it had brought relief for Ray Burrill from what he had felt was the penetrative gaze of the beautiful girl's father. As he straightened up out of the huddle he thought she had given him a little wave. This seemed to suggest that his reputation had not as yet been blitzed by paternal revelations and accusations. But how long could this be delayed, Ray Burrill asked himself? He was forced to turn his attention back to the game as a new batsman presented himself. This was Ed Fylder who wore Ray Burrill's air of distraction. His arrival at the crease had been preceded by a bout of banter in the dressing-room with Fred Ranger and Tom Amwell, who were listed to bat below him. Although Doredell's opening bowlers had both seen Winston Jenkins bowl last year and thought they knew his true ability, his extraordinary salvo off his long run had fuelled their teasing of Ed Fylder. In the ordinary way he deserved to bat above Fred Ranger and Tom Amwell. By the time he actually walked out to the pitch, this had become much more questionable. The beamer which flew past his nose finally broke his spirit.

Morale was similarly low in another part of Doredell. The Japanese tourists were now divided into three groups. Some had remained inside the cabin to face the challenge of tea prepared by Connie Stillmarch, a larger number had disappeared into the maze whilst some others, who had left the tea-room, hovered indecisively between the two. This turned out to be the group which fortune teased. Their misfortunes were a little later in coming. At first it might not have seemed so. The most weary and infirm had sought space on two nearby benches. Their very limited understanding of the English language spared them any embarrassment from the obscenities which indigenous youth had carved into the wood. Their companions were forced to stand. This increased their restlessness, but, again, a very limited understanding of the English language denied them a sustained verbal assault on their tour leader. A Mr Tamamura with the help of his cane tried to communicate by sign language the question which interested them all: where was their transport? However, had Mr Tamamura been able to make his enquiry in perfect English, Roger Trysom would not have known the answer.

The wait of this group outside the tea-room was not without incident. The chatter of discontent was stilled by the sight and sound of Mrs Nagase moving at speed but in obvious distress from the door of the tea-room to the shelter of the public convenience, which was very conveniently adjacent. Two of the watching ladies went to support and comfort their stricken fellow tourist, their seats being unceremoniously snatched by two of the standing onlookers who put their own comfort before that of Mrs Nagase. Less out of curiosity about the cause of Mrs Nagase's condition than a desire to escape the menacing stares and mutterings of the outside group, Roger Trysom returned to the tea-room. He found no respite there.

Ed Fylder's collapse at the crease was so dramatic and at the same time undignified that any question of this being stigmatised as a 'no ball' went completely out of Umpire Corrington's mind. It was said to happen to criminals as the moment of public execution becomes imminent. So it happened to Ed Fylder. A stretcher was called for, the umpires having the sense to see that this would spare the unfortunate batsman the added humiliation of having to walk off the field of play. Discerning cricket-lovers among the spectators were not fooled. Mirth was in greater evidence than concern as Ed Fylder was conveyed into the refuge of the pavilion. It was no refuge from the scathing tongue of Farley Richardson who was scandalously in disregard of the mote in his own eye. The stretcher-bearers resolutely carried the stricken batsman through this verbal fusillade into the relative sanctuary of the changing-room where extensive repairs were required to both mind and body.

Remorse and revenge were both in Fred Ranger's mind as he stepped out to take Ed Fylder's place. He knew that he had played a part in winding up the unfortunate Ed. The consequences he had not foreseen. Indeed his first reaction had been to laugh uproariously at Ed's plight when the beamer had been unleashed. Now he was the wiser and so, somewhat ashamed of himself, he wanted to atone. As he walked to the wicket he assessed the prospects.

It seemed hardly any time at all since he had last stepped out to face the bowling of Winston Jenkins. It had not seemed like this then. Frankly, there was no more than sparse (admittedly dramatic) evidence that the Winston Jenkins of this year was other than the Winston Jenkins he had previously encountered. After all, he had persuaded himself by the time he reached the wicket, if Winston Jenkins had turned himself into anything matching a genuinely fast bowler, he would surely have opened the bowling in that mode. It was an impeccable piece of deduction and Fred Ranger fought to keep it lodged in his mind as Winston Jenkins took strides ever further away from him.

Cranley Nice, too, had been putting his best foot forward. His first off-site visit was to the village store. On the way he had an odd experience. As he passed some bushes he had the uneasy feeling that he was being observed. Perhaps somebody was hiding. Probably kids. Without altering his pace he stared into the bushes. He locked on to a pair of eyes. Their shape was distinctive. He blinked and looked again. Nothing. Cranley Nice told himself that he must have been hallucinating.

It was the sun. He should have worn a hat. Shivering slightly, despite the temperature, he continued on his path towards Iris Pearlhammer's emporium.

The pair of eyes watched him pass. They belonged to Ashoki Ebihara. In the ordinary way there was nothing furtive about Ashoki Ebihara. Ordinary was the word which could most appropriately be applied to his life. It would therefore have astonished those who knew him to learn that he should have so far departed from the ordinary as to be lurking in the bushes somewhere in rural England. Desperation can sometimes locate hidden depths in a man and it was certainly desperation that had driven Ashoki Ebihara into the hidden depths of Doredell's bushes. He was the one who had got away.

Roger Trysom had not, of course, been counting. It is to be doubted whether he would have shown any more diligence had he had a party of children in his charge. He had blithely assumed that adults – even elderly adults – were capable of looking after themselves. Any supervisory duty which he should properly have exercised had given way to a mounting feeling of self-preservation as the tour had turned into a travesty. So Roger Trysom had easily failed to detect that there was a rebel in his ranks. How could he have known that Ashoki Ebihara had always been troubled by his feet since his days as a postman? The mooted trek to the tea-room had assumed nightmare proportions in the mind of the former postman. He had dragged himself most reluctantly from the bus, but shown unexpected sprightliness in peeling off the end of the column of trudging tourists when the camouflage of the bushes had presented itself. Sitting down in their midst he had dozed off. It was a practice to which he had not been unused during his daily postal rounds. Awake again, Ashoki Ebihara was trying to re-orientate himself when his thoughts were disturbed by the sound of Cranley Nice passing by. Panic overtook him much as it had momentarily affected Cranley Nice. Ashoki Ebihara wanted to be abroad no more in this miserable village: he determined to make for the sanctuary (as he misguidedly saw it) of the bus.

After the dreadful start Doredell's middle order had flourished. The recovery had begun with Clive Matheson and George Summermore. It had been materially assisted by, first, Winston Jenkins and Phil Cole. Their performance had very soon led Alan Birch as captain to discover hitherto unnoticed features in the pitch. Having pored over it in hope rather than recognition, he came to the grandiose conclusion that the pitch was poorly prepared and his spinners might be able to get something from it. They did. It was a hiding. They too were poorly prepared. It did not take long for Alan Birch to realise that the pair would have disgraced a shove ha'penny team. Preposterously they both took wickets, but by this time the captain had already decided that he would be better off with the re-introduction of, first, Phil Cole to be followed shortly and much more dubiously by Winston Jenkins. Bill Chance, who had succeeded George Summermore, had continued to keep the runs coming, but Winston Jenkins removed his partner with an audacious piece of good fortune. He had had no such luck with Fred Ranger whose brief but entertaining innings was entirely at his expense.

It was with such recollection that for his part Fred Ranger now steadied himself as Winston Jenkins tore towards him. There followed two wild swishes to two wild deliveries. No harm was done to himself, his wicket or the ball. They were enough to persuade Fred Ranger that his instinctive judgement was right. Nothing had really changed from last year. By the time Winston Jenkins sent down the last ball of his over, it was apparent that the bubble had burst. It was on the slow side of medium pace, short and slanting towards a point wide of leg stump. Fred Ranger wound himself up and mowed the ball hard and high. Contact was more top edge than middle of bat. The height the ball attained was of greater measure than the lateral distance travelled. Ray Burrill settled beneath it.

Roger Trysom was concerned for Mrs Nagase, but he knew that it was a tricky business for a male to enter a female lavatory. The hazards were all the greater if he could not communicate and he was unsure whether any of the current inmates possessed between them any smattering of English. He had chosen therefore to investigate the source of the difficulty. There was a commotion inside the tea-room. Connie Stillmarch was under siege. All bar one of the Japanese visitors remaining indoors were congregated in front of the counter. Angry words were being exchanged. To that moment Roger Trysom had not realised the extent of the basic (very basic) English vocabulary possessed by some of his clients. It is surprising what idiomatic language skills anger can bring out in people. In the whole of the East of England it would have been difficult to have found anyone who could out-swear Connie Stillmarch. Roger Trysom had time to notice that a close contest was under way before bellowing for silence. Resuming her version of a more polite form of speech, a defiant Connie Stillmarch said to Roger Trysom, 'I told 'em they bloody well 'ad to pay'. One of the Japanese tugged at Roger Trysom's sleeve and said, 'She poison us. Mrs Nagase sick – and Mr Demimoto, look.' The finger pointed to a forlorn gentleman still seated. His pallor was, very unusually, grey. Before him lay a half-eaten fig biscuit.

Belatedly Connie Stillmarch had remembered that Japanese tourists were meant to be affluent. Having had her afternoon disturbed she decided that she might after all try to maximise her profits from the invasion. Tea was to be £1 per mug rather than the usual 30p. With biscuits she could charge £2.50. She had found an already-opened packet of fig biscuits in a cupboard. Failing to notice that the opening of the packet had not been carried out by a human agency, she threw away some crumbs and laid out the rest on a cracked plate. Friends of Mrs Nagase from childhood, had they been on hand, would have testified to her indiscriminate appetite. It would not have surprised them to see her tuck into the fig biscuits so greedily. Eating too quickly is no aid to digestion, and decidedly not with biscuits of this provenance. She was through no more than three sips of tea before calamity overtook her, whereupon Mr Demimoto froze mid-biscuit.

Various thoughts flew through Roger Trysom's mind. The Vale of Widdle District Council must have an environmental health inspector. There was surely a question of trading standards as well. Wasn't there now a Food Standards Agency? But the very words 'standards' and 'inspector' sounded a note of caution in his mind. He had no wish in indicting others to bring attention towards his own little business.

So he decided to do that at which he was best. He cut and ran. Slamming a £10 note on the counter ('I think that'll cover it'), he herded the tourists towards the door. Roger Trysom relieved his feelings with one last gesture. Stepping back to the counter, he emptied the contents of an unsold mug of tea on to Connie Stillmarch's cast-aside knitting. At least, he felt, there was someone somewhere who had cause to be grateful for what he had done that day. Roger Trysom felt better as he went outside, but the feeling did not last. No one had yet emerged from the maze.

The ball thudded into the grass. The batsmen ran three –

coincidentally the number of reasons why Ray Burrill spilled the catch. The ball had gone incredibly high, but Ray thought that he had got himself into the correct position to pouch it. He could have done without a belated and quite superfluous call from Winston Jenkins, 'it's yours, Ray'. Taking his eye off the ball, he was suddenly aware that the girl's father was no longer standing beside her. What did that mean? Then as he re-focused on the descending ball it became blurred. To his horror it began to change shape. Like a great blob of mercury it looked to be about to divide into two. He screwed up his eyes, he blinked, but it was too late. The ball was through his outstretched hands and on the ground. Ray stared in a mixture of dismay and disbelief at the all too real singularity and regularity of its shape. His captain called again, 'well, don't just stare at the bloody thing, Ray, at least chuck it back'.

Despite the dropped catch Winston Jenkins finished the over in a more optimistic frame of mind. He now thought that the Outcasts had a chance of winning the match on the thin evidence that they had seen off two batsmen within a short space of time. True, Ed Fylder could return, but Winston Jenkins discounted him. He regarded Fred Ranger as a hit-or-miss merchant and he was convinced on last year's evidence that Tom Amwell was a rabbit. George Summermore was the problem, but, if they could keep him off-strike, surely they ought to be able to prevent Doredell scoring more than eight an over. From this lofty overview of proceedings, Winston Jenkins then had to descend to the reality of deciding which of his bowlers was to be the first to show that he could give away less than eight runs. Although he was unsure how much a suspiciously cheerful David Pelham had drunk and why Ray Burrill was not his usual self, the weakest link was still Greg Roberts. Winston Jenkins decided to get another of Greg's overs out of the way. Fred Ranger licked his lips.

Ray Burrill pursed his and frowned. He looked towards her, but she was not looking towards him. As he tried to follow her gaze he spotted her father who had moved across to join in animated conversation with a lady standing by a silver sports car. Ray had not noticed its entry into the ground. Now he ogled it. His eyes were still turned in that direction when the voice of his captain penetrated his thoughts with a polite suggestion that the game could continue if he was sure he was ready. Ray swivelled hurriedly back to the playing area without fully taking in the person who had evidently driven the car. His thoughts were jolted back to cricket and the mess he was making of it. Having allowed himself to be distracted, he realised that he had probably only made a fool of himself in every direction. He swallowed hard and launched a mental fight to get on top of his game. Had he turned round again and seen the longing look being directed towards him from beyond the boundary his resolve would surely have weakened.

Greg Roberts told himself that he could bowl to Winston Jenkins' prescription – but this was rather different from actually bowling with the consistent economy it dictated. After all, he argued, what he had to do was just bowl his next four overs for no greater cost than his previous four. He had given away twenty-one runs which was barely more than five an over. And now he was bowling at lower order batsmen. With new-found confidence he commenced his run. Greg was sure he could do it. But he couldn't. Perhaps trying too hard, he bowled a ball which bore his usual hallmark. It was short and it was wide. Syd Breakwell was teetering on the brink of calling a wide when Fred Ranger lashed the ball to the point boundary. The batsman would have done something similar to Greg's second ball if it had not bounced twice and then scuttled along the ground. Patience, thought Fred Ranger, would bring its reward. And it did.

In the village shop pleasantries were exchanged between Cranley Nice and Iris Pearlhammer. The factory owner felt obliged on such occasions to make a token purchase. Choosing something was never easy for in all truth there was no item in the shop in which Cranley Nice was remotely interested. However, there was something else on offer which was of enormous interest to him. Iris Pearlhammer had information. She was by nature inquisitive and also acquisitive. Cranley Nice recognised something of himself in her. Like him she had had to overcome hardships in early life, but like him she had been a fighter. Like him she was now comfortable; the only difference was that his comfort was buttressed by a multi-million-pound fortune. Nevertheless there was one trait they both still shared: a penchant for the pursuit of easy money.

Iris Pearlhammer's life in her Essex habitat could accurately be described as being spent as an active citizen. The causes which attracted her were not those most usually associated with the image of active citizenry. In truth they were an odd-ball jumble of prejudice and eccentricity. Not for her a front-of-crowd rallying role. Her style was to move in the background, but in amongst the movers and shakers, prompting and manoeuvring with a word here and a comment there. And she listened. The more she listened, the more she picked up. She confined her activities to the parts of the Vale of Widdle which lay beyond Doredell, because she observed the old axiom that politics and business did not mix.

Early in their series of occasional encounters Cranley Nice had discovered that Iris Pearlhammer was a mine of information about that part (which meant most) of the district with which he was least familiar. Early in their series of occasional encounters, Iris Pearlhammer had realised that Cranley Nice was keen to exploit that mine. A commercial arrangement had soon suggested itself. And so it was that whilst Cranley Nice might leave the village store with a comb or a tablet of soap or a bottle of aspirins he always left behind a brown envelope.

The brown envelopes had become thicker as the acquaintanceship had grown. Cranley Nice had never been explicit about the precise nature of his interest, giving away no more than general hints. Iris Pearlhammer had not taken long to get the gist and she then understood why Cranley Nice was keen to know about the men and women who were the elected representatives on the Vale of Widdle District Council. As his queries became more specific so her price edged up. As she was made aware of the potential benefit to her business of several hundred more houses in the area (Cranley Nice did his best to encourage the thought) her information-gathering became more comprehensive – and more valuable. It had not taken long for her income from Cranley Nice to dwarf the shop's weekly takings. From Cranley Nice's point of view he felt that he was getting near the point (Iris Pearlhammer did her best to encourage the thought) when with a successful by-election result behind him, he would be close to a majority on the District Council for approval of his development plans. As he bade farewell to Iris Pearlhammer with a smile and a wave and a bar of chocolate in his hand, he envisioned the store being bulldozed. He was sure he could entice one of the supermarket chains to take the site in the wake of a major growth in population.

Iris Pearlhammer's next customers were a woman and a man, in that order.

Feeling humiliated by the ball which had bounced twice, Greg Roberts presented Fred Ranger with a juicy full toss. Had Fred been a more accomplished batsman he would have hit it for six. Being more basic and rustic than accomplished, Fred could get only four, but he was quite satisfied as he waited for the next helping. With this one, technique again let him down. The ball was inviting enough: short and on a line which would have taken it past leg stump. It was actually too inviting. Fred was pumped up for action and launched what has become known as a slog sweep. All he got was an edge and a single. The ball had slid towards fine leg. It was George Summermore's call. To Fred Ranger's irritation he was forced to give up the strike. The remaining two balls of the over yielded only three runs to add to the nine already scored. George Summermore missed entirely a slow, drifting full toss (claiming afterwards that someone had moved behind the bowler's arm) and then missed a boundary when a well executed square drive was interrupted by the boot of a motionless John Furness who was still day-dreaming.

An assertive Ray Burrill presented himself to Winston Jenkins. Having undergone mental chastisement Ray Burrill had now convinced himself that notwithstanding aching heart and aching leg, he could come to the rescue of the team. Before converging on his captain he had sneaked a final glance at that section of off-field activity which interested him. She was still there, seemingly watching him. That was good. The lady in the silver sports car had emerged from the pavilion and was getting ready to go. The girl's father had disappeared. That was a relief. As the sports car began to move away, Ray thought that there was something familiar about the woman, and then with a shock it came to him. The worry set in. They must have talked about him. He was rumbled. He found himself trying to remember the name on the credit card slip which Mitsos Deflopolous had shown him in case of repercussions. Some at least of the people in the ground had no such difficulty in knowing who she was. What they could not work out was why she had been in animated, even angry, discussion with their most prominent local estate agent. The conversation had been sharp and focussed and had had nothing at all to do with Ray. Neither the observers nor Ray gave any thought to what the lady might have been doing in the pavilion. Ray, with no real peace of mind, swallowed hard and forced himself to concentrate on the job in hand: 'I'm your man, skip.'

Winston Jenkins was not immediately convinced. Seventeen runs had come from Ray Burrill's last over and Greg Roberts had just gone for twelve. For him, Ray was unusually insistent. Winston conceded that he looked to have more about him than a short while ago. Ray continued to plead his case. His leg felt better. He could bowl in his quicker style. He would do the business. Winston with a soft heart (more like a soft head he thought to himself) and few options finally cracked. 'If you're sure', he muttered, pressing the ball into Ray's hands. It was hard to say whose confidence grew more, that of the bowler or the captain, as the over progressed. It was almost immaculate. Possibly the pitch was more responsive to the off-cutter and the in-swinging ball. Bowling in this style Ray Burrill appeared to capture a rhythm which had previously eluded him. He actually got one or two to lift and George Summermore, who had not been expecting any problems, was suitably disconcerted. Ray Burrill very nearly achieved a maiden over, but the last delivery slipped off-line allowing the batsman to dab it down in the direction of the square-leg umpire and obtain a single. It was now Fred Ranger's turn to be disconcerted as he was once again denied the strike.

Nor was Cranley Nice a happy man. There had been a detectable spring in his step as he had left the village shop. Before returning to the sanctuary of his company premises for the climax of the match he wanted to feast his eyes on the Longbirch estate which was the object of his desire. He imagined that it would be a sensational property coup, massively augmenting his wealth. His anticipated pleasure was rudely obliterated when he rounded a corner and found a Japanese phalanx advancing towards him. The advance, which was definitely not a product of his imagination, could hardly be described as a surge. Nor, bearing in mind the age and infirmity of its components, could any aggressive motive remotely be ascribed to it. The psychiatrist's couch would be the only appropriate place to tease out the reasons why an otherwise coldly calculating businessman could be gripped to the point of panic by Nippon phobia. Cranley Nice did not wait for the rational explanation for the Japanese presence to become obvious. He turned and fled.

A deal had been done. It might have been pertinent to wonder whether Roger Trysom or Bill Blimp had been taken for the greater ride. However, no more inappropriate metaphor could have been invoked in the circumstances as the coaches in question were not (with one very slight exception) destined ever to take anyone for an actual ride again. The Bilsdon brothers could not believe their luck. (Strangely at the time neither could Bill Blimp.) It was a barefaced piece of commercial opportunism: remarkable in that they had encountered two gullible people within a short space of time; and remarkable for being another example in the shape of the Bilsdon brothers of men of little education and poor skills having extraordinary savvy when it came to making a quick buck. They were surely a loss to the financial markets. The ancient coaches were promptly removed from Doredell to await collection by Bill Blimp from the Bilsdons' yard in Hayste. In words which echoed the advice of a previous owner the Bilsdon brothers generously mentioned to Bill Blimp that the vehicles would 'need a bit of work on them'. After a short bout of negotiation Bill Blimp's promise to pay £1500 was even more generous.

All was now clear to Winston Jenkins. He had a plan. The apparently rehabilitated Ray Burrill would bowl the remaining three overs of his allocation from the Doredell end of the ground to be followed by the captain himself who had one over left. At the Hayste end, he would alternate Greg Roberts and David Pelham. Winston Jenkins tried to pretend to himself that this was not a reckless gamble. To bolster this disposition of his bowlers he threw in the thought that, if they captured the remaining three wickets, they might not have to bowl as many as forty overs. He even threw in the possibility that the shattered Ed Fylder might not return so that only two wickets would be needed. This plan or reckless gamble began with an invitation to Greg Roberts to bowl a third consecutive over. The man was after all sober – the final consideration constantly if vainly weighed in Winston Jenkins' desperate mind. What followed was mayhem.

Such a state of affairs had not yet been achieved at the maze, but it was hovering. The Japanese tourists, who had been pushed out of the tea-room, coalesced with those hanging about outside. At first

Roger Trysom tried to get it across to them that they should stay put and await their relief transport. However, he found it difficult to dislodge the idea from their minds that their transport was in fact where they had left it outside the pub. The visitors showed every sign of wanting to move in its direction despite having no alternative but to walk. It then suddenly occurred to Roger Trysom that Bill Blimp had been given the Pink Pedlar as the rendezvous point. He would not know that they had moved on to the maze. So Roger Trysom had let them begin the slow trudge back.

There was no trudging for Mrs. Nagase. She had emerged from the public convenience, but not on her own two feet. She was partly dragged, partly carried by the two ladies who had originally gone to her assistance. None of them looked in good shape which would be no surprise to anyone with experience of this particular lavatory. It seemed to have suffered damage to a degree which defied rational explanation. The vandals of East Anglia must have made it their prime target, always ensuring that a bowl was cracked or a ballcock twisted. Such was their efficiency that month after month *Convenience News* listed the ladies' toilet in Doredell as the nation's most disgusting. Poor Mrs Nagase was parked on the bench unfit for further movement. Next to her sat Mr Demimoto whose greyness was now tinged with green. Intimidated though he felt by the presence of this quartet, Roger Trysom realised that another group of the overall party was still missing. Why were they spending so long in the maze? What was so intriguing about it? The answers when they came only provoked other and more disturbing questions.

Greg Roberts began what was by now his sixth over – some kind of personal achievement record during his association with the Outcasts – with two wides. He gave equal favour to both sides of the pitch which at least had the merit of confusing the batsman although fortunately for his team not the wicket-keeper. Rashid Ali knew his man. Greg Roberts landed his third ball on line, but immediately wished he hadn't as George Summermore lifted it back over his head for a straight six. The charitable description of the next ball would be that Greg Roberts gave it a lot of air. So too did the batsman. Struck slightly less straight, true, but another six nonetheless. Whether in panic or through fear of the ribald reaction he could expect from his team-mates, Greg redoubled his concentration and managed to produce a ball of passable length and direction. Even so it was not good enough to staunch the flow of runs. In George Summermore there was an adrenalin rush. This time the technique was less than perfect. The shot lacked sufficient power to reach the boundary. Two runs were scored although Fred Ranger, anxious to be more than a spectator at the feast, had tried to make it three.

The second half of the over began with a no-ball (an error not always spotted by Syd Breakwell). This so surprised Greg Roberts that he then bowled a wide. Winston Jenkins was not sure whether to offer advice and encouragement in case it made matters worse. Unfortunately his hesitation was not shared by everyone. Raucous elements in the crowd were all too ready to give voice. With enthusiasm whetted by the over's significant contribution to the afternoon's entertainment, there were some wounding enquiries: 'Who taught you to bowl, yer granny?', 'Where's yer compass, mate?', 'What about another sixpenn'orth?' Some of the other comments were much less polite than this. The strange thing was that this chorus of critical banter instead of unsettling Greg Roberts somehow brought about his composure. There was a steely serenity about him as he bowled the rest of his over. It was not enough to ensure that he escaped further punishment. As Greg forlornly thought, it was probably the critical over of the match. And in a strange way it was.

Iris Pearlhammer had been brought up in a hard school. One thing drilled into her at an early age was that so few opportunities would be likely to come your way in life that you should exploit to the full any that did. What is more when you found yourself with a commodity which other people wanted you should make what you could out of it. Iris Pearlhammer had information which Mr. Cranley Nice seemed to find valuable. If Mrs Cranley Nice was willing to pay her for it as well, Iris Pearlhammer was not disposed to argue. That kind of money over the counter did not have to go through (what passed for) her books. If Iris Pearlhammer had any pang of anxiety that her double payment would be uncovered in pillow or other talk, she need not have worried. She knew exactly what she was doing and would soon share her knowledge with the man who would be her next caller. The operations of Cranley Nice and his wife were not only covert, but also mutually independent. Covert was too mild a word to apply to Mrs Nice's activities. Treachery was afoot (or rather in motion) as, topped up with the latest news from Iris Pearlhammer, Mrs. Cranley Nice drove away avoiding the cricket ground. She had done her business there for the day. Or so she thought.

James Saito's second reunion of the afternoon with Roger Trysom had very much the good-news/absolutely-bloody-awful-news syndrome about it. The latter's relief on seeing his travel companion and interpreter outweighed the displeasure he had felt about his inebriation and then his disappearance. The news which James brought with him quickly extinguished any feeling of relief or pleasure. He had reappeared from the direction of the maze entrance waving the coloured map and proceeded to denounce it in terms which turned the air blue. Roger Trysom quickly and dreadfully got the message. The map was either the wrong map or was full of misprints. It bore scant relation to the actual layout. James Saito had just been plain lucky to find his way back. An unspecified number of elderly Japanese tourists had not so far shared his good fortune. They remained prisoners of the maze.

The fourth legitimate ball of the Roberts over could have been modelled on a coaching manual. There was – purely by chance – nothing wrong with it at all. Unfortunately it was bowled to a batsman who was in every danger of playing out of character. The stroke which George Summermore launched was entirely unorthodox, but, it so happened, entirely effective in that it earned him four runs. Fired up still further by the sight of a wide-ish full toss (the next Greg Roberts offering)· George Summermore's backlift reached a new height, but its downward swing missed the ball by several inches. Undeterred, he tried something similar to what appeared to be a similar delivery. The chance meeting of bat and ball occurred only because Greg Roberts had imparted (not by design) a higher trajectory to the ball. By equal chance the ball left the bat for a sector of the arena guarded by two of the (by now) least alert members of the fielding side. To Fred Ranger's annoyance, Winston Jenkins's incredulity and the crowd's delight they ran five.

Doredell passed the two hundred and fifty mark, George Summermore kept the bowling and was one short of his own half-century.

Apart from one spell in the field and some work as assistant beer steward, Tim Jackson had had a fairly idle afternoon. One or two phone calls had confirmed that satisfactory party arrangements were in place for those of the squad who were set for a night of revels. He had been relieved to hear that most of the fancy dress costumes they had chosen were unlikely to be replicated, but there would be one or two others going as policemen. Whilst keeping regular checks on the progress of the game Tim was left with plenty of opportunity to fraternise. Apart from passing time he saw it as another way of mending such fences as remained broken from the Outcasts' last visit to Doredell. Once embarked he warmed to his task. In political parlance he worked the room. His encounters varied in length and intensity. Farley Richardson's demeanour did not encourage much of an exchange. The most intriguing conversation came last. Tim Jackson found Adrian Wills in a corner thumbing through a file of press cuttings. 'What's with this election then?', Tim greeted him. Checking first that Jim Flote was out of earshot, Adrian Wills told him.

Bill Blimp had been too absorbed in what he fondly imagined was a coup over the coaches to pay much attention to the absence of their former passengers, who, after all, were the reason for him being in Doredell. When eventually he came to think about it, Bill Blimp could see nothing in any way resembling a coach party, but he was no more than momentarily fazed. The pub looked an obvious enquiry point. He found a distracted Geraint Poppledown trying to sort out a problem with one of his pumps and not in the mood for an extended conversation. It was confined to a single exchange. Bill's opening gambit 'I'm looking for the coach party' received the response 'They've gone to the maze straight on down the road'. This was accompanied by a straight arm and a pointing finger. This gesture sufficed to send Bill Blimp and the double-decker on their way. There was no reason why Geraint Poppledown should have fleshed out his statement by mentioning the predominant nationality of the group. Absolutely none. Nor, as it happens, had Roger Trysom covered this detail when engaging Bill Blimp for the rescue mission. So the struggling column of Japanese tourists meant nothing to him when, breasting a gentle rise, he came upon them at some speed. Bill Blimp had been galvanised not by any pang of conscience that he had already kept his client waiting too long, but by the sudden recollection that he was meant to be going to a boxing tournament that evening.

Just as Cranley Nice had been put into retreat by the Japanese, so were they scattered by the onrushing double-decker. Even though their anticipation of the unexpected might have been well honed by their experiences since embarking on Roger Trysom's supposedly cultural tour, a large, speeding double-decker bus in this remote rural location still came as a shock. Their sluggish reaction certainly betrayed a dulling of the senses. No one was actually struck by the vehicle. In the circumstances the agility with which seventy-three-year-old Mrs Irikaki leapt at the last moment from its path could only have been born of terror. She cannoned into two of her companions. All three fell heavily to the ground. Rapidly it became clear that one of them would not rise again without the intervention of medical assistance. Yet even this incident would turn out not to be the severest of the privations to befall the wretched Japanese visitors.

Two of the inner ring turned in pursuit and John Furness set off from deep mid-on in the same direction.

Fred Ranger realised that there was no chance of taking just a single. So, if the ball was not going to reach the boundary, he would try and run three. He was quick off the mark. George Summermore, thinking that two would do nicely and being heavier of build, was less hurried. By the time he turned for the second run Fred Ranger was halfway down the pitch on the return journey. When George turned on completion of the second run with a view to checking the whereabouts of the ball he was almost knocked over by Fred Ranger who had been charging after him. Too astonished to hold his ground and too much of a gentleman to argue, George made a desperate but futile effort to reach the other end. John Furness had been first to the ball. He had thrust out his foot to stop it reaching the boundary and had unintentionally struck it back in the direction of Harry Northwood who was converging in company with Winston Jenkins. The former gathered the ball whilst the latter acted as navigation officer. They were aided by the fact that the wicket-keeper appeared to be guarding a batsman-free zone. It was not Harry Northwood's best throw, but there was time for Rashid Ali to gather the ball and get back to break the wicket before a gasping and groaning George Summermore was anywhere near. It was another of those examples which litter the annals of cricket where it was the bowler at the other end (Greg Roberts) who, without touching the ball and completely unknowingly, had induced the fall of the wicket.

As George Summermore walked ponderously back to the pavilion, Farley Richardson was preparing to greet him with the news that he was to go straight back out again as runner for Ed Fylder. This was altogether a dubious proposition. Ed Fylder had not suffered an actual physical injury; it was more a case of nerves. However, Ed had had to admit to his demanding captain that his guts were in such a state that he could not trust himself to run. It was customary for the opposing captain to be consulted before a runner was employed, but never having been an adherent of a consensual approach to life, Farley Richardson was set on bluffing it out. The second dubiety about George Summermore as runner was his comparative lack of speed. Nevertheless, Farley Richardson reckoned, what he lacked in speed he contributed in terms of experience. A wise head was a desirable attribute in a runner, because experience even at the highest level of cricket showed that a third batsman on the field could trigger confusion. Unfortunately Farley Richardson was to be denied the wise head he had selected as an emergency suddenly presented itself.

When Bill Blimp pulled up at what seemed to be the entrance to the maze, he remained puzzled. Apart from a huddled quartet of geriatrics on a bench he could see no sign of anything resembling a sixty-strong band of tourists. No one else was around and Bill Blimp's gaze dwelt on the tea-room for no more than a second before assuming it was derelict. With a loud curse he turned his vehicle round and headed back for the Pink Pedlar. He had not come all this way to the wilds of Essex to be denied his payload. Clearly the publican knew something and he seemed to be the only source of information. In his search for it Bill Blimp totally ignored the speed limit which safety-conscious legislators had imposed (with the full range of street furniture) on this lightly-trafficked village.

Roger Trysom and James Saito had been invisible to Bill Blimp's cursory glance, because they had been inside the tea-room in lively negotiation with Connie Stillmarch. The encounter was so lively that neither man had noticed the arrival of the rescue double-decker. They were wholly absorbed in trying to mount a different kind of rescue. Roger Trysom had not expected to have to return to the tea-room. The manner of his leaving had not exactly paved the way for supplication. But he was confronted with an extraordinary situation. He was also confronted with Connie Stillmarch whose natural negative cordiality factor had been many times multiplied. No, she had said with some satisfaction, there was no telephone in the tea-room. There would have been no answer to this blatant mis-statement if the tense atmosphere had not been disturbed by the sound of a phone ringing. Being a jingle rather than a ring it was clear that Connie Stillmarch was the owner of a mobile. Without a blush she dug it out of her bag, listened a moment, uttered the single word 'sausages' and ended the call. She glared at Roger Trysom and James Saito as if to defy them even to ask to borrow it. His desperation was such that Roger Trysom was not deterred. Some agitated exchanges took place before Connie Stillmarch relented. Then, having overcome her distaste for Roger

Trysom and her prejudice against the Japanese (serve 'em right she had thought, on being acquainted with their plight), Connie Stillmarch revealed that the maze-keeper was very probably playing cricket and could possibly be contacted by ringing the factory.

The pedestrian Japanese contingent minus Mrs Irikaki and her two shaken but otherwise uninjured companions had arrived at the Pink Pedlar where amidst much agitation and repeated use of the words 'accident' and 'ambulance' Geraint Poppledown made the necessary 999 call. In stilted English he did his best to explain to the thoroughly cowed Japanese that their replacement bus had gone to the maze to collect them. With one eye on his commercial interests he tried to suggest to them that they would be better off resting where they were until the bus returned. The visitors were so thoroughly racked by fear that they would have none of it. Out they streamed into the road with one thought in their minds: to find the bus. They found it soon enough.

The security guard burst into the pavilion, his shirt stained with blood. He had lately been involved in putting down the disturbance surrounding Andy Lizzard and his allies. The blood had not belonged to the guard himself, but he had not had time to clean up before the emergency call came. He was told to run across to inform Mr Richardson as a matter of urgency. Being a cricket lover it was instinctive for the security guard to take in the action on the field before completing his mission. At once he saw a snag. The man needed to unlock the key to the maze was at the crease preparing to take strike. Naturally the security guard paused. As any cricket enthusiast would, he enjoyed what followed, especially as the mounting score was yelled out from the scorebox. He cheered as loudly as anyone when George Summermore's fifty was announced and was finally brought out of his reverie when the wicket fell. Again he contributed generously to the applause, but then remembered that duty called. Farley Richardson was forced to agree that releasing people trapped in the maze was a stronger claim on George Summermore's time than a return to the middle as Ed Fylder's runner.

Mysteriously Kris Vertz was still wearing his pads and other equipment. With the umpires showing signs of impatience at what was a mounting delay he stood out as the obvious second choice runner. There was no time to instruct him in the finer points of the job. He showed such eagerness that, having been given the nod by Farley Richardson, he practically dragged Ed Fylder out on to the ground. Making every allowance for circumstances it remained an awful decision.

Bill Blimp and his bus roared up the slight incline barely noticing the pathetic sight of Mrs Irikaki being consoled by those who waited with her. The party of Japanese which had so peremptorily left the Pink Pedlar had learned nothing from their previous walk through the rustic bliss of Doredell. They were strung across the road when first they heard and then saw the bus bearing down on them. Salvation. They waved enthusiastically. They soon stopped when it became horrifically clear that the bus would not. Again not everyone escaped unscathed. One Zimmer frame was caught by a rear wheel and irredeemably mangled. Mr Katsuragi would probably have come to less grief if he had not tried to hang on. 'Bloody hikers!', Bill Blimp bawled as he swerved round the main body of the Japanese and pressed on back to the pub.

One of the delights of cricket is its sheer unpredictability. It is a game of almost infinite variables. Taking place over several hours (over several days when played at a higher level) cricket is susceptible to so many influences. The pitch may be green or brown, worn or lushly covered with grass. It can change in the course of a match. The ball can be shiny or dull with a seam raised or otherwise. Sunshine, showers and cloud all play their part. The toss of the coin and the use of the roller may swing a game. Even the length of a boundary may have an effect. And all that is before the form of particular batsmen and bowlers is taken into account. It is something indefinable which causes a batsman to time the ball perfectly one day and have difficulty in finding the middle of his bat the next. A bowler can be metronomically accurate in one spell and without length or direction in the next. Any or all of these things can effect the outcome of a cricket match. None of these factors decisively influenced the match between the Outcasts and Doredell. Instead it was a marauding miscreant called Shane Bott.

Twelve-year-olds do not always go to cricket to watch the match or, if they do, their attention can wander. In the case of Shane Bott, it had wandered to the receptacles which had been placed around the boundary. He had quickly gathered that they contained some form of refreshment. When no one (on the field) was looking, Shane got himself alongside one of these receptacles and sampled the contents. Not everyone (Brian Sachin Crossley being an honourable exception) takes to beer at the first tasting. In the modern age a disturbing number of young people continue to reject true bitter beer in favour of lager. It was not perhaps surprising that Shane Bott reacted badly to Hoppenhall's Charger bitter. However, he did not have to take his dislike to the extent of emptying the remaining contents of the vessel on to the grass. It was sheer vindictiveness which led him progressively to empty the rest. Incredibly this treachery had gone unnoticed by the Outcasts, who on finding their nearest receptacle empty had simply assumed that their team-mates had got there first. When they returned from their latest huddle they were disappointed that there had been no refills. Attempts to attract the attention of Tim Jackson or Adrienne Palmer were unavailing. All were unaware of the sadism which had invaded the ground in the shape of a twelve-year-old boy. Having traced the drink back to its source Shane Bott had cheerfully informed Adrienne Palmer that he had 'had a piss' into the funtub.

So it was that in reverting to his original selection Winston Jenkins found David Pelham three pints drier than he might otherwise have been. This was still two pints wetter than when he had bowled the eighteenth over. Winston Jenkins knew that he was moving into risk territory. Why, he asked himself when it was too late, had he not bowled David Pelham out? Well, he knew the answer and it was too late. He had to hope that David Pelham could go for less than twenty-seven an over otherwise the match was over. The off-spinner seemed to take little interest in the field setting. That was a bad sign. As he took the ball David Pelham winked and gave his captain an encouraging grin. That was a better sign. Optimism proved to be short-lived.

'Oh Christ', exclaimed Bill Blimp on digesting a small but crucial piece of information which had hitherto been denied him. Bloody hikers had not been bloody hikers after all, but bloody Japanese tourists. And the numbers did not seem to add up. From Geraint

Poppledown's account there were many more of them than Bill Blimp had seen (or perhaps not seen) on the road. The publican was sure that they had gone to the maze. Perhaps, he suggested, in what he could not possibly know was a massive understatement, they were in the maze. Bill Blimp thereupon returned to the driver's seat to embark on a programme of repair to Anglo-Japanese relations. Early obstacles were placed in his path. His first sighting was discouraging. A lady caring for a stricken Mr Katsuragi shook her fist at him. Nor, a few yards further on, was there any sign of friendliness on the part of those tending Mrs Irikaki. Bill Blimp decided not to stop, but then strangely found that he had reached the maze without seeing anyone else at all. However, at the maze itself there was a Caucasian male whom Bill Blimp greeted with all the relief Stanley must have felt when finding Livingstone. Unlike Stanley and Livingstone each had to admit to the other that he had lost a party of Japanese. The only advantage held by Roger Trysom was that he knew (approximately) where his were.

Spared the twin threats of food poisoning (courtesy of Connie Stillmarch) and claustrophobia in the maze, the Japanese who had shuttled between the Pink Pedlar and the tea-room now felt that the greatest risks had been reserved for them. Getting off the street of death before the traffic notched up its first fatality seemed a priority for those still upright. One of them recognised the overflowing ornamental village waste bin which marked the otherwise anonymous path to Iris Pearlhammer's shop. With mixed expectations they took this escape route. At its end they found the shop-keeper welcoming but wary. In her experience a crowd could mean turnover, but it could also be a cover for pilfering. Nevertheless she erred on the side of friendliness as she sensed some more ancient stock clearance possibilities. It was this refuge in retail therapy that had caused his prospective passengers to be out of Bill Blimp's sight.

'Oh Christ', exclaimed Winston Jenkins in a restrained but audible voice after the third ball of David Pelham's over had followed the first two to the boundary. The bowler seemed unable to target off stump or even middle. Deliveries drifting down the leg side were food and drink to Fred Ranger. He may have had a restricted range

Winston Jenkins, whose expectations of victory had been severely jolted by what had happened to Greg Roberts's last over, could not possibly have known the invisible but intimate connection between events on the field and the welfare of the Japanese in Doredell. He was now more reliant than ever on Ray Burrill maintaining the frugal accuracy of his second coming. To his pleasure and relief that was how the over began. The free-scoring George Summermore of the previous over was forced back into his shell. At this point impatience became the Outcasts' unexpected ally. Whether the batsman's prime motivation was to reach his fifty or to get to the other end so that he might continue the mayhem was unclear. His lunge at a dipping off-cutter got a minimal contact and he took the chance of a scampered single. Fred Ranger joined in the congratulations to his partner, but could not help feeling peeved. Uncharitably he supposed he was being denied the chance of easy runs at the other end. He had one ball to face from Ray Burrill with which to redress this situation.

It was Rashid Ali behind the stumps who detected the grimace of reluctance which had passed across Fred Ranger's face when he was pressed into the last run. He communicated the thought to Winston Jenkins, who was in a mood for any inspiration at this stage. It seemed worth the bluff. Ostentatiously calling 'you OK, Greg?' with a significant nod in the direction of the Hayste end, Winston Jenkins next had a word with his bowler. 'Tempt them with another single, Ray' was his instruction. It was, of course, ludicrous to suppose that a plan based upon such a hopelessly flimsy foundation could be implemented with the slightest possibility of success. Striving to deliver the perfect ball just short of a length, which might conceivably encourage a quick single, Ray Burrill produced a rank long-hop. Fred Ranger had been starved of the strike for too long for his liking. He had been thinking how he might contrive a single so that with any luck in the next over he would be able to have a go at the unfortunate Greg Roberts who seemed likely to be bowling it. Now he was faced with a dilemma. He was being presented with a four ball. Should he just bag the boundary and forfeit the strike? He had a fraction of a second in which to decide. The hesitation undid him. He went for the big shot, but his timing was awry. The ball easily beat the inner ring of fielders which Winston Jenkins had positioned and was destined for distant parts.

of shots, but the scoop to leg was prominent amongst them and he was able to employ it to great effect. This had the advantage to the batting side of a more than useful spurt towards their target and it also meant that running between the wickets was not required. The importance of this was not immediately recognised. After what in post-match discussion David Pelham lightly and not wholly accurately dismissed as 'one or two looseners' he managed to concentrate sufficiently to find a line which obliged the batsman to work a little harder to obtain reward. Fred Ranger dabbed a good length ball past where slip might have been (Winston Jenkins had not even thought of posting one) and took a single, the ball being fielded by an advancing third man. The single had presented Kris Vertz with no difficulty. He had dutifully run to the striker's end and then given way to Ed Fylder, who approached the crease without the look of a man who meant business. However, after taking guard he played the same shot as Fred Ranger to a similar ball from David Pelham. What followed was not similar. Kris Vertz's limited experience of the game had plainly not embraced the essential duties associated with acting as runner for another player. He was deficient in two respects. First, he was slow off the mark, taking a moment or two to realise that Ed Fylder himself was not moving. Secondly, the Austrian seemed to think that he had to run directly to the wicket at the other end. Accordingly, instead of running straight he took a diagonal route. The combination of these factors gave the advancing fielder vital extra time to throw to the bowler's end. David Pelham did not so much catch the ball, but grasp and spill it. Nevertheless he spilt it on to the stumps decisively ahead of Kris Vertz's arrival. The ninth wicket had fortuitously fallen.

'Oh Christ', said Farley Richardson. He said one or two more things as well. Suddenly defeat loomed. Two wickets had been carelessly thrown away and now there was only Tom Amwell left to bat. There were thirty-seven balls left in the innings and thirty-eight runs were needed from them. As his number eleven batsman headed towards the pavilion steps Farley Richardson was going to say that he should do his best to give the strike to Fred Ranger. He stopped himself, thinking that could be a perfect formula for another run-out. For the moment Fred Ranger did have the bowling. Unfortunately there was only one ball left in the over. Tom Amwell would soon be exposed which left little ground for optimism.

'Oh Christ', said Bill Blimp again vehemently as the situation at the maze sank in. The prospect of an evening's boxing began to recede. Not one of the three men present – Roger Trysom, James Saito or Bill Blimp – felt able to initiate a rescue. Bearing in mind how comprehensively the maze had swallowed what Roger Trysom had to admit was an unknown number of Japanese, no one was brave enough to volunteer to step very far into it (least of all James Saito who had begun to think his own exit from it was a divine deliverance). Roger Trysom explained that help had been called for, but this was information which might have been more valued by the entrapped Japanese. Feeling that he needed to mend fences with the visitors Bill Blimp made a show of concern for the still ailing Mrs Nagase and Mr Demimoto. Even when his words had been translated by James Saito, they made little impression. One of the minders of the stricken pair did manage a couple of words in response. To avoid aggravating an already tense situation, James Saito decided not to translate them.

'Oh Christ', said George Summermore when he finally arrived on the scene and was acquainted with the problem. Though still in cricket whites he had at least swapped bat and pads for his own master plan of the maze and a ball of string. One quick glance with his expert eye was all he needed to see the glaring errors in the new maze guide which had been innocently handed to the Japanese. Tying one end of the string to the bench, George Summermore beckoned a reluctant Roger Trysom to follow him in the direction of the maze entrance. James Saito was quite certain that he did not wish to experience again the torment from which he had so recently escaped. Bill Blimp tried to pretend that he was still fussing over the ailing tourists who were firmly outside the maze..

Tom Amwell approached the wicket with as much enthusiasm as Roger Trysom faced the maze. Unlike many number elevens who were duffers with the bat, Tom Amwell never dreamed of glory. He was utterly realistic. He did not see himself as capable of delivering a match-winning innings. He did not actually relish batting. He was too often marked down as a rabbit, effectively a gift wicket for a quick bowler. At least that blond paceman (Colin Banks) was not playing in this year's match. In that game, Tom Amwell remembered, he had batted at ten, ahead of Darren Tilt.

His time at the crease had been downright uncomfortable. Colin Banks had been tearing in looking for his fifth wicket. Before he had hit the stumps he had hit several parts of Tom Amwell's anatomy. To one delivery he had flung up his bat to protect his head and earned two runs as the ball had looped over the wicket-keeper's upstretched arms. He had finally been bowled off his toecap and forced to limp back to the pavilion. His bruises had remained a source of solicitous enquiry (and sometimes amusement) throughout the closed season.

Tom Amwell could not even get enthused about facing slow bowlers. Too often he had failed against them as well. Not for him the joy of a great cow-heave which sent the ball soaring into the crowd. He knew that any kind of ambitious or reckless shot would end in disaster. He would make his usual show of defending. And that was very much the advice which Fred Ranger gave him in a few pungent sentences. Fred, of course, was in two minds. If the opportunity presented itself (as with David Pelham bowling it very well could), should he go for the boundary thereby leaving Tom Amwell exposed at the start of the next over or was the priority to steal the strike? His dilemma was resolved by the bowler. David Pelham decided that he would produce his faster ball with a view to surprising the batsman. He succeeded in his primary aim. The ball was past Fred Ranger's bat before he could adjust his stroke. It would have been better if David Pelham had thought to signal his intention to Rashid Ali behind the stumps. The wicket-keeper was as unprepared as the batsman. The ball sped past him with such force that it reached the boundary before a similarly surprised Boris Wigmouth at third man could get to it. That took the score to 271-9 and Tom Amwell effectively to the front line.

As soon as they entered the maze they heard the wailing. The thickness of the hedge must previously have muffled the piteous cries of the trapped tourists. As George Summermore expertly led the way, Roger Trysom became gradually reacquainted with his clients. The first encounter unnerved him. Mrs. Ashimoro rushed forwards with the intention of embracing her saviour. Roger Trysom was unsure of her intention and feared an attack. He flung himself to one side and interrupted the frenzied approach with his outstretched foot. It took fully five minutes before Mrs

Ashimoro was fit to continue. Meanwhile the wailing grew in volume. Roger Trysom sought to stem the panic by shouting a short message which only a few of the Japanese understood: 'Shut up'. The words failed in their purpose. The sound of the foreign tongue merely intensified the cries of those (bar one) who had started to think that they would end their days in this monstrous enclosure.

It was the likely end of his employment with Nice Spice which was of most concern to Tom Amwell. At the end of the previous over Fred Ranger had administered further advice in such direct terms that Tom had felt more intimidated than encouraged. Worse, far worse, was his sighting of Farley Richardson in front of the pavilion. His captain did not have to impart any advice. His visible presence was sufficient reminder of how seriously Farley Richardson took defeat. If he, Tom, was seen as the instrument of that defeat, he feared that his future at Nice Spice could be in jeopardy. Had their senses been more finely honed, Winston Jenkins and Ray Burrill might have detected the smell of fear. The sharper perception of Rashid Ali was not trained on the situation as he was taking time out to adjust his protection. Tom Amwell watched whilst the wicket-keeper made himself ready and then had to be reminded by his partner to take guard. Not appreciating that the psychological battle had already been won, Ray Burrill trotted in to bowl. All it needed was a straight ball.

Cranley Nice was not a witness to the approaching climax of the match. The apparent invasion of the village of Doredell by the Japanese had thrown him off balance. He had retreated to his office whence he had launched a series of enquiries of his bankers, his stockbrokers, his accountants and his solicitors. This was no problem to Cranley Nice on a Saturday afternoon. It was a contractual requirement that professional service providers to Nice Spice had to be available at all times to tender advice. Cranley Nice had access to the home, office and mobile telephone numbers of the key people on whom he relied. He was now engaged in obtaining their assurance and confirmation that there were no happenings of any kind in the UK or abroad which might be about to threaten the integrity of his company.

The assurance and confirmation were obtained, but not without a loss of goodwill. The four professionals Cranley Nice succeeded (of course) in reaching were aware of his whims and eccentricities, but on the whole these had mostly disturbed their office hours. Only occasionally had an evening at the ballet been disturbed by a throbbing in the trouser pocket as a mobile phone had insistently vibrated; or a Sunday lunch party been disrupted. Saturday afternoons, especially Saturday afternoons in the cricket season, had very rarely been intruded upon by their rich but demanding client. So the sense of being on duty at all hours had subsided. They were comprehensively off-guard when the call came.

Ralph Odur, senior executive director of the exclusive merchant bank, Baskton Bliny, was in a deeply compromising situation with one of his junior accounts clerks to whom he had become quite inadvisably attracted. In the tangle of clothing and bedding the mobile phone had taken some finding. Ralph Odur was uncharacteristically out of breath whilst trying to mouth solemn sentences to assure Cranley Nice that in the commodities sector all he could see was in perfectly good order. What at that moment he could actually see was anything but.

'Damn'. Lawrence Coombs-Frobisher threw down his putter in disgust. He knew that the Murlion Valley Golf Club forbade mobile phones on the course. The cause of his disgust was not his breach of club rules, but the error which the sudden ringing induced. They were on the 17th green and he was one down with two to play. He needed that putt to square the match. The ball had veered to the right of the hole and with it had gone £500. The accountant did his best to soothe Cranley Nice's jangled nerves. 'Bloody maniac', he muttered to soothe his own feelings as he snapped shut the cover on the mobile. He knew where he would eventually recover that £500.

Cranley Nice's stockbroker, Cyril Gooderson, was doing something about which he would rather his client remained ignorant. There was nothing in the least bit disgraceful about what he did. Many would think that it reflected credit on him. Equally, however, there would be many, Cyril Gooderson feared, who would be all too ready to mock him. His reputation as one of the most perceptive and slickest operators on the exchange could be adversely affected. He had discovered his talent as a ventriloquist at the age of six and had been paraded by proud parents at many a talent contest and concert party. He had pursued his skills (privately) at school with a doll which bore an uncanny resemblance to the head teacher. Later, as a student, he had acquired a new doll which now formed the basis of his act. But these days as a bastion of the city establishment he was forced to indulge his deeply-engrained hobby in secret. Adopting heavy disguise in the persona of Old Charlie, a cross between a village yokel and a scarecrow, he performed at concerts in old people's homes and hospitals. His doll took the form of an elderly lady with a razor-sharp tongue and an encyclopaedic fund of double-entendres.

Old Charlie made people laugh, but Cyril Gooderson was not laughing when his mobile phone sounded – yet another man in thrall to Cranley Nice. Had someone been available with a video camera to record what ensued that afternoon at the Hillcrest Residential Home for the Elderly and Downcast a wider audience might have judged that Cyril Gooderson had missed his calling. His improvisation as he answered what he regarded as the fevered ramblings of Cranley Nice, whilst continuing a dialogue with his doll was sheer brilliance. Cranley Nice could not make sense of the laughter in the background, but he was somehow convinced that the

markets showed no irregularity which could be of any concern to the welfare of Nice Spice.
Last to be tracked down was his solicitor, who was not working in his office, as one at least of his girlfriends believed. Hugo Furwell had a brilliant legal mind. Without this asset he would not have been taken on at the age of thirty-three by Cranley Nice. At the point when the phone call was made the brilliance of Hugo Furwell's mind was somewhat impaired. The solicitor on whom Nice Spice could usually lean with total reliability was now slumped at the base of a pillar under the new grandstand at Lord's Cricket Ground. He had intended no more than a couple of beers and a couple of hours of cricket. However, once within the majesty of Lord's, even on the usually quiet third day of a county championship match, diversions and distractions can occur. Hugo Furwell's plans were amended first by a stirring performance by one of Middlesex's young hopefuls, which looked as though it might turn around what was until then an unpromising position. Could the young player get his hundred? Hugo Furwell had dallied and – naturally – taken a third pint. And then he had bumped into Matt Lumsdell.

Hugo Furwell had not realised that his old college chum was back in the country. They had not seen each other for three years. It would have been unforgivable, Hugo Furwell later rationalised to himself, to have declined to take up the spare place at lunch which he had been promptly offered. Stripey and Boggo (they had been fellow students) had also been there. Many past memories and misdeeds had been relived. Two bottles of Gewurztraminer, six bottles of Côte de Rhone and three rounds of Cognac later the young batsman had passed one hundred and fifty and Middlesex had a lead of over two hundred. These details barely registered with Hugo as he was marched to the back of the grandstand in search of 'a bevvy or two'. After the third Hugo had sat down with the pillar of the stand at his back. He reckoned that he must have nodded off for the next voice he heard said, 'aren't you going to answer that thing?' And the next voice after that undoubtedly belonged to Cranley Nice. Hugo's blood froze, but he would later (much later) dine out on the story of how he had managed to string together a sober-sounding sentence which seemed to satisfy his client. Of what happened in the remainder of the day he claimed no recollection whatsoever.

Roger Trysom and George Summermore on their way to the heart of the maze had liberated twenty Japanese tourists in various states of distress. At its centre another problem, which Roger Trysom had in no way anticipated, loudly presented itself. Ignoring for a moment the man asleep in the chair by the fountain, Roger Trysom realised from noises off that there were still further members of his party somewhere else in blind alleys of the maze. Not until that moment did it strike him that he had no idea how many of the Japanese had entered the maze in the first place. Nor for that matter could he remember how many had been left outside. Fortunately George Summermore had sufficient string and patience systematically to clear people out from the parts in which they had become lost. At last the shouting produced no tremulous replies. There was silence. Strangely the babble and bustle had had no effect on the remaining tourist in his seat by the fountain. Roger Trysom gently tugged at his sleeve. The man fell forward. Roger Trysom was the second person that day whose blood froze.

Tom Amwell's state of health was less extreme, but that was not to say that he felt good as he prepared to shape up to the bowling. By contrast Ray felt that he was now in the groove. With the girl's father out of sight he was better able to concentrate and was thus in greater command of himself than hitherto. The first ball nevertheless was not what was required but it was far too good for Tom Amwell. It pitched outside off stump and jagged back, passing just over middle stump and into the hands of Rashid Ali. Ray Burrill was so pleased with it that he strove for a repeat performance. He almost exactly achieved it, but this time the ball lifted over the keeper's gloves and went into open space. Fred Ranger had seen enough. 'Come one', he yelled. Tom Amwell did not argue. The bye took him to safety.

Having observed the first two deliveries, Fred Ranger reckoned that he was up to dealing with Ray Burrill's bowling. Scoring from it was another matter. His first priority was to be watchful. That was just as well, for Ray produced another couple of beauties on which Fred Ranger was unable to lay the bat. The bowler's high standard lapsed with his fifth delivery as a bolt of pain shot through his leg. Had he been better prepared for the full toss, Fred Ranger might have struck it for four, but by the time he played his shot it lacked force. He got two. There was no chance of turning it into three to get himself to the other end in preparation for the next over. A single off the last ball became an urgent necessity if Tom Amwell was to be shielded and some easy runs plundered. In the event it was more by luck than judgement that Fred Ranger achieved his objective. Having warned Tom Amwell of what he intended, he pushed the ball down a yard or two in front of him and ran. Forewarned, Tom Amwell was quick to react; Ray Burrill was slow. But in his headlong rush, Tom Amwell tripped over the ball, and as he stumbled did not see Rashid Ali, who had been advancing in the opposite direction to attempt to retrieve the ball. Batsman and wicket-keeper crashed and for a moment neither moved in any direction. The ball meanwhile had changed direction. Having come into contact with Tom Amwell's foot it had been propelled forward, narrowly missing the now unguarded stumps. Thinking for a flash of a second that a run-out might be on the cards, Ray Burrill excitedly appealed. Before the ball could be fielded, Tom Amwell had extracted himself from the mini-melee and belatedly made his ground – but not before the umpires had moved into conclave.

Being the keeper of the maze was only a part-time occupation. George Summermore's main calling in life was death. He was the local undertaker. No more appropriate person could have been on hand to hear Roger Trysom's call for help. George Summermore, having guided the tourists clear of their verdant prison, came running. There had been something distinctive in what he had heard, apart from the words being in English. It was fear – fear that transcended the recent wailing distress of the visitors. George's professional eye had only to alight on the crumpled form for a second to be sure of his verdict. 'He's a goner', he told Roger Trysom who felt as cold as the man at his feet. The tour operator's first instinct was to flee. The undertaker's first instinct was to caution him. 'The police', he said solemnly, 'will need to satisfy themselves that the gentleman died of natural causes. After all', he added, 'you were the only person with him at the end. It'll look bad for you if you scarper.' It seemed to Roger Trysom pretty bad as it was. This group of Japanese tourists must have a curse on them. Some ill, some injured (George Summermore had mentioned seeing an ambulance) and one now dead. In a burst of self-righteousness Roger Trysom was sure it was nothing to do with him. So why did he feel so afraid? He would soon find out.

Insisting that the body must in no way be disturbed before the arrival of the police, George Summermore conceded that Roger Trysom could retreat to the maze entrance. Between them certain arrangements had to be made and the only means of making them could well turn out to be the mobile phone belonging to Connie Stillmarch. They found the lady in the process of closing down the tea-room for the day. She was not pleased to be delayed, but she was more prepared to pay attention to George Summermore than to Roger Trysom. It transpired that nothing could have more powerfully gripped her attention than a mysterious death. She had not read the whole Agatha Christie lexicon without developing a taste for a real life drama. She had already concluded that it must be murder.

It would have been far too simple if the village doctor had been found at home. 'I can give you his mobile number', said his wife. She did not say that her husband had gone fishing. In any case she would not have known that his favoured fishing haunt was in a dead area for his mobile network as she had never dared to disturb him when he was engrossed in his sport. To make doubly sure the phone was switched off. George Summermore's next try was the health centre in Hayste. He was asked by a recorded voice whether he had a touch-tone phone. He hoped that a mobile qualified and depressed the signified button twice. He was then regaled with an extensive menu which challenged not only his memory, but the capacity of the phone. He passed over options covering his possible pregnancy, immunisation, heart disease, obesity therapy, mental health, minor cuts and bruises, cancer screening and communicable diseases. Finally he was advised to hold for an operator. However, it was not an operator who interrupted an over-lengthy recital of 'Greensleeves', but another recorded voice advising that 'all our agents (sic) are busy – please try later'. George Summermore thereupon decided to thrust the whole matter into the hands of the police: they would surely be able to drag a police surgeon out with them.

Whilst the undertaker was thus occupied, Roger Trysom had an opportunity to make some plans of his own. It was not so much a matter of cutting his losses, but stopping them from mounting. If he was not careful, he recognised that he would find himself footing the bill for overnight accommodation for his customers. That he could not risk. Urgently he instructed James Saito and Bill Blimp to gather the Japanese wherever they were and get them back to London and off his hands as quickly as possible. Bill Blimp needed no prompting. He could recognise a bad situation when he saw it – and anyway that boxing tournament might still be on the cards. He assisted James Saito in unceremoniously bundling Mrs Nagase, Mr Demimoto and their friends who had stayed with them into the double-decker, together with the refugees from the maze. He then set out to collect the other survivors, who by now (and with extreme caution) had manifested themselves by the ornamental waste bin, weighed down with all the bric-a-brac skilfully off-loaded by Iris Pearlhammer. George Summermore and Roger Trysom were left with only a highly curious Connie Stillmarch for company. She offered to make some tea. Roger Trysom hastily declined.

When he was beckoned by Syd Breakwell, Rodney Corrington assumed it had something to do with a possible run-out. Yet even from his vantage point there seemed no doubt that the ball had not hit the stumps. Perhaps Syd Breakwell had seen it differently. However, he soon found that Syd was excited about an altogether more unusual consideration. The former policeman, an international test umpire manqué, was troubled. His knowledge of the laws of cricket was comprehensive, but slight; he knew a little about a lot. He thought he had witnessed a situation to which a particular law applied. He had never had to adjudicate on this matter before, but was quite keen to parade his concern in front of Rodney Corrington. In any case he had not the first idea whether the decision lay with him or his opposite number. Rodney Corrington was taken aback by what was in Syd Breakwell's mind. He was even more hazy about how this law operated, but having thought about it doubted whether it would be in accordance with the spirit of cricket if a match at this level was decided in this way. In the end the two umpires agreed. The players were nonplussed by what seemed to be the wholly superfluous 'not out' decision. Tom Amwell being given out for obstructing the field would not have been an appropriate way to end the match.

Acting Inspector Barry Foxdene was the wrong man in the wrong place at the wrong time. It was true that policing was in his blood. His grandfathers (maternal and paternal) had both been police officers, his father and two uncles were in the force and he himself was the second of three brothers who had also enlisted. Barry was enthusiastic, bordering on impetuous. So far as ordinary policing was concerned his approach was zero tolerance, but his ambition was to be a detective. His superiors had decided that a rural posting might help to calm him down and allow him a more measured view of life. The uplift to the rank of Acting Inspector may have sprung from a confusion of orders, Barry having a brother called Brian. Whatever the explanation, a rural part of the county of Essex fell that spring afternoon under the command of an officer who had an appetite for conspiracy.

Winston Jenkins was beginning to think that in Greg Roberts and David Pelham he had the wrong men in the wrong place at the wrong time. Doredell needed thirty runs from five remaining overs. That was not a great ask even if they did have only one wicket left. Ray Burrill might not give away much, but, if Fred Ranger kept chancing his arm against Greg Roberts and David Pelham, the match could very quickly be lost. They had to try to get Tom Amwell on strike, but instructing Greg Roberts to give away a single was to engage in a degree of sophistication well outside Greg's compass. Winston feared that the same was true of David Pelham on the strength of his current capability. Coming to the conclusion that what he really needed was an outrageous piece of luck, Winston kept to his preconceived plan and threw the ball to Greg Roberts. Fred Ranger licked his lips – again.

Greg Roberts was acutely aware of his limitations. The friendly advice from Phil Cole in passing that Greg should 'try to tuck him up' as a means of limiting Fred Ranger's strokeplay was not easily put into effect. In so far as he tried, the ball twice drifted towards leg and was twice lifted by Fred Ranger for four and (with practice) for six. The next delivery which pitched almost a foot outside off stump must have taken the batsman by surprise and he missed it. Greg aimed in that direction again, but this time went wider of off stump. He was lucky that Syd Breakwell, who was still ruminating about the lost opportunity to add 'obstructing the field' to his catalogue of dismissals, did not stir. When the fifth ball of the over reverted to a leg stump line Fred Ranger, confused, played around it. There was then one ball left to get the single needed to spare Tom Amwell from Ray Burrill.

It took only one call. George Summermore was put through to the acting inspector. The combination of a dead man – Japanese – in the middle of a maze with paramedics attending to two other incidents – both involving Japanese – in the same village was quite enough for Acting Inspector Barry Foxdene. The words 'elderly' and 'tourist' were not used. Even if they had been, it is doubtful whether they would have caused the acting inspector to stay his hand. He saw the headline in his mind's eye: Slaughter in Essex Village; and then again more upliftingly: Police Inspector's Prompt Action Foils International Gang. He gave the order. A cordon (in Barry Foxdene's mind a ring of steel) was to be thrown round Doredell. By the time it was in place, Bill Blimp's double-decker was already well clear of the village on the last journey of its day – and life.

Greg Roberts was not helped by the reminder that there was one ball left in his over and that Fred Ranger needed to be deprived of the single which would allow him to protect Tom Amwell. As he was not managing to be in control of either his line or his length there was little good in his theorising about where ideally he should be seeking to pitch this final delivery. Advice from Winston Jenkins and then separately from Jon Palmer was of all too little avail. Miserably he ran in and as though in haste to be rid of the ball banged it in woefully short. At least it made the batsman think. Fred Ranger could see a boundary for the taking. Just in time he checked himself, realising the strategic situation. Hesitation caused the false stroke. Instead of smashing the ball he found himself chipping it off a leading edge between point and cover. Without conviction Fred Ranger ran the single, not daring to look at the fate of the shot. By pure chance he had found a relatively untenanted part of the field. Cover (John Furness) and point (Phil Cole) moved, but each seemed more preoccupied with the movement of the other than with the flight of the ball. Thus they broke the basic rule. When Phil Cole finally said 'yours', he was unfortunately echoed by a similar call from John Furness. The players were abreast when the ball bounced harmlessly a yard away from them. Doredell's innings remained alive.

This was more than could be said, of course, about Mr Aoki Yanada to whose companionship Roger Trysom had been re-committed by the undertaker and maze-keeper. It was a union which would have been no more welcome in life than Roger Trysom found it in death. George Summermore had gone away to collect his undertaking apparatus. Connie Stillmarch's appetite for the mysterious and the macabre had waned at the thought of being left in close proximity to the body. Shivering, she hurried away from the maze which had now taken on a sinister aura. After two large brandies in the Pink Pedlar, the sound of police cars racing by almost restored her resolve and for a few moments she contemplated a return to watch the law at work. Then she decided on another brandy.

The police found the maze without difficulty. The body was more of a problem. Eight officers – the complement of two cars – entered the maze with zeal, but without the guiding string which George Summermore, after posting Roger Trysom as sentinel of the body, had removed (just in case). The six men and two women were quickly absorbed. None had reached their objective by the time Acting Inspector Barry Foxdene arrived on a scene deserted but for two empty cars in which he noted with disapproval the keys had been left. This act of carelessness was matched only by his own in not removing them. Spurred on by the need to reprove the officers in charge of the vehicles, Barry Foxdene plunged into the maze. Rank did not equip him with greater insights into the right direction to tread.

For the next twenty minutes the police investigation made no progress. Exceptionally in the modern age this failure could not be put down to lack of manpower. Several officers were on the spot, but equally in a spot. Even though they dispersed in search of the true path, no advance was made towards what their commanding officer in giving his orders had described quite unfairly as their quarry. For his part Roger Trysom had begun to feel that he was a hunted man. The shouts he could hear did not seem at all friendly. He preferred to stay silent rather than offer any clue as to his exact whereabouts. The sound of a police siren did nothing to improve his sense of well-being. The same sound encouraged in Acting Inspector Barry Foxdene the belief that reinforcements had arrived and were being signalled to him. Of the two false reactions his was the wider of the mark.

Having had his metaphorical dragons slain, Cranley Nice recovered himself sufficiently to remember that there was an unfinished cricket match close at hand. He hoped that it would provide the final antidote to his anxiety, the balm for his mental wounds. As he drew near he could see that the match was still in progress. That had to be an encouraging sign for his team. Of the score there was no sign, but as Cranley Nice reached the perimeter of the ground, Simon Crossley obligingly lent out of the box to bellow '286 for 9, four overs left'. This bulletin was insufficient to convey the good news that Fred Ranger was going strong with over forty to his name and the bad news that Tom Amwell was his partner. As a general proposition nineteen runs to win off four overs did not sound so bad. By the time Cranley Nice was reunited with his team captain in the pavilion the equation looked rather less good.

Craig and Ryan arrived at the place from which Acting Inspector Barry Foxdene had just exited. The two young lads had left the cricket ground where they had been under orders to stay. The prospect of an exciting finish had not held them in its grip. Having extracted amusement from every other diversion which they had been able to discover during their stay at the ground (the punch-up had been the most entertaining) they had made their escape, curious to see whether there were any new attractions in the village. Tempting panes of fresh glass in the telephone box were always a possibility. The public toilets were also worth a visit so long as Craig's spray paint can had remained undiscovered in its handy cache. The sight of the two police cars alongside the acting inspector's saloon might have been expected to act as a deterrent. For a short while this was so, but gradually they became objects of attraction. Which small boy has not yearned to operate a police siren and set the blue lamp flashing? Regrettably with the two boys in question this proved not to be the limit of their ambition.

Every credit had to be given to Ray Burrill. Here was a man rising above his earlier mental and physical doubts. Responding to his team's needs, his pacier style of bowling seemed to match the conditions. Ray grew in confidence as his inner turmoil diminished. It helped him to discount the recurring pain in his injured leg. Many more illustrious bowlers would have been proud to claim ownership of the over which he sent down to Fred Ranger. The outcome might have been different had Fred been able to lay any forcible bat on ball, because that would have brought fielders into play. By this time they could roughly be divided into those who had had too much of the boundary-side refreshment and those who had had too little. There was no way of assessing which category would have been encountered had Fred Ranger managed any half-decent stroke. Of the only two deliveries where bat and ball actually made contact, the batsman might have been caught, but the state of the match and the state of the Outcasts by this time in the afternoon meant that the fielding positions of short leg and silly mid-off were vacant. The over was wicket-less, but also run-less. Nineteen runs to get with three overs left and Tom Amwell's turn to be on strike signified a possibly final and decisive shift in fortune.

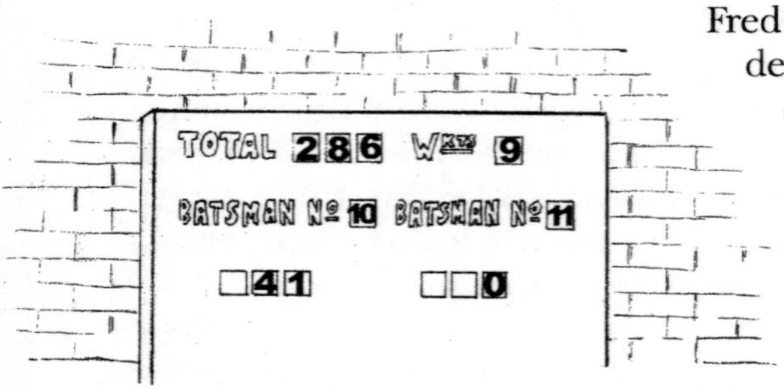

Inside the maze a variety of emotions was on display. Roger Trysom had experienced a growing sense of unease over being alone with the body of a stranger in the centre of this rural gaol. What had seemed a sensible albeit unattractive suggestion when made by George Summermore had now acquired a different and more sinister character. Roger Trysom's stomach tightened. Noises off gave the impression of a net closing. It was in the normal course of things an entirely irrational thought (perhaps less so had he been aware of Barry Foxdene's approach to policing), but it provoked an entirely irrational reaction. Suddenly Roger Trysom wanted to put distance between himself and the corpse. He did not stop to think that he did not know which way to go and that he would almost inevitably run into the arms of an advancing policeman. All he could remember was the pathway leading from the centre of the maze which he and George Summermore had previously used. He went for it.

The maze had also had its effect on Acting Inspector Barry Foxdene. The more he thrashed around inside, turning first one way and then the other, the more he allowed himself to believe that he was grappling with a sinister crime of far-ranging implications. His brain was infused with the idea that he had been lured into this labyrinth by a cunning mastermind. Holmesian images flitted before his eyes. Doubtless a score of bodies awaited him at the core of the maze – if ever he could find it. He entertained the thought that his fellow officers whom he could not locate might have been led to their doom. But as his imagination soared to fever pitch, he made two left turns to an anticlimax. It was now Barry Foxdene's chance to be alone with a deceased elderly Japanese male. Almost simultaneously and with extraordinary luck the former companion of the corpse found his way out of the maze. Roger Trysom was in time to witness the crash.

In a far corner of the maze two police officers had come together. The encounter had not been intended. Although colleagues in the same force, PC Carol Flather and PC Leonard Hupkins had seen each other up to now only at a distance. This had not prevented a mutual quickening of the pulse. Whether through reticence, a sense of professional decorum or plain lack of opportunity, curiosity had gone unsatisfied. Having blundered their independent ways to the same end of the maze, they found that they could not escape each other. With an eye to duty they each retraced their steps in search of their supposed quarry. Again and again they found themselves back in the same place with an eye more and more for each other. At the fourth involuntary rendezvous they literally fell into each other's arms. Rustic isolation may have been the catalyst, but duty very swiftly gave way to passion as if they were in the Maze of Eden. The climax was nothing if not sensational.

The two brothers, Craig and Ryan, were extremely lucky to avoid injury. Both were comfortably below the legal driving age but they had nevertheless manoeuvred the police vehicles on to the open road, although in Ryan's case this had only been accomplished after badly scraping Barry Foxdene's saloon and removing its nearside wing mirror. Their longer term plans were not clear. Ryan, and by now Roger Trysom, watched as Craig revved the engine. To add authenticity Craig had donned a chequered police cap and seat-belt. The car lurched forward. Its journey was short. Whatever driving skills the boy possessed obviously did not extend to command of the gearbox. With some force, but still in first gear, the car struck the exterior of the maze. A long, lingering cry rang out.

It was soon clear that it was not emitted by the driver. He was out of the vehicle in a trice. His brother took the hint. Cutting the engine of his vehicle Ryan joined his brother in flight back whence they had come. They missed the final act in their motoring adventure. Ryan in his haste had forgotten the handbrake. The car gently rolled forward and embedded itself in the offside of the Acting Inspector's car. What the boys did not miss was the end of the match in which their father was playing a crucial part.

For the two police constables it was more than the earth that moved as the car struck – by dramatic irony the selfsame vehicle which such a short while before PC Leonard Hupkins had himself driven to the scene. He could never have anticipated how soon he might come close to being impaled on its bonnet. The long, lingering cry to which its intrusion had contributed had two effects. It fuelled the suspicion of Barry Foxdene that the maze was after all a place where dark deeds were still being done. However, having found one body he was unwilling to plunge into the unknown to look for a second. Some of his fellow officers were less fettered and, being close to the source of the sound, sought to move towards it. The noise of their approach communicated itself to the sprawling couple. The ruptured hedge provided them with a fortuitous means of escape from major embarrassment in front of their colleagues to minor embarrassment elsewhere. The dubious pleasure of witnessing two dishevelled, partly uniformed officers staggering to freedom was confined to Roger Trysom.

Winston Jenkins's strategy had undergone a further review. Unchanged, it meant David Pelham bowling the next over, himself the captain bowling the penultimate and Greg Roberts the final. With the palpably weaker batsman, Tom Amwell, now on strike, Winston Jenkins was hugely tempted to have a go. How fitting (the thought crossed his mind) that the captain should take the last wicket and win the match for his side. Then again, if David Pelham could keep Tom Amwell tied down at one end, he as captain could take on the greater responsibility of containing Fred Ranger. Neither scenario stood up to serious scrutiny, while allowing Greg Roberts his final over earlier than was strictly necessary would be just plain foolhardy. So after such weighty calculations, Winston Jenkins exerted his leadership. He let things be and David Pelham was thrown the ball.

David Pelham, not having been invited to share his captain's thinking, had been doing some of his own. Surprisingly this had been about the game and not about the entertainment which might follow it. The strategy at which David Pelham had arrived was to bowl straight. This might not have been thought a revolutionary theory, but everything is relative. What David Pelham had persuaded himself was that direction had to have priority over length. He was sufficiently realistic to recognise that by this time of day he was incapable of commanding both line and length. Equally he was sufficiently alert to believe that a batsman of Tom Amwell's calibre was probably incapable of profiting from over-pitched balls. The full toss would be a threat rather than an opportunity. That at any rate was the theory which he had determined to put to the test. It was not without realism.

George Summermore's return to the maze (driving a hearse) helped to bring a measure of order. Constables Flather and Hupkins thought that they had regained their propriety, but the state of their hair might have told another story. Their newly liberated colleagues were airing some suspicions amongst themselves – about passion rather than crime. The acting inspector's mind was still firmly on the latter. (The damaged cars were a further contribution to his conspiracy fixation.) Any disappointment he felt at the news that his subordinates had found no further bodies was balanced by the preposterous notion that Mr Aoki Yanada's death may have come about by other than natural causes. He had reached this conclusion without himself having been within six feet of the supposed victim. Barry Foxdene associated people from the East with deadly toxins. There was no one as yet on hand to dispel this theory.

The police surgeon, Dr Prendilove, had proved easy to locate, but hard to summons. Engaged himself in a tense village cricket match some twenty miles away, his pager sounded when he was within ten runs of his first ever half-century. With one wicket left his team needed fifteen to win the match. Dr Prendilove knew where his duty lay. Thus for the moment there was no restraint on the acting inspector's imagination. After George Summermore's casual mention of the Doredell cricket match at which for a while there had been a strong Japanese presence, Barry Foxdene felt that he should extend the scope of his investigations. Leaving two officers at the maze – fortunately not Constables Flather and Hupkins – to carry out a minute search for clues with the help of a diagram thoughtfully supplied by George, Barry Foxdene headed for the Nice Spice sports ground. He was assisted by the fortuitous arrival of another detachment of uniformed officers. He believed he had the numbers to keep the village in an iron grip until the true magnitude of the threat had been assessed and overcome.

Having no sense of cricket (nor of much else it might appear), Barry Foxdene might well have ordered play to halt for the purpose of assisting his murder hunt. However, the match had already ended. The remaining spectators were trying to disperse with the Pink Pedlar a prime destination – or so they thought. The players were on their way to the pavilion with showers in mind as a preliminary, in the Outcasts' case, to an entertainment which of necessity was taking place elsewhere – or so they thought. There was animated discussion about the result and the way in which it had been achieved. Inevitably it triggered memories of how the last match had ended.

Having left the Outcasts on what had seemed an easy march to victory, Colin Banks, returning from the vicarage that fateful September found himself confronted by something which looked more nearly a rout. Eight wickets were down and Greg Roberts was on his way to the crease. At the other end stood Phil Cole with three to his name. The Outcasts were still six runs short of their target. John Furness had been dismissed on the last ball of the over and so Phil Cole was on strike. Phil, however, was not the side's big hitter. He prodded and probed, usually getting his runs in singles. Colin's team-mates descended on him complaining about his absence and urging him to get padded up without further delay. There was barely time.

Off the fifth ball of the over Phil Cole nudged a single which to his chagrin was called a leg-bye. Greg Roberts was exposed to one ball and that was all it took. In emulation of his partner Greg also prodded, but the ball went into the hands of short leg and this time the umpire did think that it had come off the bat.

The next over had followed a similar pattern – too similar. A leg-bye off the fifth ball – this time Phil Cole could not complain – left Colin Banks on strike with four to win. To be fair to him he was still shaken both physically and mentally by his adventure at the vicarage. His mind, reeling with questions, was not fully attuned to the responsibility which now descended upon him. Sensing that his attention span might be short and ignoring the entreaties of his partner, Colin decided that the issue must be resolved with one mighty blow. He had taken guard and looked around the field, but it was when his hand subconsciously moved to adjust his box that his certainty wavered. He was not wearing a box because he was not wearing a jockstrap, this having been left behind in his headlong rush to escape the scene of his intended conquest. There had been no time to borrow anyone else's equipment. The bowler approached; the batsman retreated. The ball just short of a length appeared to be heading for the tender zone. With his bat not sufficiently advanced in its downward arc, Colin took another defensive step back and trod on his wicket. The innings (and the match) ended.

The merits of single-mindedness had been immediately demonstrated by David Pelham as he began the thirty-eighth over. There was no argument that his first ball was straight, but it was a stomach-high full toss which Tom Amwell took in the stomach. As the delivery had no great velocity the batsman was only temporarily winded. The next ball was a more orthodox full toss which had the batsman in all manner of confusion. The spectacle offered by the over so far had done nothing for Fred Ranger's peace of mind. By the time of the third ball he was in a mood to run for anything, but it presented no such opportunity. Again of full flight, it lodged in the flap of Tom Amwell's pad. By this time David Pelham could see that one of his thoughts was close to the truth. The over-pitched ball was indeed causing the batsman a problem. Unfortunately David lacked the capacity to exploit this recognition. He maintained the line, but the ball pitched short. Tom Amwell almost ran towards it in gratitude, but, having blocked it, he stopped as though in satisfaction for a job well done. Fred Ranger, however, was on his way. So too was Rashid Ali. With all three stumps to aim at, he propelled the ball well in advance of a late-galvanised Tom Amwell.

With all the three stumps to aim at Rashid Ali, the soundest and usually most sober member of the fielding side, missed. David Pelham, having discharged his function of bowling the ball, had allowed his mind to wander. Neither he nor anyone else was in position at the stumps to gather the errant ball and complete the run-out. Tom Amwell had got a run to his name and the more aggressive Fred Ranger was back on strike. At this point David Pelham excelled himself. He got a ball to turn. In the context of the afternoon this was a minor miracle. It was also a major piece of luck. David Pelham had not schemed a good length ball and he could not have anticipated that it would pitch on a crack or some irregularity of the strip, deviate and then so completely confuse the batsman. Fred Ranger's lunge at it missed by a generous margin. With two overs and one ball left the batsman was then faced with the familiar need to farm the bowling. There was no risk of a similar delivery from David Pelham. To his credit he again maintained line, but length was lacking. Fred Ranger stabbed down on it, but his bat jarred the ground in the process. The ball squirted out towards mid-off. Tom Amwell watched it in uncertainty, deaf to Fred Ranger's call. When he belatedly set off he should have had no chance. Harry Northwood galloped in and smoothly gathered the ball. Had he chosen to keep on running he would probably have beaten Tom Amwell to the other end. That would have been the better option for in his excitement Harry's aim was wild. The throw missed the wicket, the wicket-keeper and fine leg. Its journey ended only when it passed the boundary rope and hit the cool-bag of an adjacent spectator. In all Fred Ranger gained five precious runs and it was then a matter of Doredell getting thirteen off twelve balls.

Come the hour, come the man. Some such thought passed through Winston Jenkins' mind and he was sure the man was not Greg Roberts even though in the end it might come to that. Winston Jenkins reminded himself silently of the responsibilities of captaincy. He planned accuracy at the expense of speed and there was certainly nothing quick about the implementation of the strategy. His first ball was fortunate not to be called a wide. He was lucky too with the second, because hesitation on Rodney Corrington's part was resolved by none on Fred Ranger's part. It was smashed to the point boundary for four. Fred's half-century was warmly applauded. Winston's third ball was an improvement, but Fred Ranger pushed it past cover's left hand. 'Two', he yelled for the benefit of Tom Amwell and of everyone within a quarter-mile radius. Thus forewarned Ray Burrill charged in from where he had been lurking at deep extra cover. Tom Amwell was well short of his ground. Winston Jenkins caught the ball and immediately dropped it again in his rush to sweep off the bails.

Winston Jenkins was then doubly conscious of his responsibility. He rallied well. Daring to bring the field in closer (there was nothing left to anchor them to the boundary) he prevented Fred Ranger scoring off the fourth and fifth balls of the over. Placement became extremely important if the batsman was to get the single he needed to steal the strike. Harry Northwood was again at mid-off standing parallel with the stumps at the bowler's end. Fred Ranger's stroke was firm and almost straight to him. On the evidence of the last over Fred decided that Harry's arm could be taken on: Tom Amwell should be safe. He had not reckoned that Harry would use the other option. Stopping the ball with his left hand (smartly it has to be said) and transferring to his right Harry executed an underarm roll at the one stump he could see. Strike! Fred Ranger was not to know how many hundreds of hours Harry had spent in the ten-pin bowling alley. He was run out by a yard. Winston Jenkins smiled in triumph. Came the hour, came the man – even if it was not the man he had had in mind.

OUTCASTS

Palmer	b. Amwell		34
Pelham	run out		49
Faulds	c. Beckett	b. Richardson	47
Rashid Ali	b. Fylder		88
Jenkins	b. Flote		47
Cole	not out		18
Burrill	did not bat		
Northwood	did not bat		
Newton	did not bat		
Furness	did not bat		
Roberts	did not bat		
Extras			21
TOTAL	**(for 5 wickets)**		**304**

Bowling	**o**	**m**	**r**	**w**
Ranger	8	2	39	0
Amwell	8	0	65	1
Vertz	7	0	24	0
Richardson	8	0	119	1
Fylder	8	1	25	1
Flote	1	0	20	1

DOREDELL

Flote	run out	71
Tiller	run out	7
Bliss	run out	28
Wills	run out	49
Beckett	run out	18
Vertz	run out	0
Summermore	run out	50
Richardson	run out	0
Fylder	run out	0
Ranger	run out	52
Amwell	not out	1
Extras		22
TOTAL	**(all out)**	**298**

Bowling	**o**	**m**	**r**	**w**
Jenkins	8	0	64	0
Cole	8	0	65	0
Pelham	8	2	41	0
Roberts	7	0	71	0
Burrill	8	1	43	0

Outcasts won by 6 runs

CLOSE OF PLAY

One of the players did not immediately head back to the pavilion. After the customary back-slapping and high-fiving, Ray Burrill had detached himself from his team-mates. He went in search of his female fan-club from whom he hoped he might get some physical approbation better than a back-slap or high-fives. He also had questions on his mind. After receiving a warm smile and a promisingly affectionate hug he began to try to unravel the knots inside his head. What Ray Burrill heard made him realise that the unravelling process could be extensive. Without actually taking her number and with no more than a distracted 'I'll call you later' he turned back to the pavilion to mull over what she had told him. There was something not quite right.

There was absolutely nothing right about the investigation being conducted by Acting Inspector Barry Foxdene. By wild exaggeration of the situation he had been called to examine he found himself in command of more police officers than would have been deployed for the protection of a visiting head of state. Strict orders had been given to prevent anyone leaving the ground without any corresponding instruction to stop people entering. The police and security guards simply did as they had been told. Those who were in the pavilion, the acting inspector decided to keep there for the convenience of interrogation. In the meantime all vehicles were stopped from entering or leaving the village. It would have been bad enough if the acting inspector had then pursued his enquiries with an open mind. However, with a preposterous idea already colonising his brain, what he was about to hear made matters even worse.

The first expostulation came from Farley Richardson. In the presence of the chairman of the company he was pomposity personified. In enraged tones and with a suitably elevated voice (Cranley Nice was several feet distant) he told Barry Foxdene how monstrous it was that private property was being invaded in this way. Habeas corpus, human rights, wrongful imprisonment, aggravated trespass and violation of property all got a mention as Farley Richardson's rhetoric took flight. With restraint which was untypical Barry Foxdene waited until the tirade exhausted itself. He then told Farley Richardson to shut up. When the factory manager countered with the insistence that he was in charge, Barry Foxdene flatly contradicted him and to underline his assumed authority went on to say that he was investigating a diabolical crime with far-reaching international ramifications. Climactically he roared at Farley Richardson: 'Don't you know there's a man lying dead out there?' In so saying his thumb was jerked vaguely in the direction of the factory. Farley Richardson's eyes followed the general line and saw the by now reduced gathering of spectators on that side of the ground. He gasped. Surely to goodness the earlier fracas had not led to a fatality. The thought silenced him – temporarily.

Whether they were spectators or prisoners was not yet a question bothering the Outcasts. For the moment as they hovered between changing room and shower they had something much more intriguing to discuss. It had begun with Tim Jackson reporting his conversation with Adrian Wills. He concluded his account with the summary: 'So that's what this by-election is all about.' He was surprised to be contradicted by the rejoinder from Ray Burrill: 'I don't think it's that simple.' Ray, having passed back effortlessly into the ground, recounted what he had gleaned from his new friend of the afternoon, adding the account of his old acquaintance with the man and the woman (now he had remembered her name) who featured in the piece. Whichever way one looked at it, land was the issue. After that things became much less straightforward.

By contrast Bill Blimp thought that his assignment had shed its complications and that he was on course to execute his mission and settle down to a contented evening watching a series of guys knock hell out of each other. The first indication that this dream might not be quite so easy to fulfil came early in the journey. James Saito had become Bill Blimp's route-master. The bus driver, having no better idea of the route back to London than he had had of his journey to the Cambridgeshire border, and still bereft of road maps, was all too ready to take advice. Equally without access to a road map, James Saito had a sufficient sense of direction to be sure that there was a better way to get back to London than the one Roger Trysom had chosen for the outgoing journey. What is more James Saito believed in motorways. He advised Bill Blimp to head for the M11. For a Saturday it was an entirely reasonable proposition. But not, as it turned out, this particular Saturday.

The approach to the motorway was via a major dual carriageway. The double-decker found the right road with little difficulty and the bus was getting nicely up to speed when Bill Blimp was obliged to apply the brakes with some force. The vehicle came to a halt within a foot of a green people carrier (of Japanese manufacture naturally) from the back of which a young boy very elaborately and very emphatically gave Bill Blimp a V-sign. At another time Bill Blimp might have engaged in a nuclear reaction, but in the first instance other (conflicting) thoughts took precedence. He was furious that progress had been brought to a halt by what looked like serious traffic congestion, but he had to acknowledge some relief that the double-decker's brakes had responded. At the last service he had been advised that the brake linings were forty-five percent worn, but he had decided to chance it and leave their replacement until the next service. Or was it the service before last, he briefly wondered, when the wear had first been mentioned? But back to the moment – it was clear that they were stuck. Bill Blimp stared ahead. His only reward was another V-sign.

If Cranley Nice had not said 'bloody Japanese – how I hate them' in too loud a voice, he would not have drawn attention to himself, more especially not the attention of Acting Inspector Barry Foxdene. The relative eminence in these surroundings of Cranley Nice was not known to the policeman. It is doubtful whether the knowledge would have made any difference. Barry Foxdene had already brushed aside Farley Richardson who exuded authority even if he did not fully possess it. Cranley Nice, who did fully possess it, was of medium frame and outwardly mild demeanour. Without hesitation Barry Foxdene acted. Two of his officers lifted the chairman of Nice Spice off his feet and heaved him through a nearby door for private interrogation. Rodney Corrington was surprised to find his ablutions disturbed by his boss being dumped upon him like a sack of coal. This was the umpires' room. With Barry Foxdene's finger pointing at him accompanied by the single word 'out' said far more peremptorily than to any batsman he had himself dispatched, Rodney Corrington got out. He stared sheepishly at the people in the main area of the pavilion whose eyes had been riveted on the door through which Cranley Nice had disappeared. After no more than a moment – it seemed to Rodney Corrington longer – it opened once more and his clothes followed.

These latest developments were lost on the Outcasts. Whilst one or two of them had vaguely noticed a Japanese element in the ring of spectators, the closest connection most of them had with anything Japanese amounted to two mobile phones and three mini-disc players. Only Harry Northwood and Sophie Crossley had had any direct contact, but the geriatric tourists of their casual acquaintance had not seemed the stuff of a terrorist network. As the hubbub continued in the other part of the pavilion the Outcasts continued in their efforts to make sense of the land issue and the persons connected with it.

Longbirch House might have gone and its last owner been imprisoned, but the estate remained. It was in the hands of administrators, but it would be an exaggeration to say that it was in their care. Only by special arrangement had the maze received attention. As no one had come forward with any interest in rebuilding the house, thought had drifted to disposing separately of the fifty-acre estate. However, planning restrictions appeared to block the way to development and local farmers had problems enough squeezing a living from their existing acreage without adding to their liabilities. The hopes of the administrators had been momentarily lifted when they read that the Home Office was searching for sites to accommodate asylum seekers, but these were quickly dashed. Doredell was deemed to be too isolated and too far from an airport. Prospects of a purchaser for the Longbirch site had receded until, that is, the nearby spice factory had changed hands.

After the purchase of Fingerbarrows had been completed, Cranley Nice had wasted no time in discovering what other potential was offered by the area into which he had bought. The Longbirch estate had soon caught his eye without any prompting from his wife. It held no attraction to him as the site for a future country home. Cranley Nice's mind had concentrated on how many houses could be built on those acres. He was, of course, advised that development of the land for housing was expressly ruled out by the terms of the Vale of Widdle District Plan. But Cranley Nice did not see that as any kind of obstacle. He had a deep loathing of planning regulations; many such petty restrictions in his path had been surmounted in the past. Each victory had bolstered the belief in him that nothing was impossible. Meanwhile there was extra satisfaction (let alone profit) to be gained by purchase of the land at a fraction of the price which planning permission would have given it.

Similarly Cranley Nice's interest in Doredell Cricket Club had not been purely related to his love of cricket. Doredell's ground had stood on part of the Longbirch estate. Persuading the club to move to the spice factory's recreation ground, apart from giving him a controlling interest in its affairs, had neatly removed a complication. It also, Cranley Nice had calculated, created space for another thirty dwellings. He had eyed the maze with disfavour, but, as that was covered by a restrictive covenant, he had decided that its removal could be secured at a later date.

With Cranley Nice's attention distracted by a number of business problems – the international spice industry was hotting up – progress towards an agreement on the land purchase had been slow. This had not been due to any laxity on the part of Cranley Nice's agents and solicitor. What had frustrated them in their tenacity to achieve their client's goal was an unexpected complication affecting the administrators – one of them had been sent to prison. Although his financial irregularity (described in his local newspapers as fraud) had been confined to his own personal affairs, the case had cast a shadow over his colleagues and some regrouping had to take place – after a suitable pause. And then when it had looked as though negotiations could be finalised another unexpected complication had intervened. A second offer was received. Despite some hectoring by Cranley Nice's advisers, the administrators, chastened by their indirect association with financial impropriety, insisted that they had to give the new offer full and fair consideration. Cranley

Nice's fury had been full and monstrously unfair. Part of his fury was directed at the continued anonymity of the competitive bidder. Unbeknown to him and to them this was a matter on which the Outcasts could have been of assistance.

Little assistance was available to Bill Blimp and his unfortunate passengers. Nothing had moved for twenty minutes except the fingers of the young boy in the green people carrier. They were capable of a wide degree of versatility as insulting gesture followed insulting gesture in Bill Blimp's direction. The bus owner's verbal responses were fortunately inaudible to the boy and to Bill's passengers, many of whom had been overtaken by sleep which would not be untroubled. There was no public address system in the double-decker and Bill Blimp was in no mood to get out of his cab and give a message of explanation and apology to his customers. Had he actually stirred himself into action it might have taken the form of a message of admonition to the boy's parents. And Bill Blimp knew about road rage and did not fancy a knife between his ribs. Then suddenly, without forewarning, the traffic began to move. The green people carrier lurched forward taking the young boy by surprise. He was promptly sick all over the back window of the vehicle which then had to weave its way to the verge. Bill Blimp allowed himself a smile. It would be his last of the day.

Assistance was not immediately available to Cranley Nice in the umpires's room. He had naturally demanded the right to phone his solicitor. The state of preparedness of Hugo Furwell to receive the call had deteriorated further since the previous exchange. When he had fallen asleep he had been deserted by his friends, but not abandoned. At close of play – earlier than the appointed hour for the official reason of bad light (which often shines at Lord's) – Hugo Furwell had been revived by Matt Lumsdell with the stimulating words, 'you look as though you're in need of a drink'. Their slurring did not inspire confidence in the acuity of Matt Lumsdell's judgement in the matter, but Hugo Furwell allowed himself to accept the advice. The four friends departed for a pub which Boggo said was just around the corner, but seemed an overlong walk away. On a day when his mind was functioning better Hugo would have recognised the Bug and Beetle as a shrine for the real ale enthusiast. But that was not to be the way of things. It also served champagne at very competitive prices.

The first bottle had disappeared within ten minutes of their arrival. The landlord used larger than traditional champagne glasses on the theory that what his low prices cost him in margin was made up by volume. Five more bottles had been disposed of before Matt Lumsdell (on whom champagne had seemed to bestow restorative powers) suggested that they should go to Martine's. This was an exclusive men's club which provided gourmet meals and specialised personal services of a discreet nature. Hugo Furwell would probably have been better off had he managed to get there, but that was not the case. On leaving the Bug and Beetle he chose instead to embrace rather too vigorously an extremely good-looking policewoman. He insisted on dancing with her. They were not easily separated. Police reinforcements appeared. Hugo's friends disappeared, and when Cranley Nice made his second call his solicitor was in a police cell facing a charge of racially-aggravated assault. The mobile was in fact being counted amongst the prisoner's possessions by the policewoman, who had had the pleasure of making the arrest (but of little else), when it rang. 'No way, baby', was all Cranley Nice received by way of reply, and the phone was then switched off.

Hugo Furwell could not know what an asset he might have been to the Outcasts Cricket Club.

'And that's it, darling, I'm afraid', were the words which ended the conversation. They had been spoken by Cecilia Fossington through whom Tim Jackson had procured access for himself and his friends to the exclusive post-race fancy dress party. Tim snapped his mobile phone shut in exasperation. He had known that the party host was an autocratic type whose renowned parties were run to an exacting (but exciting) schedule. Faced with his own utterly unscheduled detention in Doredell, Tim had thought it wise to raise with his friend and intermediary the growing risk of late arrival. The advice he had received was unambiguous. They had to be at the party venue by 8.30 pm at the absolute latest or they would find the gates closed. Already attired in his white dinner jacket Tim acquainted his fellow partygoers with this serious news. The police investigation had to be completed quickly or they would have to consider breaking out. Glumly they contemplated the prospects.

Had the spice factory ceased operation its site would have had obvious potential as a secure prison. There were only three entrances all of which were easily guarded, provided, of course, that the task was not entrusted exclusively to Stopp Security Systems. The remainder of the perimeter comprised a high wall capped with spikes or an impenetrable hedge. Given time and ingenuity a group of determined escapees would doubtless have found means of overcoming these obstacles with the same flair as had been shown by the internees of Colditz Castle in World War II. The Outcasts did not match this specification. There appeared to be no way out until Acting Inspector Barry Foxdene gave his approval. Movement in the reverse direction remained no problem. So Andy Lizzard had not encountered any hindrance in returning to the scene of his machinations.

The would-be trade union organiser presented a very different picture from the man who had clocked on at the factory earlier in the day. He was now heavily bandaged in a manner which concealed the actual extent of his bruising. Some of the bandages bore a red stain, but it was not blood. He was on crutches which were a wholly unnecessary accoutrement. One of his eyes was covered by a patch to imply, falsely, that it might be damaged. He was flanked by two battle-scarred associates whose apparent role was to help him to keep his feet on his path to the sports ground. The overall effect was dramatic, but it did not earn him the response he had envisaged when he had cooked up this charade.

The man with whom Andy Lizzard had planned an angry confrontation could not have been more fulsome in his greeting. Farley Richardson, in light of Barry Foxdene's description of his investigation, had entertained a vision of Andy Lizzard trampled to death, a fate which Ashley Bright's assurances had not completely extinguished. It was with a surge of relief that he welcomed Andy Lizzard although he held back from embracing him. The word 'compensation' had barely begun to form on Andy Lizzard's lips when the door to the umpires' room opened and Barry Foxdene emerged. The sight of the bandaged cripple seemed to excite him and he at once began to question the poor unfortunate. Had he been the victim of attack? Andy Lizzard responded energetically to that, but was deflated by the second question. Had the attacker been Japanese? Andy Lizzard wondered which answer would best suit his purposes, but in the end could see no sense in being other than honest. Was he sure? Andy Lizzard hesitated a second time. Barry Foxdene took this to be suspicious. 'Are you sure?' he roared. And Andy Lizzard confessed, trying to judge which way advantage lay, that he was not. The admission had dramatic results. Immediately a detachment of the by now plentiful force of police was allocated to this new line of enquiry into what was clearly (in Barry Foxdene's mind) a burgeoning international crime wave. The adjacent scorebox was commandeered. Robert Vine and Simon Crossley, who had been engaged in a painstaking transfer of match information for the former's benefit, were brusquely expelled. Andy Lizzard was pushed past Simon Crossley and made to await detailed interrogation. Farley Richardson was put under warning that he would shortly be questioned in the mess room.

This latest complication weighted the scales against those of the Outcasts who under, Tim Jackson's leadership, were bent on an evening of superior partying. As they stood around letting their general misfortune sink in it was Harry Northwood who came up with a suggestion. 'If we're going to be stuck here for God knows how long, why don't we play a ten-over thrash? It's still daylight.'

The question was first answered by the acting inspector. 'I don't care what you do as long as you stay in sight. You're not yet eliminated from my enquiries.' The expression on Farley Richardson's face did not look in the least bit enthusiastic, but before he could pronounce a veto he was whisked off for interview by Barry Foxdene in the mess room. It was left to Fred Ranger to say 'Why not?'

The double-decker with the contingent of Japanese had just reached the motorway when there was an insistent tapping on the glass panel which separated the driver from the lower saloon. Bill Blimp slid the panel open, an action which seconds later he regretted. It was James Saito and he was the purveyor of bad news. Some of the passengers needed to relieve themselves. Bill Blimp was disposed to argue. The hard shoulder of a motorway was not hospitable to this need. A services area was about twenty miles ahead. There was surely a bucket somewhere on board. James Saito was unimpressed by these observations and said that he could not be responsible for what might happen unless the bus was halted. These words sent a chill through Bill Blimp. He had heard that the Japanese had one or two extreme habits and he did not want anyone doing anything silly on his vehicle. Cursing and swearing he steered the bus on to the hard shoulder by a grassy bank topped by a few trees. 'This'll have to do', he snarled and then lent back in malicious satisfaction, competing with impatience, as the elderly Japanese, desperate enough to overcome their embarrassment, scrambled – with difficulty – up the grassy bank.

There was particular difficulty for a man with a Zimmer frame. He had almost scaled the summit when one of the legs of the frame sank into a hole. The frame reared and toppled back causing its owner to lose his grip and his footing. He slid not ungracefully down the slope to be followed seconds later by the Zimmer frame itself which gave him a sharp blow on the head. Mr Kowisaki was not easily repulsed. Yesterday's hero of three failed kamikaze missions battled once again up the embankment. He almost made it. Unfortunately as he was making the final push one of his travelling companions appeared from the other side and collided with the frame, knocking it out of Mr Kowisaki's grasp. Deprived of its support Mr Kowisaki toppled and slid once again down the slope this time less gracefully and on his back. Confused for a moment he forgot the frame. Seeming almost to be drawn by an invisible cord it reunited with its owner giving him another painful rap.

Whether out of confusion or extreme physical necessity, Mr. Kowisaki declined a third assault on the grassy bank. He had quickly to resolve the tricky question as to facing inwards or outwards. Should he affront his fellow travellers who were returning to the bus or those who had never left it and whose attention had locked on to his travails? He chose the latter. It was the most embarrassing moment of his life made more acute seconds later as the motorway patrol car glided to a halt beside the bus.

Meanwhile a game of cricket was set to begin.

THE TEN-OVER MATCH

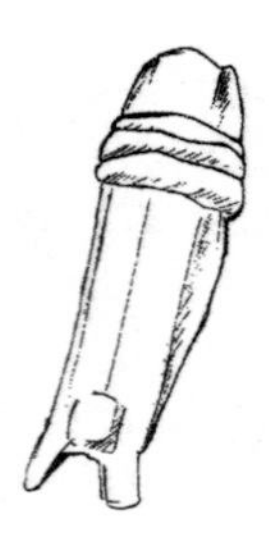

It could not be said that the teams which took to the field in the decline of the day's light were complete in any sense of the word. In a hastily improvised toss of the coin, Winston Jenkins had chosen to bat. Some would have said that this was the obvious decision in order to get the best of the light. If so, it was reinforced by other more pressing considerations. The captain was unsure how many men he actually had at his disposal. The Outcasts were never normally engaged actively in cricket at this hour of the day. Winston Jenkins had felt that another hour without booze might suit his fielding resources better than his batting. He had talked to Jon Palmer and found him up to opening the batting. It had quickly become apparent that this time David Pelham was not ready to accompany him to the crease. As his bowling would be essential later it looked wise to give him maximum time for recovery. And that was it. Winston did not know how many of his pathetically few bowlers would be capable of performing (even to their standard) when it came to the point. He naturally excused himself from this private stricture. The ever-willing and usually more sober Rashid Ali readily agreed to partner Jon Palmer.

When the two openers surveyed the field they quickly recognised that the home team was not without its own problems. No more than nine of them were at the disposal of the stand-in captain, Fred Ranger. Farley Richardson was under interrogation and George Summermore was about his professional business. Doredell's twelfth man, Hugh Smith, in a fit of pique had declared himself unavailable. If he was not reckoned good enough to play in the proper (he had laid emphasis on this word) match, he was dashed if he was going to take part in what he dismissed as a 'farcical frolic'.

Winston Jenkins's own forecast of what was to take place was not so far removed from Hugh Smith's, but he had modified his doubts with the rationalisation that they were stuck for the moment in Doredell and they might as well make the best of it. Yet he continued to doubt whether there would be any 'best' on offer. It was therefore a major surprise when, after three overs, the Outcasts had accumulated fifty runs. This information was conveyed with chalk on a blackboard which Robert Vine had borrowed from the company training school. Such prolific scoring could be explained by a number of factors of which a nine-man fielding side was not immediately the most potent. In the absence on death duty of George Summermore the gloves had been snatched by Kris Vertz. There had been no rush to compete with him.

The Austrian's knowledge of wicket-keeping had been gleaned from no more than observation. He had never previously kept wicket and his performance therefore manifested several early limitations. He had not known that it was good practice to wear inner gloves. So the actual wicket-keeping gloves were loose on his hands and uncomfortable. His spillage rate was disconcerting. The third ball of the innings brought home to him the otherwise unanticipated necessity of wearing abdominal protection. There was a painful pause before the fourth ball of the innings could be delivered. With less than the full complement of fielders, acting captain Fred Ranger was loath to post a long-stop. After twenty-four byes had been conceded he could no longer give Kris Vertz the benefit of the doubt. Wider gaps in the field began to allow punishing shots, but extras continued to keep pace. Jon Palmer and Rashid Ali had scored only fourteen runs between them when the team total reached fifty.

The scorers, Robert Vine and Simon Crossley, had the use of no more than a bench as vantage point. Sophie Crossley wheeled a now sleeping Brian Sachin alongside, the still clinging aroma of hops providing his father with an appreciative longing. Sophie's greeting had a sharp edge to it as her eye was drawn to a reddish-brown smear on the elegant designer polo shirt she had given Simon on his birthday. Scolded, Simon was at a loss to explain the offending mark, but the pained expression of his wife put him under pressure to try to remember where he had been and what he had done. A further burst of scoring – not all from the bat – slowed his power of recollection.

By this time Bill Blimp and his chastened party of Japanese tourists were on their way again. It had been a desperately humiliating encounter with the police officers in the patrol car. Sergeant Brendan Lockitt, who had led the investigation, was not the openly aggressive type often associated with the genre. If anything this made matters worse. Sergeant Lockitt underplayed the whole thing: 'Having a little trouble, sir?' Rightly assuming that the cluster of elderly Japanese might possess minimal English, the sergeant had directed his question to Bill Blimp whom he had reached after a slow (very slow) and deliberate (very deliberate) march around the bus to the driver's cabin. Invited to say what was going on, Bill Blimp's every sentence was repeated slowly and with subtle emphasis by Sergeant Lockitt with sidelong glances to PC Phil O'Goff, his travelling companion, and James Saito who were in attendance. The bus driver was reminded that there were laws covering 'this kind of thing'. Even while uttering this warning, the sergeant had begun to think that securing a successful conviction against a foreign visitor before he departed the country (or this life in the case of Mr Kowisaki) might not be easy. His command of the law was insufficient to be sure whether a charge might lie against the bus company. Sergeant Lockitt had enjoyed his few minutes piling on the agony, but, having sensed diminishing returns, he let them go with the predictable command, 'don't let me catch you doing that again'.

The Outcasts' score continued to mount. Being late in the day it was a case of Fred Ranger and Tom Amwell not at their freshest. For their part Jon Palmer and Rashid Ali had begun to relax. Inhibition left their strokeplay. Behind the stumps Kris Vertz played his own fumbling part in the run-feast which had begun to ensue. After seven overs the score had not quite doubled. The blackboard read ninety-eight. As the bowlers made an extra effort to get their line right so that less reliance could be placed on their keeper, the batsmen were contributing a higher proportion of the runs. No wicket had fallen.

It was not until the seventh over had been bowled that Winston Jenkins made what in the context of the game was an important discovery. He and Fred Ranger had not discussed a limitation on the number of overs to be bowled by any one bowler. Naively Winston had assumed proportionality and had gloomily imagined that five bowlers would each have to send down two overs. By now he had caught up with the fact that Fred Ranger had bowled four and it looked as though Tom Amwell was all set for the same number. In the Outcasts' straitened circumstances this had joyful implications for Winston Jenkins. Whether Fred Ranger had intended to use himself and Tom Amwell for the entire ten overs was not clear for after Jon Palmer had smacked Tom Amwell for six successive boundaries (bringing up his own half-century in the process) there was a change of bowling.

Rather late in the day Fred Ranger remembered the rarely-employed leg-spinner. He had no hang-ups about calling on Adrian Wills to have a bowl. The rarely-employed leg-spinner (Fred Ranger scolded himself for taking so long to recall) had wreaked havoc amongst the Outcasts in their last encounter. Perhaps he might have a similar effect this time. Adrian Wills himself was not so sure. The imperfections of the pitch at the old Doredell cricket ground had assisted him; he was not as confident about the surface at the company's sports ground. Confidence is part of a leg-spinner's armoury. He does not want to see it in his adversaries. Jon Palmer, who had not been part of the Outcasts' team last year, looked in murderously good form. However, Adrian Wills bucked himself up with the realisation that he would be bowling in the first place to Rashid Ali, who on the last occasion had adopted a very defensive approach to him. And after all, he was limited to a mere six balls. His inner reassurance was wholly misplaced.

Had he paid any attention to detail, Bill Blimp would have known that the double-decker's fuel gauge was faulty. There had been a note in his in-tray, but it had been covered by the programme for the boxing tournament. He first registered that the indicator had been sitting on the half-full mark for far too long only half a minute before the engine began to splutter and then cough and finally to die. In serene silence the bus came to a halt on the hard shoulder of the motorway. The cruellest impact was on those passengers who had dozed off. They awoke believing that they might have arrived at the sanctuary of journey's end. The services area was thirteen miles to the north of them. Any alternative source of fuel was a long way to the south. To add insult to injury the double-decker had come to rest just about equidistant between the emergency telephones.

John Furness was in a turmoil. He was confined when, more than anything, he wished to be free. His mood of desperation had been brought on by a chance question from Adrienne Palmer: 'Didn't I see you lurking furtively in the garden centre earlier?' His 'why, were you there?' had led to a complete revision of the interpretation which John had put on the scene he had witnessed. He told himself (but not Adrienne) what a fool he had been. Would the garden centre still be open? Could he still try and catch up with Fern Sadler? What a diabolical situation to be under virtual house arrest on the orders of that preposterous police officer. He cursed the policeman over and over again until at last desperation lubricated the cogs of his brain which had been slowed by the afternoon's imbibing. Police officer. That was it. Now he remembered. Excusing himself from Adrienne's company he retreated into the visitors' changing-room.

The rarely-employed leg-spinner knew that he had pitched his first ball too full and was relieved that Rashid Ali did no more than prod forward in safe defence. The impression given was false. At this level of cricket Rashid Ali was a superb player of spin. He had not had the opportunity to do much against Adrian Wills in the previous contest. He had done no more than inspect him before his unfortunate run-out. The inspection this time was of necessity brief: one delivery and he had to be satisfied. Adrian Wills tried to correct his length, but over-corrected. Rashid Ali went down on one knee and sent the ball soaring over the boundary. Adrian Wills tried again, but was still short. Rashid Ali stepped to leg, waited for the turn (he discounted a wrong'un) and sent the ball crashing through an obliging gap square on the off side. Trying to make up length, Adrian Wills overstepped and was no-balled by Umpire Breakwell in full throat and gesture. Rashid Ali needed no further invitation and executed a handsome on-drive. Inclined to doubt that he had got his run-up wrong, Adrian Wills declined to re-measure it. His reward was another stentorian shout from Syd Breakwell, a straight six from Rashid Ali and a bewildered glare from Fred Ranger. Enforced re-measurement brought no relief – except from the enthusiastic attention of the umpire. Adrian Wills managed two balls of fairly good length and fairly good spin. They were met by a fairly good late cut for four and a fairly good piece of luck when a miscued scoop to leg fell tantalisingly close to Jim Flote who came in from the deep and embarrassingly overran it. The over would have been further extended if the batsman had chosen to disdain the bowler's last delivery which was plainly wide of leg stump and would probably (but not definitely) have been called as such by Syd Breakwell. Instead, Rashid Ali danced towards it and flicked it effortlessly over Jim Flote, who was saved the necessity of moving at all. The over had cost thirty-two runs. The Outcasts had avenged their previous weakness against the rarely-employed leg-spin of Adrian Wills.

'It's blood', announced Simon Crossley, suddenly and loudly to puzzled looks from his wife and Robert Vine. Between recording the spate of boundaries scored by Jon Palmer and Rashid Ali he had been trying to think back to how he could have acquired the disfiguring mark on his polo shirt. He eventually retraced his movements back to expulsion from the score-box when he had brushed past the bandaged, wounded figure of Andy Lizzard. Blood must have been weeping from the bandages. Simon Crossley looked triumphant. At least he was innocent of the charge of carelessness that Sophie might have levelled at him. At the end of the over he whipped off his shirt and took a confirmatory sniff at the stained part. The look of triumph gave way to one of astonishment. Since when had blood smelt like tomato ketchup? Something was very wrong. Whatever this scam was, Simon felt that the police needed to know. Never had he wanted a quicker end to the innings.

This wish was devoutly shared by two others. Fred Ranger was clear that he could not risk Tom Amwell getting another mauling from Jon Palmer and he had no appetite for subjecting himself to similar punishment. Short of taking Kris Vertz from behind the stumps, the only remaining option was Ed Fylder. In the light of earlier events this could be deemed a foolhardy move, but Fred Ranger felt the need for a conciliatory gesture. Yet it was an avowed risk. Fred Ranger's hesitation lasted only as long as it took to notice that Farley Richardson was descending the pavilion steps albeit in the company of a police officer. Ed Fylder was instructed to get on with it. An off-spinner given the chance of a long bowl with a well-placed field is often as good a container of batsmen as any other type of bowler. Neither of these conditions applied and Ed Fylder was soon made to suffer. Fred Ranger suffered alongside him as he felt the glare of a far from patient (or understanding) Farley Richardson from beyond the boundary.

It was a bad start when Jon Palmer miscued and sent the ball to a part of the field which was especially sparsely populated. They ran five. The second ball of the over – Ed Fylder's arm ball – was missed by Rashid Ali, who was possibly out of breath, and also by Kris Vertz, who had no such excuse. They collected three byes. A full toss went for four and a short ball got similar treatment. Driven by despair and yet much to his credit, Ed Fylder rallied with a ball spot on length from which Jon Palmer could scramble only a single. The final ball erred on the side of full. Rashid Ali drove. The bowler dived. The ball was stopped. No run was taken. The Outcasts' innings closed on 171. Grimacing with pain, Ed Fylder was surrounded by team-mates congratulating him on a brilliant piece of fielding. It was uncertain whether their over-enthusiastic handshakes or his fielding effort caused the broken fingers which a hospital visit later confirmed.

Farley Richardson was not under arrest, but he had been left with the impression by Acting Inspector Barry Foxdene that he was within an ace of attaining that status. The only reason for delaying the formality was the acting inspector's inability to identify the exact offence which might form the basis of a charge. Barry Foxdene was not without his suspicions. His problem was that there were too many of them. He had ended his interview with Farley Richardson by detailing one of his constables to stick with the suspect like glue. The order had been meticulously observed. Farley Richardson had been refused permission by his police escort to re-enter the field of play even though two extra fielders at that juncture might have been a crucially beneficial boost to the Doredell cause.

There had been a minor dispute between John Furness and Dean Faulds about a fortnight before the match (and party) in Doredell.

For fancy dress, both had opted to go as policemen. Over a seven-pint session at the Sink and Plumber they had resolved their differences. The clinching argument was that Dean's elder brother was actually a police officer with a southern county force and was prepared to lend Dean his uniform whilst coincidentally he would be on leave. John, it was finally agreed, would be in the guise of a burglar 'under arrest'. All this had come flooding back as John had pined for an escape route from the cricket ground. The police uniform was hanging on a coat hanger above Dean's bag. The flat cap (fortunately not a helmet) was in the bag. Dean, he had established, being next man in, was engrossed in watching the fireworks of the Rashid Ali/Jon Palmer batting partnership. After a quick change, John Furness looked to the manner born. The absence of handcuffs, baton and radio was made up for by the presence of sergeant's stripes. With the number of police officers swarming around John was unnoticed and his authority easily carried him through the cordon at the factory gates leading into Hayste. His pace then accelerated towards the garden centre.

Bill Blimp and James Saito had argued as to which of them would walk to the nearest emergency telephone. Consequently Bill Blimp was accelerating grumpily and gaspingly towards his objective. He had gambled twice and lost. Despite James Saito arguing that, as a Japanese speaker, he was the one who should stay to look after the passengers, Bill Blimp had insisted that they should toss for it. He lost. The next question was whether the nearer telephone was north or south of where they were. Again the coin decided it. After fifteen minutes – Bill Blimp was not a fit man – it was clear that James Saito had been right. No one was around to hear the language Bill Blimp used when he found that the phone had been vandalised.

Dramatic events occurred between innings. The thrust of Acting Inspector Barry Foxdene's investigation had to be reassessed and assessed again. The assimilation of Simon Crossley's information led to a detachment of four police officers being ordered to sniff the bandages of Andy Lizzard. This bizarre exercise confirmed the suspicion that all was not what it had at first seemed. Overriding blustering protests that a doctor had to be present, Barry Foxdene removed the eye patch and saw an eye which showed signs of bruising, but was otherwise undamaged. He snatched the crutches. Andy Lizzard did not have the wit to collapse; he instinctively steadied himself. Then Barry Foxdene gave the order that the bandages should be unwound. The final effect of what was revealed could not persuade even Barry Foxdene that he was faced with a man who had been a victim of international terrorism. Refusing to accept that sundry bruises and cuts had been inflicted by management ('I shall listen to no more of your lies'), Barry Foxdene arrested Andy Lizzard for wasting police time. After prompting by one of his colleagues, he agreed with a trace of reluctance that Farley Richardson might now be eliminated from the enquiry.

Barry Foxdene was not happy. Andy Lizzard was a poor bag for the large-scale operation he had initiated. He could not see any connection between this fraudster and the death of the Japanese visitor. The only lead he had so far was the prejudicial language of Cranley Nice. He marched back to the umpires' room where he found a Cranley Nice who was by now incandescent with rage over his continued detention. In his business life the force of his position, supplemented not infrequently by bombast, had usually ensured that he had got his way. A torrent of abuse fell upon Barry Foxdene, but this did no more than strengthen him in his suspicions that he was dealing with a man who could be provoked to the extremes of violence. It was therefore extremely unwise of Cranley Nice to react to the acting inspector's resumption of questioning about the dead Japanese with a raging rant to the effect that all members of that race could go to hell as far as he was concerned. Determined to have something to show for his efforts Barry Foxdene thereupon arrested him and charged him with murder.

The other dramatic event of the ten-minute interval was the repossession of the captaincy of the Doredell side by Farley Richardson. He began by making a decision which could perhaps be justified on orthodox cricket grounds (Farley Richardson would later make some such claim), namely form. Yet arguably with an asking rate of seventeen an over the situation called for a pinch hitter. Of this genre Fred Ranger had given a recent and powerful demonstration. But Farley Richardson was not keen on handing any glory to Fred Ranger and so he was out. George Summermore, being on body-gathering detail, was also out. Ray Beckett had disappointed. So it was with some surprise, especially in the latter case, that Jim Flote and Adrian Wills received the news that they were to open the innings together. Farley Richardson was obviously unaware of the non-cricketing sub-text of the earlier Doredell innings.

There had been an intruder. Connie Stillmarch was in no doubt about that. Brandy had not dulled her senses to that extent. She had returned home, entering by the front door, and at first nothing seemed amiss. It was only when she reached the kitchen that she knew something was wrong. The net curtains were swinging in the breeze. Connie then noticed that the window was very slightly ajar. She was certain that she had left it firmly shut. With a cry she rushed to check her porcelain collection in the living room and her jewellery box in the bedroom. Both were intact and there was no other sign of disturbance. Connie Stillmarch was not easily panicked, but her anxiety level had risen in the wake of the death and the presence in the village of the Japanese, who, despite their age, she distrusted. Armed with a poker she checked behind every door and satisfied herself that there was no one lurking. Perhaps after all she had not shut her window firmly enough. Everything seemed absolutely in order. Connie Stillmarch calmed down, but instead of making a cup of tea, she poured herself a large glass of sherry. It was not brandy, but it would have to do. What she had not done was to examine closely the kitchen window-frame or check the contents of her wardrobe. The extra brandy had had some effect after all.

Bill Blimp's day had not improved. His choice was between walking back northwards towards the bus (and the possible scorn of James Saito) and advancing towards the south in search of the next emergency telephone. He chose the latter and was within distant sight of a telephone column when there was an odd sequence of events. A familiar police patrol car passed by on the northbound carriageway. He thought that he detected a wave in his direction. A few seconds later he thought that he also detected the engagement of a siren, but it could have been his imagination. The reason why it was probably not his imagination made itself clear with the blast of the horn and a screech of the brakes as James Saito brought the double-decker to a halt within feet of its owner.

In contrast Farley Richardson felt that his day was improving. The fact that his employer had been charged with murder (the story was spreading like a bush fire) had not darkened his mood. He was sure that such an absurd suggestion would be dismissed as readily as the accusation, never properly specified, against himself. No, Farley Richardson's satisfaction stemmed from witnessing the apparent chaos into which his cricketing opponents had descended. He was growing in confidence that the afternoon's defeat was going to be avenged. Ignoring the unequal nature of the contest he at least would get some pleasure from such an outcome.

Winston Jenkins had taken the field followed only by seven other members of the team. The first disappointment was Ray Burrill's refusal to play. He had suffered a relapse. To help his team-mates and impress his new-found girlfriend (probably in reverse order of priority) he had made a supreme effort to bowl his overs in the main match. But the pain had come back. When he examined his leg the wound looked angry. Gone was the balanced judgement of a veterinarian (admittedly one of only recent vintage) and back in full force was the fear of the hypochondriac whose imagination ran the full gamut through amputation, rabies and death. Limping, he longed for comfort, but not the comfort which came from bowling a man out.

The second disappointment was that David Pelham was paralytic. He had become sufficiently desperate for a drink that he had been prepared to put the Shane Bott confession to the test. It transpired that he had taken a small beaker from the changing room and scooped a sample from the funtub. He had regarded this as a controlled experiment but as he lacked a control sample it was difficult to tell whether or not the beer had been adulterated. David Pelham had been so unsure that it was evident, when discovered, that he had consumed many a beaker full. Winston Jenkins was furious, but at least paid David Pelham the compliment that Shane Bott must have told a mischievous lie, for an Outcast would (hopefully) never have drunk bad bitter.

The third disappointment was the absence of John Furness, whose disappearance apparently had no witnesses. The final disappointment was the point-blank refusal of the twelfth man, Tim Jackson, to do what a twelfth man was meant to do in the circumstances. He was still lording it in his white dinner jacket, practising his Noël Coward voice. 'No, dear boy, I couldn't possibly play. Perspiration is so vulgar, don't you think?' Winston Jenkins did not answer. Had the match mattered, his reaction might have been different, but he reckoned he knew what Brian Close would have thought of a ten-over thrash.

The two consolations which Winston Jenkins carried on to the field with him were that the other side was not at full strength either and that he could reckon (rely would have been too strong a word) on himself and Phil Cole to bowl the whole ten overs. Such hopes were bordering on the desperate. The sight of Jim Flote and Adrian Wills approaching the middle was also a cause for encouragement in view of how they had reacted when last they batted together. The encouragement was to be no more than momentary. To avenge the honour of Doredell the two openers had agreed a truce. In any case one look at the depleted ranks of the fielding side had convinced them that the runs could be got in boundaries without much need for running between the wickets.

Winston Jenkins bowled the first over. He felt reasonably in the groove and his line was generally good. It did not prevent him being struck for three boundaries. He told himself that this was below the asking rate. If Doredell scored only at this rate, the Outcasts should achieve a comfortable win. His confidence persisted through the next over, bowled by Phil Cole to Adrian Wills, as again it cost no more than three boundaries. When Winston Jenkins' second over yielded only ten runs to the batting side the Outcasts' captain allowed himself to think that they were getting on top. His belief survived another over from Phil Cole even though it had contained two very short balls which Adrian Wills had hooked for six, another boundary all along the ground and four leg-byes. With half the overs bowled the Doredell score had advanced to seventy-five. Jim Flote had begun to perfect the art of placement. He found five routes to the boundary which were not obstructed by a fielder. For the last ball of his over, in a mix of luck and exasperation, Winston Jenkins had produced an excellent yorker. Jim Flote managed to stab down on it. As no fieldsman was remotely close he called Adrian Wills for a single, saying as they crossed, 'You might like a go at this bloke'.

Surprise, relief and then rising anger were the emotions with which Bill Blimp greeted James Saito, who jumped down from the driver's cab of the double-decker with a broad grin on his face. Bill Blimp had not expected to be rescued by his own bus. The reason for the resumption of its journey was the discovery by James Saito of two jerry-cans of diesel in a compartment under the stairs, put there as a precaution by Bill Blimp's son, without telling anyone else in the firm. Highly pleased with himself James Saito had tried his hand at bus-driving. By the time he reached the lonely, plodding figure of Bill Blimp he had begun to get the hang of it, eliminating the early jerks in the motion which had induced sickness in a couple of the passengers.

Bill Blimp's success in suppressing his anger owed everything to panic. He put to the back of his mind James Saito's lack of a licence to drive such a vehicle. He doused his suspicion that the tour guide had probably not overcome the effects of some earlier drinking. In a blinding flash (which for him was a rare event) Bill Blimp realised that the police in the patrol car had seen him and then seen the bus being driven obviously not by him. Having already carried out an inspection as to who was on the bus, a police officer of average intelligence (the sardonic sergeant fitted the bill) might well be inclined to think that there had been only one licensed driver aboard. This was, of course, conjecture, but it was sufficiently plausible for Bill Blimp to reckon that they should move off at speed and leave the motorway by the next exit before the patrol car reached a junction enabling it to head south. He hit the throttle with such force that diesel fumes pervaded the interior prompting several more of the passengers to succumb to sickness.

The garden centre was closed. Strangely early, thought John Furness, whose own family business would still be trading whilst daylight remained – and even beyond in the high season. There was not a flicker of light or movement within the building. Apart from three liveried vans there were no vehicles in the staff car park. John Furness cursed his lost opportunity, the more vehemently for the ingenuity he had had to employ to try to retrieve the situation. In dejection he turned back into the main street where he was immediately embraced by a complete stranger, who was found to be male, elderly and Japanese. So omnipresent had Japanese people reportedly been since the Outcasts' arrival in Doredell that John Furness made a mental note to check whether some cult had headquartered itself in a country mansion in the area. The thought was not entirely extinguished by three decipherable words which the stranger uttered: Ebihara, escape, death. John Furness had not succeeded in making much sense of these when Mr Ashoki Ebihara sank to his knees and sobbed: 'Save me'. It was a cry shortly to be echoed by his compatriots elsewhere.

The sixth over of the Doredell innings was eventful. In striving for extra pace with his fourth ball, Phil Cole strained a muscle in his side. The search for a faster ball had been prompted by the fate which had befallen the first three of the over. They had been thrashed by Jim Flote for six, four and six respectively. The fourth might have suffered similarly if the batsman had not been distracted by the sight of the bowler pulling up in pain. Whilst Winston Jenkins and his other team-mates gathered around Phil Cole with sympathetic attention the silver sports car reappeared. The lady driver ran into the pavilion. ' I wonder what she wants', said Jim Flote, who had obviously not seen her earlier visit to the ground. He added, when he saw Rashid Ali, who had stayed behind the stumps, looking at him quizzically, 'we don't often see the boss's wife on site, especially if there's cricket going on.' 'But', said Rashid Ali, 'I thought it was ...' And then each learnt something which they had not previously known. Before Rashid Ali could share his thoughts with Adrian Wills the over was resumed.

Although suffering, Phil Cole had sportingly agreed to stay on the field, but he could not bowl – not even underarm he had muttered in response to a discreet enquiry from Winston Jenkins. There was no alternative but to summon Greg Roberts to continue the over by bowling the two outstanding deliveries. In fact it took Greg four attempts to complete the task as two wides were interspersed with two long-hops. The second was less costly than the first. The charitable view was that it was fielded by Boris Wigmouth (aka Kevin Newton). More accurately it was blocked as Boris/Kevin had his back to proceedings at the moment of impact. The score had advanced to ninety-nine, Doredell's most productive over to date.

When he had been confined to the pavilion earlier John Furness had become vaguely aware that at the root of the commotion was the death of a person unknown, but probably Japanese. He now found himself almost umbilically linked to someone who fitted this description and was babbling about escaping death. Mr Ebihara's choice of words from his extremely limited English vocabulary may have accurately reflected his experience (or rather his imagination), but it permitted an interpretation which was to produce a remarkable reaction. Having been conveyed while he slumbered (in the shelter of the coach which had originally brought him to Doredell), Mr Ebihara awoke in the yard belonging to the Bilsdon brothers. The next-door premises were operated by a car breaker. The first sight which met Mr Ebihara's bleary eyes as he peered through the window of the coach was the crusher, the grabber hook and a pile of squashed metal objects. The fact that there was no actual activity at this hour on a Saturday was not a detail taken in by Mr Ebihara. The picture told its own story and it was not one of which he wished to be part. He stumbled off the coach and fled the yard at the best speed he could manage. He was both a bundle of joy and distress when he ran into what he judged to be the safe arms of the law.

At the start of the seventh over Winston Jenkins still clung to the belief that seventy-three more runs off (hopefully) no more than twenty-four balls was too big an ask. By the end of the over he was much less sure. In truce the two batsmen might be, but it did not eliminate the inner desire of Adrian Wills to outscore his partner. For so late in the day and in the light of the heavy punishment he had suffered there was much to admire in the steadiness of Winston Jenkins' fourth over. The trouble was that it was bowled to a batsman prepared to take risks and who was confronted with an under-manned field. Using his feet Adrian Wills cut and drove well wide of the fielders. His fifth shot in any case made them redundant as it sailed high over the boundary. During the delay whilst the ball was retrieved, Rashid Ali acquainted Adrian Wills with the information which had emerged from his exchange with Jim Flote. He was surprised by the reaction he received. 'I know', said Adrian Wills. But then Rashid Ali added something which plainly Adrian Wills did not know. The batsman was still cogitating when he pushed the last ball of the over for a gentle single, but he remembered to say to Jim Flote in mid-run, 'thanks, I enjoyed that'. Rashid Ali was left to speculate.

By now Winston Jenkins had a sense of déjà vu; once more he must rely on Greg Roberts. Fifty runs off eighteen balls in the ordinary way would be a very tall order. Things were far from ordinary though, Winston Jenkins reminded himself, when twelve of those balls had to be bowled by good old Greg. At this point the number of fielders at his disposal was augmented. Put to shame by Phil Cole's example, a limping Ray Burrill returned to the field almost dragging with him David Pelham, whom moments earlier he had kicked into wakefulness (naturally remembering to use his uninjured leg). Winston Jenkins admired the gesture, but doubted whether it outweighed the risks attached to Greg's bowling. This was by far his most realistic judgement of the day.

Those Outcasts who had seen the most of Greg Roberts's bowling were ready to say that he had done well to restrict the cost of the eighth over of the innings to fourteen runs. He was helped by two poor decisions from Syd Breakwell. Most umpires would have adjudged the third and fifth balls of the over to be wides. The batsman certainly did and was successively dismayed and outraged when this particular umpire did not. Those Outcasts who had seen the most of Syd Breakwell's umpiring had grown accustomed to the guilelessly uneven nature of his judgement. What no one knew was that on this occasion an aggravating factor was present. Not expecting a further duty turn, Syd Breakwell at close of play had enjoyed several cups of his favourite Darjeeling tea from the flask which his wife had supplied. It was a treat to which he had looked forward. It had now quite suddenly become a source of discomfort; and not only physical discomfort, for Syd had begun to fear that he might be facing the onset of prostate trouble. His concentration had thereby suffered, to Greg Roberts' advantage.

The break-out from Summersley Prison had taken place in the late afternoon. It was not until its full extent had been determined by the prison authorities that local police forces were alerted. The Divisional Commander eventually reached Acting Inspector Barry Foxdene and enquired acidly what he was doing 'frigging around' in Doredell with half the police force of two counties when there were dangerous criminals on the run. Having been faced in quick succession by Mrs Cranley Nice, John Furness and Ashoki Ebihara, a deflated Barry Foxdene was asking himself the same question. He had begun to wilt under the verbal assault of Mrs Nice who demanded to know the precise reason why her husband was being held on some ridiculous charge. His explanation had not been going too well when he was presented with a person answering to the exact description of the deceased. Mr Ebihara repeated for the Acting Inspector's benefit the few words of English which had seemed to stand him in good stead with John Furness: escape, death, save me. One word formed in Barry Foxdene's mind: Lazarus. It was the nearest he had come to believing in the supernatural. Then his mind went back to the body in the maze. Who had actually pronounced the man dead? Not a doctor. Not himself. Only the undertaker, but he could have been mistaken. To Barry Foxdene one elderly Japanese gentleman looked much like any other. The more fanciful ideas he had previously entertained suddenly deserted him. There had been a misunderstanding, but all was now well. Making a mental note to build as serious a case as he could manage against Andy Lizzard, his one detainee, Barry Foxdene executed a swift and total police withdrawal from Doredell. The situation he left behind was soon far from well.

Tim Jackson's first thought was that now he could achieve an Outcasts' withdrawal from Doredell every bit as swift and total as Barry Foxdene's. For some of them a party beckoned and there was no time to lose. He wanted the match stopped immediately. The only man who would willingly have agreed with him was Syd Breakwell. In all other directions he received strong resistance. The players had their teeth into the match. So too had the remaining spectators who had had no choice but to watch eighteen overs. The biff-bang nature of proceedings had kept them amused – now they wanted to see the climax. Farley Richardson, scenting victory and revenge, grabbed Tim Jackson and quietened him down. The nineteenth over began.

The double-decker had finally reached journey's end. This turned out to be under a railway bridge in north-east London and not the Bayswater Road where the tourists' hotel was situated. Prudently, having left the motorway, Bill Blimp had stopped to refuel. The first filling station which had presented itself was one which had experienced a recent make-over. Its huge forecourt was flanked by a shop which might have rivalled a small department store. As Bill Blimp busied himself at the pump the Japanese, recognising at last a glimpse of restored civilisation, descended on the shop in search of retail therapy. What should have been no more than a ten-minute stopover extended to over half an hour. This had given precious time to Sergeant Lockitt, whose tenacity Bill Blimp had been right to suspect, to pick up the trail. As Bill Blimp eased the bus back into the stream of traffic his eye caught a flashing blue light somewhere to the rear. He did not know this part of London like the back of his hand and so there was a risk in taking evasive action. Nor did he keep in the front of his mind the height of the vehicle he was driving. He was too busy finding a direction to follow to notice the height of the bridge ahead. The two did not match. There was the ghastly sound of the scraping of metal against metal. This had barely ceased when screams of terror flooded the bus from those who had chosen to ride on the upper deck. Seconds later the whole scene was illuminated in the headlights of Sergeant Lockitt's patrol car.

The light was also fading in Doredell where Jim Flote was facing up to Winston Jenkins. This helped to balance the contest between bat and ball although after only ten runs had come from the over Winston Jenkins did claim that he had deliberately bowled a full length. Neither batsman was able to find the boundary and the strike kept changing. Pad as well as bat became the source of runs. At this critical stage of the game it had proved to be a better over for the Outcasts than for the home team. Doredell had the daunting task of scoring twenty-six off the final over if they were to win the match. This was more than they had managed to accumulate in any previous over of this mad-dash thrash. The balancing factor in this instance was that the over had to be bowled by Greg Roberts. Adrian Wills savoured the prospect.

Greg Roberts, frankly, did not. He was sure that he was not the man for the occasion. Was there no one else who could bowl the over, he enquired of Winston Jenkins? He knew the answer before he had finished putting the question. The credible alternatives even to him were handicapped to one degree or another. He at least, he was reminded by Winston for the umpteenth time, was the most sober among them. By now he wished that he wasn't. But Greg knew that he too was handicapped – by disbelief in his ability to perform at all reliably as a bowler. 'Try to pitch it up', advised Winston in an attempt to add force to what he had claimed on behalf of his own bowling. Greg nodded wisely, but despondently. The result was a first ball which was very nearly a beamer.

Four ambulances, three fire tenders and several police vehicles ringed the stricken double-decker and its even more stricken passengers. The emergency services had arrived in force. Bill Blimp was under interrogation. The Japanese – those who were not already strapped to stretchers – were useless as witnesses in the absence of an interpreter. And the on-board interpreter was absent. Yet again that day James Saito had managed to do a disappearing act. Even before the first hysterical tourist had been rescued he had found his way into a back-street pub, the Dirty Moon, and lowered a pint of stout. It would be the first of many as he tried to obliterate the memory of his nightmare day. Bill Blimp's memories would remain with him for a long time. Meanwhile all train services on the busy line supported by the bridge had been suspended for safety reasons. The ban on movements would not be lifted for four days causing widespread disruption of commuter and mainline services. A rumour spread amongst the travelling (or non-travelling) public that the bridge had been disabled by a Japanese terrorist ram-raid. It was a story which put-upon rail companies were curiously slow to deny.

Adrian Wills had felt that there would be easy pickings from Greg Roberts's bowling. It would provide him with the opportunity to win the match for his team. He could also out-score his partner (each had sixty-nine runs to his credit) and that would be an additional source of satisfaction. He had already formulated a plan. To overcome deeply defensive field-placings he would employ what cricket commentators frequently referred to as the aerial route. If twenty-six runs were to be scored from six balls, discounting the possibility of wides, he would need to clear the boundary at least once in any case. Adrian Wills felt more than equal to the task.

Having a ball heading towards his chest at a speed not previously associated with Greg Roberts's bowling produced momentary indecision in the batsman. Adrian Wills failed to react quickly enough when it was clear that no intervention would be forthcoming from the umpire. He stabbed down on the ball and, almost transfixed, watched it trickle down the pitch. Approaching more swiftly from the opposite direction was Jim Flote with a cry of 'come on'. Belatedly Adrian Wills stirred and got himself safely to the other end where he smarted at his failure. The task facing Doredell, as he glumly realised, had become a whole lot harder. At least three sixes were now required if twenty-five runs were to be scored from five balls. There was an early sign that Greg Roberts was ready to oblige. Continuing to follow the advice he had received from Winston Jenkins, he strove for a full length and produced two successive full tosses which Jim Flote drove back high and straight for six apiece. It would have taxed Greg Roberts' consistency too far to expect him to produce three like deliveries in a row in his current rattled state. The fourth ball of the over introduced variety. It was short and pitched outside off stump. Taking a leaf out of England star Michael Vaughan's book, Jim Flote pulled it brutally for a low flat six over deep mid-wicket. This brought the score to one hundred and sixty-five. Seven more runs were needed. Captain and bowler went into discussion. Syd Breakwell shifted from one foot to the other as his discomfort increased. Would this match never end?

At the Pink Pedlar Geraint Poppledown was asking himself the same question. On Saturday night he would expect to be busy, especially after a cricket match. He would need his partner behind the bar with him. So far there was no sign of either Haydn Bliss or thirsty customers. Geraint Poppledown had been sheltered from any sign of the heavy police presence in and about the village, information unlikely to have been imparted by the four youths hovering round the pool table in the public bar. The publican had charitably assumed that they were all eighteen although he could only be sure of it in the case of two familiar faces. His lounge bar was empty but for a complete stranger. She was tucked into a far corner with her head down in the remains of a morning newspaper. Unless she had more than a pint of bitter and a packet of pork scratchings, Geraint Poppledown reckoned that she wouldn't even be covering the cost of his electricity.

All the advice showered upon him was not a lot of good to Greg Roberts. Any last vestige of confidence had been removed by Jim

Flote's assault. His morale was the lower for realising that it was down to him that the match, however unimportant it might be, was slipping away from the Outcasts. A glimpse at the exuberance of Farley Richardson beyond the boundary further depressed him. His mind was a jumble as he served up his fifth ball. It was another full toss and was plainly going down the leg side. Jim Flote could have left it alone and collected the extra on the assumption that reliance could be placed on Umpire Breakwell. However, he had seen enough to doubt that and in any case he was on an adrenalin rush. With a huge swing of the bat he sent the ball sailing over the boundary. The scores were level.

After a few moments it became clear that the ball was lost. Actually it had hit the ground close to Shane Bott. The apprentice vandal, nursing his disappointment that at least one of the cricketers had called his bluff over the beer in the funtub, was on the look-out for alternative ways of doing mischief. Pinching the ball seemed a smashing ploy. He got a great deal of pleasure from watching the players come off the field in increasing numbers to join the search. If he had hoped that his action would have a major effect on the match, he would have been right, but not in the way he might have imagined. What is more, at his age and capacity for learning he would never have heard of the expression that it is an ill wind that blows nobody any good.

The first beneficiary of the interruption to play was Syd Breakwell. Muttering that it might be as well to get a spare ball from the pavilion (although he actually had one in his pocket), he left the arena at speed. His return some minutes later with a box of balls coincided with the abandonment of the search. Winston Jenkins, Greg Roberts and the batsmen grouped around him to supervise the selection of a replacement ball. It was an exercise in the blind leading the blind. All the balls in the box looked much the same. Having regained his poise and authority, Syd Breakwell took matters into his own hand and made the decision. As the balls had been passing from hand to hand no one noticed that his choice had fallen on one from out of his pocket. It happened that this ball was different from the rest in one important particular.

Ten minutes had been lost. In this time there had been a further loss of light. This had not been matched by any loss of anticipation on the part of Farley Richardson. Greg Roberts could see his grinning face. He frowned and his grip on the ball tightened. With only one run needed for Doredell to win the match Winston Jenkins chose to bring the fielders in close to cut off the single. In view of what had gone before this might have seemed a pointless strategy. With Greg Roberts in his present unfortunate groove it might be more likely that the ball would be struck to distant parts with even the (remote) possibility of a boundary-edge catch. The astute captain might have compromised with a half-in, half-out field setting. As it happened it made not one whit of difference.

It was long talked about afterwards among the Outcasts as the finest ball ever bowled by Greg Roberts. True, it did not have a great many rivals for the accolade. Someone said that there had been a really mean look on Greg's face as he ran up to bowl. If you are a poor bowler with usually little command over line and length, it is inevitable that you will spray the ball around and pay a heavy price, especially against batsmen of any competence. Yet it also has to be reckoned that once in a while, amid the dross, a passably good ball will appear. With this key delivery Greg Roberts, having had time to compose himself, got his direction right. The ball was just short of a length. Jim Flote wound himself up with the intention of doing no more than chip it over the ring of fielders. But then something happened. As the ball pitched it seamed and leapt, missing bat and gloves and only narrowly missing Jim Flote's head. Rashid Ali, who stood up to bowling of Greg Roberts's pace, rose like a salmon, with his arm extended. The ball ended in his left glove and the match ended in a tie.

Compliments were exchanged and the umpires thanked. The Outcasts dallied in congratulation. Greg Roberts was mobbed for providing them with unexpected deliverance. Though the match had not really mattered, it was pleasing to have avoided defeat. The umpires collected the stumps and Syd Breakwell retrieved the ball. As he returned it to his pocket he could not help noticing how, when he was fretting, he must have inadvertently picked at the seam. Had he but known it Winston Jenkins could once again have reflected that both the hour and the man had come.

One person who had not dallied was Adrian Wills. Suppressing his frustration with the outcome of the game, he raced off towards the pavilion where there was some unfinished business to be settled.

OUTCASTS

Palmer	not out	69
Rashid Ali	not out	51
Faulds	did not bat	
Jenkins	did not bat	
Cole	did not bat	
Burrill	did not bat	
Northwood	did not bat	
Newton	did not bat	
Roberts	did not bat	
Furness	a.w.o.l.	
Pelham	could not bat	
Extras		51
TOTAL	**(for 0 wicket)**	**171**

Bowling	**o**	**m**	**r**	**w**
Ranger	4	1	32	0
Amwell	4	0	43	0
Wills	1	0	32	0
Fylder	1	0	14	0

DOREDELL

Flote	not out	93
Wills	not out	70
Tiller	did not bat	
Bliss	did not bat	
Beckett	did not bat	
Vertz	did not bat	
Fylder	did not bat	
Ranger	did not bat	
Amwell	did not bat	
Richardson	absent	
Summermore	absent	
Extras		8
TOTAL	**(for 0 wicket)**	**171**

Bowling	**o**	**m**	**r**	**w**
Jenkins	5	0	74	0
Cole	2.4	0	44	0
Roberts	2.2	0	47	0

Match tied

END-GAME

By the time the Outcasts returned to the pavilion there was a healthy row in progress. It seemed that Mrs Cranley Nice had been tackled aggressively by Adrian Wills. The question 'what the hell are you up to?' was regularly repeated as he tore into her in a voice which became ever more shrill. The revelation that Mrs Cranley Nice was formerly Mrs Jack Jamieson was a fascinating item of news to those local people who were in earshot. The number grew as Adrian Wills's voice rose through the octaves. The joining together in matrimony of the ex-Mrs Jamieson and Cranley Nice, having taken place in a discreet and dignified ceremony in a jacuzzi in the Cayman Islands, had unsurprisingly escaped coverage in the local press. Until this moment the former Mrs Jamieson had been no more than a name to the villagers. Rumoured (incorrectly) to have had complicity in Jack Jamieson's pyrotechnic escapades, she had been popularly referred to as 'Mrs Cinders'. However it was not her identity, but her duplicity, which was the cause of Adrian Wills's rage.

When they had first met, Cranley Nice had been flattered by the attentions of Mrs Jack Jamieson. She had researched her subject thoroughly before friends had conveniently brought them together at a dinner party. Her pursuit of him thereafter had been subtle but relentless. Cranley Nice enjoyed the company of women and he soon fell under her spell. Before she let herself succumb to his proposal of marriage she had (she believed) done a deal. She had made Cranley Nice aware of her interest in her old but now ruined home. She was sparing with the details, especially the fact that she had never actually spent a night under its roof, the roof never having been there long enough for the fulfilment of this purpose. So it had become an engagement promise. Once they were married, she was assured, her new husband would set out to acquire the Longbirch estate and help her to reconstruct a country mansion. Making it crystal clear that a substantial token of his good faith would not come amiss, she persuaded Cranley Nice to deposit a six-figure sum in her bank account.

Not long after acquiring the former Mrs Jamieson, Cranley Nice in a fortuitous business move acquired Fingerbarrows Flavours. More than the promptings of his wife then gave him cause to become familiar with the exact location of the Longbirch estate, its setting – and its potential. He smelt profit (huge profit) and knew at once that he would not be honouring his promise. He loved his wife, but there was love and there was business. For her part Mrs Cranley Nice sensed a shift in her husband's priorities. It was this realisation which led her to Adrian Wills.

After due process the seat of Doredell on the Vale of Widdle District Council had been declared vacant following the extended absence of Casper Fulworth. (His letter of resignation, which he had failed to stamp, had been declared lost by the Royal Mail.) Within twenty-four hours of this announcement Jim Flote had issued a press release declaring his candidacy in the forthcoming by-election. He proposed to stand as an Independent on a platform which he described as 'bringing Doredell gently into the twenty-first century'. In carefully crafted language he talked of 'tasteful progress to enrich our rural community' and 'bringing much needed facilities for young and old'. He implied that Doredell had been singularly deprived as a consequence of decisions taken by councillors elsewhere in the district for whom Doredell was 'a faraway place of which they knew nothing'. Jim Flote's statement was a masterpiece of generality painting a picture of bounty whilst offering no specific policies. It therefore had huge vote-gathering potential. Suspecting its provenance Adrian Wills had determined to provide local electors with a choice. He presented himself as the candidate of tradition and stability. The two lines to this effect which she had gleaned from the *North West Essex Trumpeter* were much more to the taste of Mrs Cranley Nice, who saw the Flote manifesto as a cloak for unbridled development which could engulf the Longbirch estate.

This was how she came to share a fragment of her past history exclusively with Adrian Wills. She wanted to engage his sympathy and to offer discreet but generous support for his campaign. She had presented herself as a woman whose home had been torn from her and who nursed the nostalgic wish to reclaim the Longbirch estate and restore it to its former glory. This, she maintained, was a more appropriate course of action than exposing the site to large-scale housing development, which, she darkly hinted, could be the effect of his opponent's approach. Adrian Wills needed little persuading on the latter point, because he was convinced that Jim Flote was in the pocket of the new owner of the spice factory. However, this begged the question as to the apparent rift between husband and wife. It was here that tears had assisted Mrs Nice's case. Mr Nice, she told Adrian Wills, just did not understand. He was inclined to put profit before sentiment. That certainly figured, Adrian Wills had thought, and so, encouraged by Mrs Nice, he had accepted her shilling and agreed to make the preservation of the estate a feature of his campaign.

Unfortunately no such exclusive briefing had taken place when Mrs Cranley Nice, like her husband before her, had undergone a change of heart. It was a chance meeting with an estate agent from north Essex at an art gallery preview in London which had set her thoughts racing. They had later dined together and that had settled it. On second acquaintance she had found him insufferable, but a mine of useful information. Without, she hoped, letting him read her mind she saw dangling before her a profit of such magnitude that she could leave Cranley Nice far behind her. Cruise ships, exotic locations and sun-tanned young men beckoned. With the help of the betrothal nest-egg she thought she knew exactly the right strategy to select. What she did not know was that the estate agent reckoned that he had read her mind. He had noticed how her eyes had betrayed her when he had mentioned one particular type of development for which the Longbirch estate might be suitable.

The unravelling of this web of deceit and its accompanying recriminations was taking place before an attentive and growing audience in the cricket pavilion. Not the least attentive member of it was Cranley Nice. He was slow to recover his poise after the lifting of the murder charge and the sudden appearance of his wife whom he had supposed to be at home. From what he had initially been inclined to dismiss as no more than the demented rantings of a disgruntled and disloyal member of staff he began to detect a disturbing drift. He found himself taking up with his wife the question posed so insistently by Adrian Wills: 'What the hell are you up to?'

The answer was supplied by Ray Burrill. 'What she is up to is her neck in a development deal bigger than yours.' This was true but Ray could not resist gilding the lily, based on a hint he had picked up from the estate agent's daughter. 'She's only planning a ruddy theme park.' The change in colour of Mrs Cranley Nice's complexion – perhaps as she saw her dream disintegrating – showed how inspired Ray's allegation had been. She went red whilst her husband went white – with fury. What had begun as a row matured into pandemonium. The two main protagonists (Adrian Wills had now been sidelined) were practically spitting at each other. The locals, in small shocked groups, quizzed Ray Burrill, Tim Jackson, Rashid Ali and the other Outcasts. The only person detached from the proceedings was poor Mr Ashoki Ebihara. He sat in a corner bemused and thinking to himself that he had seen enough in one day to be able to rewrite the history of the British.

It was impossible for the whole of the story to emerge in the atmosphere which prevailed in the sports ground pavilion. This was partly because not all the facts were known to those present and partly because Cranley Nice had decided that the time had come to assert himself. 'Get out, the lot of you', was an unambiguous signal to the cricketers from both sides that play had finally ended for the day. Cranley Nice's command, it was clear, was for immediate implementation. Time to shower and change was not permitted. This was of particular concern to those Outcasts who had imagined themselves party-bound. Tim Jackson marched up to Cranley Nice to protest. He was unprepared for the response. The spice tycoon, by now bereft of rational judgement, punched him on the nose. Blood streamed out, mostly over the white dinner jacket. The Noël Coward effect was ruined. Any risk of a general melee was extinguished by prompt action on the part of Winston Jenkins and Jon Palmer. They restrained their injured colleague and told the other members of the side to collect their bags immediately and assemble outside.

Help was forthcoming from an unexpected quarter. Grouped outside the pavilion the Outcasts were approached by Haydn Bliss in forgiving mood. It seemed that the Outcasts had reinstated themselves if not yet in the eyes of the village as a whole, at least in the sight of one person who counted for a lot – the joint licensee of the village pub. Haydn Bliss offered them facilities at the Pink Pedlar and added the magic words: 'I think we owe you a drink.' Some members at least of the Doredell Cricket Club seemed to agree.

Until that moment the Outcasts did not realise that they had any responsibility for the welfare of Mr Ashoki Ebihara. John Furness' street rescue apart, most of the Outcasts had been unaware of a Japanese presence in their midst. Revelation was sudden. The exit of the cricketers had left the previously hidden Mr Ebihara exposed to Cranley Nice's view. He had not been a welcome sight. The company chairman's explosive reaction had needed no supplement from the Japanese language to convey the message to Mr Ebihara that his presence was unacceptable. Farley Richardson, who had stayed behind in what he regarded as his managerial capacity, virtually frogmarched him to the door. They did not know who he was or why he was in Doredell, but the Outcasts thought that they should co-opt him as far as the Pink Pedlar where some of these questions might be answered. And some would be.

Geraint Poppledown's ready acceptance of his partner's sponsorship of the return of the previously banned Outcasts was made easier by the lack of other business. He felt that full clarification could wait until a few pints had been pulled. The Outcasts fell upon these with much pleasure whilst David Pelham's powers of recovery once again earned the admiration of his friends. They were also keen to exploit the détente to recover goodwill with the locals in general. There was nevertheless an important question to be settled and this could not be delayed beyond the second round. Were those who had enlisted still going to the party?

A well-appointed gentlemen's toilet (far in excess of the usual village pub provision) afforded the Outcasts generous space both to wash and change. Those with the superior party in their sights had drifted off in turns to clean up and don their various costumes. John Furness had first to divest himself of the police uniform before it could be handed over to Dean Faulds for whom it had been intended. Curiously Tim Jackson had not injected any urgency into getting his group ready. Normally at the head of any party queue and in this instance the proud sponsor of what he had repeatedly proclaimed as an exclusive bash, his eagerness had noticeably dimmed. Although he was not prepared to admit it, the reason lay in his change of appearance. His blood-stained and crumpled white dinner jacket now made him less Noël Coward and more Sir Les Patterson. This had undoubtedly affected his amour-propre.

One by one the other Outcasts adopted their new persona. The police constable and burglar were first. They were followed by a pirate and a nun (Jon and Adrienne Palmer), an Arab prince (Kevin Newton), Dracula (Phil Cole) and a gorilla (David Pelham). This steady flow of transformed appearances from the lavatory was observed with some incredulity by the bar's original tenant, the lady keeping herself to herself in the corner, and Mr Ashoki Ebihara, who struggled to come to terms with this fresh insight into the habits of the British.

By the time everyone was ready, the point had been reached when the fate of the evening was finally balanced. Tim Jackson's feet had been getting colder as his doubts about the enterprise grew. Everyone else's body temperature had got hotter as the consumption of ale had continued barely without interruption. Those still capable of rational thought began to wonder whether the remarkable repair to relations with the village would be wrecked if half the team suddenly departed. Both the atmosphere and the ale had compelling features. Yet Tim Jackson fretted that he might lose social credit if his promised guests did not show up at the party. The scales finally tipped when suddenly but gracefully the nun collapsed.

The attention which then had to be paid to Adrienne Palmer altered not only the nature of the evening, but also the chemistry within the assembled clientele. Adrienne Palmer was quickly revived. She knew the reason why she had fainted. There was nothing wrong with her that seven and a half months would not put right. The heated atmosphere of the bar coupled with her condition (confirmed that afternoon after a visit to the pharmacy in Hayste) had caused her momentary blackout. She had not envisaged circumstances such as these for conveying the good news to her husband, but it was the only way to prevent him from thinking that something more sinister had befallen her. Once he and the others had absorbed this information another cause for festivity presented itself. Tim Jackson read Jon Palmer's mind and slid off to impart a cancellation notice to their intended hostess.

Feeling somewhat on the fringe of the baby celebration, Harry Northwood's attention had been drawn to the lonely, nonplussed figure of Mr Ashoki Ebihara. Thoughtfully he took a pint of beer and placed it before the elderly Japanese. This had been an executive decision on Harry's part, because he had rightly anticipated that he was not equipped to elicit any preference for beverage from Mr Ebihara. Judging from the speed with which it was despatched his choice was obviously satisfactory. Mr Ebihara did not dissent when Harry refilled the glass.

David Pelham had also detached himself from the main throng. His gorilla eyes had alighted on the lonely lady in the corner. Since the mass invasion she had not ventured through the thick of bodies to the bar. The glass in front of her was empty. With each glance in her direction and with each pint consumed, David Pelham had persuaded himself that she was quite attractive. It was therefore an obvious move to ask her whether she would like another drink. Whether it was a case of the lady being thirsty or the novelty of being bought a pint of beer by a gorilla, David Pelham got an affirmative answer. The drink was gratefully received, but she was less sure about the continuing attention. Her benefactor sat down beside her with a clear intention to engage in chat – and maybe more.

Love of cricket is one of life's most useful balms. Amid other excitements several discussions about the game were under way. In lively denunciation of the crass foolishness of the England Test selectors, much common ground was forged and goodwill established. However, what had done most to convert the Outcasts from villains to heroes was their (fortuitous) part in unmasking the predatory but ultimately competing intentions of Cranley Nice and his scheming wife. It had slowly dawned on Jim Flote that he had been backed in his candidacy by Cranley Nice not on account of his intrinsic worth nor to bridge the gap between business and local government, but purely and simply to be his employer's mouthpiece. Before the end of the evening he had announced to great cheers that he would withdraw from the contest and set up a citizens' action group, Doredell against Development (DAD), even if it cost him his job (more cheers).

The pained expression on Ray Burrill's face had caused a solicitous enquiry from Haydn Bliss. Ray felt inhibited about mentioning his aching heart, but was voluble on the subject of his aching leg. 'Why not come through to the back room, whip your trousers off and let me have a look at it?' the publican suggested. Ray Burrill thought of one immediate reason, but very properly suppressed it. He realised that he had talked himself into an uncomfortable situation. His doubts were eased when Haydn Bliss mentioned that he had more than a passing knowledge of first-aid derived from his rugby-playing days. Ray Burrill ought to have had some passing knowledge himself but was inclined to over-fuss where his own welfare was concerned. There was no doubt that the area of the bite had become inflamed. Haydn Bliss cleaned the wound and applied some ointment which stung so much that Ray Burrill, not sufficiently anaesthetised by the amount of alcohol he had consumed, gasped. However, by the time he was re-clad in his trousers and on his feet he felt much better. His improvement was meteoric when the first person he saw on his return to the bar was his new female acquaintance of the afternoon.

The fact that she had tracked him down after all the complications at the ground and the likelihood of his early return to London did wonders for Ray Burrill's morale. They settled themselves some distance from the rest and Ray brought her up-to-date with what had happened. She listened approvingly to the twists and turns of the drama and to the news of the mood of reconciliation which had subsequently pervaded proceedings in the pub. After Ray had finished she put her hand on his arm and said, 'it can only get better'. It was not until much later that Ray discovered that she meant more than the state of their personal relationship.

In another part of the bar David Pelham laid his hairy hand on the arm of his companion. It did not seem to have penetrated his brain that there was little chance of a personal relationship burgeoning while he was still encased in a gorilla outfit. It was extraordinary that he was not peremptorily repulsed. Far from rejection he felt his companion's hand suddenly grip his arm, but this move was not accompanied by any encouraging look. The lady was staring straight ahead, but all David Pelham could see was the elderly Japanese man treading cautiously towards the men's room. When Mr Ebihara had disappeared she did turn to look at David Pelham, but when she spoke her voice had changed and was much deeper and what she said in no way fitted the intimate mood which David Pelham thought he had established. 'For Christ's sake can you get me out of this f---ing place?' Roger Trysom suddenly feared that he might have blown his cover.

The rota of ladies who looked after the café at the maze had been affixed to a side wall together with their addresses and telephone numbers. Roger Trysom had picked up what proved to be a crucial item of information. He knew exactly where Connie Stillmarch lived and he had made good use of his knowledge. His acquired skills in make-up came easily back to him. Thus protected against prying eyes and neatly avoiding Connie Stillmarch, who was travelling in the opposite direction, he had made his way eventually to the refuge of the Pink Pedlar to remain there unnoticed until the storm had passed and, he hoped, taken the wretched Japanese with it. The sight of Mr Ashoki Ebihara had come as a nasty shock to him. He suddenly felt less confident in his disguise. He had almost blown it with the man in the ridiculous gorilla costume who had been pestering him, but it did occur to him that these boisterous cricketers could provide his passage back to London. He set out to retrieve the situation with his unexpected companion. At the same time he needed to know whether he had to run the gauntlet of yet more Japanese. Whatever had happened to that damned bus?

The bus remained firmly wedged under the railway bridge, a source of mounting chaos for motorists and rail travellers alike. A galaxy of emergency service workers, police, safety officers and engineering advisers would ensure that it remained so for as long as possible. The injured had been removed from the scene. After exhaustive interviewing the words 'Rising Sun Hotel' and 'Bayswater' had been gleaned from what seemed to be the only passenger who combined the essential attributes of an unshocked condition and a smattering of English. This had led to the uninjured tourists being taken at last to the place from which they had started their memorable day. Late on a Saturday evening they were at least assured of the familiar comforts of a closed restaurant, a night porter off duty and a faulty heating system which delivered neither hot water nor warmth to their rooms. Bill Blimp, however, was by this time well immersed in hot water.

All good things must come to an end even if well beyond the time envisaged by the licensing justices. The consumption capacity of the Outcasts was a regular source of temptation to landlords to carry on serving. In this case a halt was called at the joint behest of Greg Roberts and Jon Palmer. Greg, already committed to drive one minibus back to London, had consumed as much orange juice and spring-derived mineral water as a self-respecting real ale drinker could be expected to take. By midnight the occasion had lost its savour. The only person left who could legally drive the second minibus was Adrienne Palmer. Her husband intervened on her behalf. She insisted that her little turn was safely behind her and that she was perfectly fit to drive. After his ninth pint Jon was anxious that the journey should be no longer delayed. Goodbyes were said in an atmosphere of cordiality (and in one case tenderness), something that could not have been imagined months and even hours ago.

There were two extra passengers for the return journey. David Pelham had decided that there was not a lot to be gained from investing in an extended conversation with the 'lady' in the corner. He had remained with her long enough to pick up the message that, having been left behind by a tour bus, she was desperate to get back to London. In pouring Mr Ebihara's fourth pint of Hoppenhall's Charger bitter, Geraint Poppledown had chanced to remark to Harry Northwood, 'I guess that old guy's stranded'. He went on to remind Harry that there had been two coach-loads of Japanese around the village earlier in the day. He was sure that they had gone some hours ago. Being full of goodwill as well as good ale, Harry Northwood saw himself as the agent of kindly deliverance. With much repetition of the word 'London' interspersed with mime, Harry made Mr Ebihara understand that his passage to the capital was assured. For the second time in the day, Mr. Ebihara went down on his knees in gratitude. Having already drunk most of four pints of Hoppenhall's Charger bitter, he experienced more than a little difficulty in righting himself. Harry reported his initiative to Winston Jenkins for approval at the same time as David Pelham was also seeking to book a place. Winston Jenkins said that he was very happy to accommodate both. So happy was he by this stage of the night that he could easily have waved another dozen on board.

David Pelham, still with a largely full glass in his hand, chivalrously gave prior attention to passing on the news to his erstwhile companion that her problem was solved. His words, 'don't worry, we'll soon have you both back in London', were not received with the reaction he had expected. Instead of delight, a look of sheer panic passed over the lady's face. Roger Trysom, willing himself to ask who was meant by 'both', feared that he knew the answer. 'Some old Japanese guy', replied David Pelham, but seeing that this did not lift the gloom, he added, 'don't worry, we've got loads of space in our mini-buses'. In spite of the background noise in the pub, Roger Trysom thought that he had caught the plural. But he had to check. His voice, dipping in tone and almost betraying himself a second time, queried, 'buses?'. On confirmation he grabbed David Pelham in a conspiratorial embrace. Dean Faulds, who happened to glance in their direction, thought that they were about to dance. Roger Trysom asked David Pelham to do him a favour and make sure that he travelled on a separate bus from the Japanese man. 'I can't help it', he said inventively, 'it's a family thing. The war, you know.' David Pelham's gorilla head nodded as if he knew very well.

Remembering his responsibilities both as captain and match manager, Winston Jenkins decreed that they should waste no time changing. The Outcasts collected their clothes and kit and departed in an atmosphere of bonhomie which could not have contrasted more sharply with last year's humiliating exit. As if forgetting that the occasion was past, the frustrated partygoers all headed towards the same mini-bus. Having tired of the rather weird lady's company, David Pelham dumped her on the other mini-bus and emerged just in time to prevent Harry Northwood boarding with Mr Ebihara. Being escorted by a man in a gorilla suit was just another feature of what had been an extraordinary day. (On his eventual return home it would be the inclusion of this item which would cast doubt on the plausibility of the whole account of his trip.) The mini-bus with Greg Roberts at the wheel took the lead. He told Adrienne Palmer that he knew a good short-cut to the

M11. As she did not expect to be getting much by way of directional help from her passengers she readily agreed to follow him. They made fast progress down the motorway before plunging into the suburbs of North-East London.

There was no warning. Had one of the mini-bus radios been tuned into the appropriate channel, they would not have been better informed. The exact location of the road closure had not been reported to the broadcasters with pinpoint accuracy and so even the most avid and attentive listener would have remained ignorant. The Outcasts were not put to the worry of having to guess. The radio in the rear mini-bus was silent in deference to an apparent desire to sleep. In the leading mini-bus the cassette player was engaged in reproducing the album, 'Bawdy Songs for Bawdy Cricketers: Volume 1'. Many old favourites were performed to general hilarity. Roger Trysom had to stop himself joining in as he felt that it would not conform to his disguise. The amateur chorus died in the middle of the popular ditty, 'She was only a stumper's daughter', as the mini-bus was forced to a sudden halt by a police barrier.

Two constables sauntered towards them, partly to explain the diversion and partly out of a curious and instinctive reaction to late night traffic. Greg received the information about the accident and prepared to turn his vehicle round. At that moment two things happened. The officer tackling the second mini-bus was alerted by the sight of a nun at the wheel. Mr Ebihara's eyes had focused on a familiar-looking bus now illuminated by arc lights. He let out a banshee wail and tried to get out of the bus. This cry had almost curdled the blood of the young policeman who had just remembered a report he had recently read about a gang of thieves dressed as nuns. In no time at all, Mr Ebihara's wish was granted and both he and his fellow passengers were lined up in the street. The similarity of the two vehicles linked them in the minds of the police and so Greg Roberts and his passengers were asked to parade as well. Together they presented an intriguing sight.

It took a while for the Outcasts to disentangle themselves from this situation. Explaining to the police why a group of cricketers in the company of a gorilla, a nun, a pirate, a policeman, an improbable-looking burglar, an Arab prince and Dracula were driving through north-east London in the early hours of the morning was not the most straightforward of exercises. The blood on Tim Jackson's white dinner jacket was treated as suspicious in itself. A powerful smell of beer was another factor to increase police uneasiness. It did not help when Winston Jenkins mentioned the word 'harassment', because one of the policemen took this the wrong way and thought that Winston was trying to make a racial incident out of it. In the end, with Greg Roberts and Adrienne Palmer doing most of the talking (they were the sober ones) the situation was cooled. By providing the police with a list of names and addresses backed up with one or two driving licences, they were free to go. It was only when Greg had begun to write down the names of the people in his mini-bus that he realised that one of their number had already gone.

Mr Ashoki Ebihara had not been the only person to see and recognise the back end of the bus protruding from the bridge. The shock had made Roger Trysom duck behind the rear seats of the mini-bus. None of his travelling companions had noticed that he had failed to emerge. The policemen were dealing with such an eclectic bunch of people that they just assumed it was the complete passenger load. The exchanges were intense and seemingly long-winded. Roger Trysom surreptitiously scanned them. He could see that his absence was unremarked, but he had no means of knowing how long this would last and whether or not they might all be carted off to a police station. He noticed that the door of the mini-bus had been left open and as Greg Roberts had half-turned the vehicle he had a concealed escape route. He stole furtively away in the gloom. After turning left and then twice right he found a secluded, unlit street. Almost immediately, he tripped and fell over an obstacle on the pavement, it was James Saito – reunification was achieved for the third time.

As they cleared up before going to bed (they were house-proud people) Geraint Poppledown and Haydn Bliss had found a solitary discarded jockstrap in the gentlemen's toilet. They were not best placed to recognise the almost poetic symmetry of this discovery.

AFTERMATH

On the following Monday a number of meetings took place. The planning officers of the Vale of Widdle District Council told a prominent local estate agent acting on behalf of a wealthy Indian businessman that they would have no difficulty recommending to the appropriate council committee acceptance of a planning application to develop the Longbirch estate as a centre of cricketing excellence for deprived teenagers from all cricket-loving nations. Such a land use was very much consistent with the principles underlying the new District Plan currently being compiled. Iris Pearlhammer had known this for some time. She was a staunch defender of rural village interests. Those who really knew her had heard her say that she had not left the East End only to see the East End come to Doredell. She had had no compunction in feeding contrary and entirely false information both to Cranley Nice and the former Mrs Jack Jamieson once she had sensed her little game. It had been a lucrative income stream while it had lasted.

The day was more advanced before Bill Blimp could track down Roger Trysom and James Saito. The owner of Executive Sporting Coachways had eventually been released by the police after his brief had improbably persuaded them that his client was more sinned against than sinning. Without any trace of James Saito there was no means of proving that the double-decker had been driven illegally on the motorway. The damage to the bridge was as nothing in comparison with the damage to his client's vehicle, and the rail network company when they had assessed the damage would doubtless pursue him. On regaining his freedom, Bill Blimp's first thought was to pursue the hirer for his money.

The office of Culture Coachtours was located in a one-room flat above a massage parlour in a dingy part of north London. The entrance door at street level had peeling paint and a sheet of plywood where glass had once been. It was not until he was in the upstairs room that Bill Blimp appreciated that the company's 'coach yard' amounted to two spaces opposite some lock-up garages at the rear. It was a simpler operation even than his own. Despite the somewhat odd nature of the circumstances which had first brought them together and later forced them apart, the reunion was cordiality itself. There was a mild haggle over the hire charge previously agreed. Bill Blimp wanted to claim for extra time; Roger Trysom talked of compensation for delay. However a deal was quickly done and Roger Trysom made no great fuss over the amount for which he presented his cheque. There was no need. He knew that the cheque would bounce, for he had cleared out his account that morning with a view to setting up business elsewhere – in a faraway country. For a while the men chatted, both Bill Blimp and Roger Trysom lamenting the loss of their buses on the same day. Neither of them realised that they were at cross-purposes and that Bill Blimp would soon be grieving over the identical vehicles.

At a meeting of the local coroner's court it was ruled that an elderly Japanese man had died of natural causes.

As a meeting could not be arranged, Ray Burrill sent six red roses to an address in Doredell. He would have liked to have sent twelve, but it was near the end of the month.

The administrator of the Longbirch estate answered an urgent summons to convene at six o'clock to consider a sensational third offer which had been submitted on behalf of an Indian businessman. The sum in question seemed to assume planning permission and was greatly in excess of anything previously on the table. The administrators gave it prudent and dispassionate consideration in line with their legal responsibilities. After fully five minutes they decided to invoke the ancient wisdom: grab it while you can.

Finally the Outcasts were reunited in the Sink and Plumber to make preparations for their next fixture. In fact most of the evening was spent in a beery recapitulation of Saturday's events. Extra rounds were bought to celebrate victory, restoration of the Outcasts' reputation in Doredell and the impending fatherhood of Jon Palmer. Many a laugh – and round – was had at the expense of Ray Burrill and John Furness. And more rounds were bought for no particular reason whatsoever. The landlord felt that all was well with the world.

It was not until the following day that Rashid Ali noticed a short piece in one of the broadsheets reporting that the Japanese Ambassador had had an urgent meeting at the Foreign and Commonwealth Office. No reason was given.

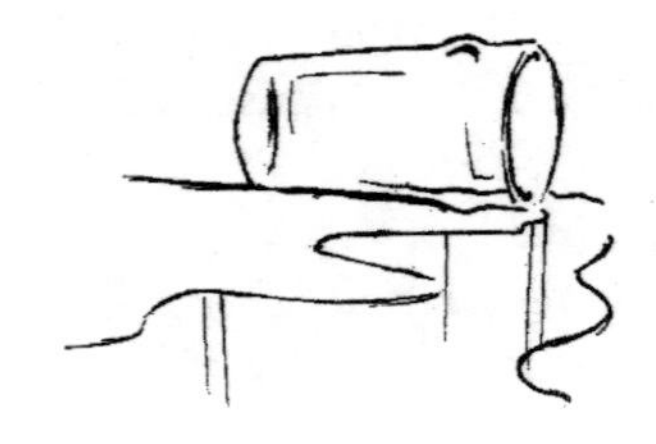